INSTRUCTOR'S MANUAL

LEO P. CONNELLY

ASTRONOMY
TODAY

SECOND EDITION

ERIC CHAISSON

STEVE MCMILLAN

Prentice Hall, Upper Saddle River, NJ. 07458

© 1996 by **PRENTICE-HALL, INC.**
Simon & Schuster / A Viacom Company
Upper Saddle River, NJ 07458

10 9 8 7 6 5 4 3 2 1

ISBN 0-13-532151-4
Printed in the United States of America

CONTENTS

INTRODUCTION TO THE INSTRUCTOR'S MANUAL

This manual was prepared as an aid to instructors using the Chaisson/McMillan textbook. It is based on my experiences in teaching astronomy and related courses for over 22 years and freely "borrows" ideas exchanged among my colleagues during that time. In style, the manual (and my teaching) follows from what I learned from my role models in teaching, the late Bart Bok and Raymond E. White of the University of Arizona. They made learning astronomy fun and exciting; an exploration of unknown distant places. They took their science seriously, but always as a human endeavor, and it is this human factor that makes astronomy relevant to scientist and student alike. It is in this same spirit that I believe the text has been written and I have tried to reflect this in the manual.

All of our students are quite capable of reading the text; please don't do that for them. In music, a score can be read; in theater, a script can be read. But in both cases, it is the performance that brings the work alive to the audience. Should science be any different? Perform your science! Let your students experience it first-hand as you bring them a variety of models, demonstrations, and visualizations that have been provided in the manual.

The text offers many paths, avenues, and highways to further understanding and learning. In each lecture, try to take advantage of these opportunities to involve your students in the material. Mathematical insight is sometimes given where it is felt that it will either improve the understanding of a concept or provide concrete examples of a phenomenon, though math has been kept to a minimum and generally parallels the use found in the text. In places I have improvised on the material in the text in order to further develop an idea. As in music or theater, though, improvisation must be based on the theme and have relevance. Practice your visualizations or demonstrations before class. Once comfortable with them you will want to introduce your own variations; this can bring a whole new dimension to your lectures. The bottom line is to present the subject of astronomy in as exciting and entertaining a fashion as possible. Your students will reward you, not with applause, but with learning.

Astronomy is a very visual science. The text provides an excellent selection of photographs, illustrations, and diagrams. These should be used to maximum advantage. A set of transparencies, slides, and video are among the supplemental materials provided to you through the generosity of the publisher. These greatly enhance presentations and help students retain information. Structure lectures so that midway through a presentation a demonstration or a set of slides is shown; this helps keep students involved. Ask them questions or their opinion or their ideas about the material. Have them help out with your visualizations and models.

For example, your students will likely see few asteroids during their lifetimes, but they will see numerous potatoes. By using the potato/asteroid analogy given in Chapter 14, they will understand the similarities between the two—will understand a bit more about asteroids—and be reminded of this upon sight of a potato.

The length of the text is suited for a one semester, two quarter, or two semester survey course. The chapters are not all equal in length or difficulty. You may want to try one of the following suggested schedules; they assume a 10-week quarter or 15-week semester. Each schedule includes a midterm exam and assumes a final exam during a final exam week. In the semester schedules, one midterm in the eighth week may be too long to wait before a first exam. An alternative is to give two "midterms," one in the fifth week and a second in the tenth week.

It is important to keep students involved with the material presented in the course. Strongly encourage them to take the Self-Test; it is meant to provide questions that should be easily answered if the fundamental concepts an a chapter are understood. Assignments made from the Review Questions, projects, and weekly quizzes may be used in any combination. A short weekly quiz of 10 multiple choice questions can be quickly produced using the Test Item File. Print out the exam using a 24-point font, make a transparency, and project it. Use computer-graded answer sheets and return them each week for the next

One Semester		Two Quarter		Two Semester	
Week	Chapters	Week	Chapters	Week	Chapters
1	1 & 2	1	1	1	1
2	3 & 4	2	2	2	2
3	5 & 6	3	3	3	3
4	7 & 8	4	4 & 5	4	4
5	9 & 10	5	6 & Midterm	5	5
6	11 & 12	6	7	6	6
7	13 & 14	7	8 & 9	7	7
8	15 & Midterm	8	10 & 11	8	Review & Midterm
9	16 & 17	9	12 & 13	9	8
10	17 & 18	10	14 & 15	10	9
11	19 & 20			11	10
12	21 & 22	1	16	12	11
13	23 & 24	2	17	13	12
14	25 & 26	3	18 & 19	14	13
15	27 & 28	4	20	15	14
		5	21 & Midterm		
		6	22 & 23	1	15
		7	24	2	16
		8	25	3	17
		9	26 & 27	4	18
		10	28	5	19
				6	20
				7	21
				8	22
				9	Review & Midterm
				10	23
				11	24
				12	25
				13	26
				14	27
				15	28

quiz. The sum of the quizzes easily equals the length of a midterm exam, even with the lowest quiz dropped. Upon the turn-in of answer sheets, the quiz questions can be reviewed and discussed before new material is presented in that lecture. This gives students immediate feed-back on the material they have just studied and helps prepare them for the longer exams. Such quizzes also help students get used to your style of testing.

The more you involve yourself in the teaching of astronomy, the greater the benefits to both you and your students. Let me know what you think of these ideas and about improvements and variations that you find effective or fun. I'll try them in my classes, and if I like them, I'll "borrow" them for future editions of this manual.

— Leo Connolly

CHAPTER 1

CHARTING THE HEAVENS
The Foundations of Astronomy

Large Numbers

Emphasize to students that large numbers are not only encountered in astronomy. Have students look for large numbers around them. The number of cells in their body is about 100 trillion. The annual federal budget deficit is about $400 billion (which is equal to the number of stars in our galaxy!). Bring a jar of sand to class and have them guess how many grains of sand it contains. Then ask how the number might be measured. Is it important to know the exact number or the approximate number. Measure the approximate number using the mass of a specific number of grains and total mass of grains. Extend the idea to measuring the total number of stars in the Galaxy or the number of galaxies in the universe.

Metric System

Non-science students are still typically unfamiliar with the metric system. Bring a calibrated meter stick, kilogram mass, a cubic centimeter, and gram mass to class. Relate these new units to common objects. The gram is the mass of a vitamin pill, the meter and yard are close in length, a cubic centimeter is about the volume of a sugar cube.

Density

Density is an extremely useful, but often times confusing, concept. Students confuse it with mass and/or size. A fun, but old, demonstration of density is to take a brick, a piece of foam rubber, and a lead brick of equal size and wrap them in paper. Have the students decide which is the most dense and why. Try passing around the lead brick and regular brick and talk about their difference densities. Then lift the foam brick as if it is quite heavy, ask the students what its density might be compared to the other bricks, then quickly toss it to an unsuspecting student! The effect of it having a low density, when the expectation is otherwise, will not be lost on the students.

Demonstrate the measurement of density. Use common objects that also relate to the course: water, ice, air, typical rocks, iron, and lead. Use the units of grams per cubic centimeter.

Night Sky

When introducing the night sky and stars to the students, have them observe the general locations of the brightest stars in the sky. (in cities these will be the only ones visible!) At the next class meeting ask for these locations and iden-

tify them by name and constellation using any common constellation chart. Show a photograph of the night sky for this month and time and again identify the stars and constellations.

Orientation of Earth, Moon, and Sun

When explaining the motions of the Earth, Moon, Sun, and stars, bring a common Earth globe (unmounted) to class, a light bulb you can turn on for the Sun, any sphere with a quarter diameter of the Earth globe for the Moon (baseballs often work well for some globes), and a flashlight to demonstrate seasonal effects of the Sun. Let the students be the stars!

Start your discussions using the globe upside down. Inevitably some brave or frustrated student will finally question why you are doing this. It is a perfect lead-in to discussing what is up and down in space and how orientations are arbitrary but necessary to be defined. Use the equator, direction of the poles, and the ecliptic as locations that do not vary in orientation (or at least do so very slowly). Demonstrate the normal orientation of the Earth and the directions of the Earth's rotation, lunar revolution, and Earth orbital motion.

Don't assume your students actually understand the phases of the Moon. After defining the four basic phases ask questions such as "At what time of day or night is the first quarter moon the highest in the sky?" Sunset. Demonstrate this with your model. Use a miniature doll as your observer and place it on the Earth globe surface while you rotate the Earth. It is difficult for many students to change their frame of reference to that of your model. If there is a laboratory component to your course, using such simple models can be very instructive and surprisingly satisfying to students.

Eclipses

To demonstrate eclipses use the same Earth globe and sphere for the Moon. Now set up a true scale model of this system by placing the Moon at 30 Earth diameters from the Earth. Establish the plane of the ecliptic and raise and lower the Moon by ±10 of its diameters to demonstrate the range of its inclination to the ecliptic (which is ±5° and the Moon is about 0.5° in diameter). It is not possible for any textbook picture or diagram to realistically represent the Earth-Moon system to scale. With this model students will see how easy it is for the lunar shadow to miss the Earth during the new moon phase or how the Moon misses the Earth's shadow during full moon phase (the Earth's shadow being about 2.5 lunar diameters). When describing eclipses ask the students what would be seen if standing on the Moon's surface while looking in the direction of the Earth of the Sun. Would the lunar surface be in darkness or light? What about the Earth or Sun? Remember that the Sun will appear to be the same size in the sky but the Earth will appear 4 times larger in diameter than the Moon does from Earth.

Show photographs of both lunar and solar eclipses, including partial, total, and annular solar eclipses.

Shape of the Earth

The circular shape of the Earth's shadow is compelling evidence that the Earth is spherical. Demonstrate this by casting shadows on a screen using an over-head projector and various objects such as a flat disc, sphere, small football, cone, and cylinder. The effect of latitude on the visibility of stars is easily demonstrated by using the globe of the Earth and pointing to the zenith and the horizon at various locations. A flat piece of cardboard with a tack stuck in the middle and a pencil stuck to the tack (through the eraser) so as to point perpendicular to the cardboard demonstrates the local horizon and zenith. Move this around the globe so that the students do not mistakenly think we can look over the horizon and around the sides of the globe.

Parallax

Demonstrate visual parallax by actually viewing a pencil first with one eye and then the other. This will make you look slightly ridiculous but encourage the students to try it too. Have them move the pencil to different distances to really see the inverse relationship between parallactic angle and distance.

People constantly use parallax to determine distances. Toss a piece of chalk, or some other small object, to a student near the front of the class. You have judged that distance and, knowing the weight of the object, determined how hard to throw it in order to reach the student. Now close one eye and look toward a completely different part of the classroom and try it again. Although your familiarity with the room will allow some memory of distance, your throw will probably be much less accurate. Emphasize that each of us constantly use parallax in this way. People with only one functional eye are often said to "lack depth perception." What they lack is parallax.

Ask your students why astronomers may not be able to make parallax measurements six months apart. Have them think in terms of the visibility of objects during the year and the declination of objects. Circumpolar objects are visible all year long. Objects with large southerly declinations (or large northerly declinations for the southern hemisphere) are visible for only brief periods of time during the year. Astronomers make numerous parallax measurements of specific stars as often as possible over several years. To study the parallax of stars in the entire sky they must work from observatories at various latitudes.

Motion of the Earth

Although we often assume that students in college are aware of the basic motions of the Earth, rotation and orbital, in reality it is estimated that from 10-30% of students (some would argue for a much higher percentage) have fundamental misconceptions about these motions. It is not unusual to encounter students who do not know that the Earth orbits the Sun or that the year is a measure of the orbital period. However, these same students are the least likely to speak up in class, and it is unproductive to ask the class if they understand these motions. The Aristotelian misconceptions: we would be thrown off a rotating Earth, we do not feel like we are moving, if moving why do we not feel a strong wind: are very often the exact same misconceptions of students. Why do our experiences fail us when applied to the motion of the Earth? Is the principle of mediocrity being violated? It is often beneficial to spend some time explaining the motions *and* why our every-day experiences lead us to the wrong conclusions. The best place to start is with the rotation of the Earth and the questions relating to why no wind is felt and why we are not thrown off.

Students usually have little difficulty with the concept that gravity is an attractive force and is responsible for "holding" us to the Earth. What they do not realize is that gravity also holds the atmosphere to the Earth. Just as the oceans, people, and other objects not connected directly to the Earth (as are mountains, for example) rotate with the Earth, so does the atmosphere. Thus there should be no wind experienced from Earth's rotation.

Students often overestimate the size (thickness) of the Earth's atmosphere. Draw a large circle on the blackboard with a diameter of about 1.5 meters. The thickness of the atmosphere is about the thickness of the chalk line! Earth's gravity can easily hold such a thin layer of gas. If the Earth had a large, massive atmosphere there might indeed be a wind associated with rotation, since the atmosphere would experience differential rotation (faster at the equator, slower at the poles).

The equator is moving at roughly 1,700 km/hr due to the rotation of the Earth (circumference of the Earth divided by 24 hours). That is fast! But the Earth would have to rotate in about 1.5 hours, instead of 24 hours, in order to "throw" anything off the equator. Our weight at the equator is reduced by the amount of centripetal force needed to make us move in a circle as the Earth rotates. The result is that an average person weighs about half a pound less at the equator than at the poles, but this is not a noticeable effect. The effect decreases as you move toward the poles.

The results for our motion around the Sun are similar.

We would not be thrown off the Earth because the effect is about half that due to the rotation. Remind students that there is no air out in space and therefore no wind to encounter. So in conclusion, there is really nothing wrong with our experiences or with the principle of mediocrity. We just have to properly apply these to the scale of the Earth and not be tempted to over-simplify what must happen. We have to calculate it to make sure we reach the correct result.

ANSWERS TO CHAPTER 1 REVIEW QUESTIONS

1. As given in *More Precisely*, p. 8, the Sun is about 100 times the size of the Earth. From Section 1.2, a light year is about 10^{13} km and a typical galaxy is about 100,000 Ly is diameter, or 10^{18} km. This makes a galaxy about 10^{14} times larger than Earth. Astronomers can see objects as distant as 10 billion Ly or 10^{23} km or 10^{19} times larger than Earth.

2. The "universe" is the totality of all space, time, matter, and energy.

3. A constellation is an imagined pattern of naked-eye stars typically associated with common objects, mythological beings, and animals. Although most of the constellations originated in antiquity, the constellations are now used to officially designate specific sections of the sky.

4. Although the Sun appears to rise in the east and set in the west, in fact the Sun is stationary relative to the Earth. The Earth rotates from west to east, giving rise to this apparent motion of the Sun. The Moon, stars, and all other astronomical objects appear to do the same because we view them from the surface of the rotating Earth.

5. Since the Earth moves around the Sun once in a year, the number of times you have traveled around the Sun equals your age in years.

6. The seasons of the Earth are caused by the tilt of the Earth's equator relative to its orbit around the Sun. This results in the Sun appearing higher in the sky during spring and summer months and causes higher rates of heating. In the fall and winter months the Sun appears much lower in the sky, its light falling more at an angle to the Earth's surface, and heats it less.

7. Due to the yearly motion of the Earth around the Sun, in the summer the Earth points in a direction 180° opposite of the direction it points during the winter.

8. As the Moon orbits around the Earth, different sides of it are illuminated by the Sun. In addition, our angle of view of the Moon changes during its orbit around us. The result is that we see a fully illuminated Moon (full phase), to an unilluminated Moon (new phase), to everything in-between.

9. A lunar eclipse is caused by the Moon entering the shadow of the Earth. A solar eclipse is caused by the Earth entering the shadow of the Moon.

10. A lunar or solar eclipse occurs only if there is a relatively precise alignment of the Sun, Earth, and Moon. But the Moon's orbit is tilted 5.2° to the orbit of the Earth. Each month, during full or new lunar phase, an eclipse of the Moon or Sun does not occur because the Moon is not in the ecliptic. Twice a year the Moon crosses the ecliptic when it is at one of these phases and an eclipse will likely be seen.

11. Precession is a slow shift in the direction of the tilt of the Earth's axis of rotation. Over a period of 26,000 years the axis moves through a circle, always keeping an angle of about 23.5 degrees. It is caused by the gravitational pull of the Moon and Sun.

12. Parallax is the apparent change in position of a foreground object, relative to distance background objects, due to the change in the position of the observer. Example: look at your finger with one eye and then the other. Notice how your finger seems to move relative to distant objects in the background.

13. The amount of parallax depends directly on the length of the baseline and inversely on the distance to an object. Because objects in astronomy have such large distances, a long baseline is required in order to make the parallax measurable.

14. Stars in constellation have only their direction in the sky in common. They may be separated by vast distances. From within the solar system, their positions would look very much as they do from Earth. From the nearest star there would likely be some noticable shift in the positions of stars within some constellations. From the center of the Galaxy, none of our familiar constellations would be visible.

ANSWERS TO PROBLEMS

1. Light travels at about 300,000 kilometers in a second, so it should be able to travel to the Moon in a little over one second.

2. Because the Moon appears to orbit the Earth in 29.5 days, it appears to move about 12° per day. (a) in one hour it moves 0.5° = 30' (b) in one minute it moves 0.5' = 30", (c) in one second it moves 0.5". Because the Moon's diameter is about 30', it moves its own diameter in about one hour.

3. $100 = 10^2$; $1000 = 10^3$; $1,000,000 = 10^6$; $1,000,000,000,000,000 = 10^{15}$; $0.01 = 10^{-2}$; $0.001 = 10^{-3}$; $123,000 = 1.23 \times 10^5$; $0.000456 = 4.56 \times 10^{-4}$.

4. Simple trigonometry gives this distance to be $(250)\tan(30°) = 144$ m. Students may need to do this graphically, however.

5. Using the method given in Interlude 1.4 we have (a) $1°/360° = 1000$ km$/2\pi D$. Solving for D gives 57,300 km. Similarly, (b) $1/60°/360° = 1000$ km$/2\pi D$ gives D $= 3.44 \times 10^6$ km and (c) $1/3600°/360° = 1000$ km$/2\pi D$ gives D $= 2.06 \times 10^8$ km.

6. The circumference of the Moon's orbit is about $2\pi \times 384,000$ km $= 2.41 \times 10^6$ km. The Moon is $0.5°$ across and so will have a diameter of $0.5°/360° \times 2.41 \times 10^6$ km. The diameter is 3350 km.

7. The Sun would not have changed positions had the Earth been flat. Therefore, Eratosthenes would have measured an angle of zero.

SUGGESTED READING

Bishop, Roy L., *Observer's Handbook* Toronto, Ontario Canada: University of Toronto Press Inc., published annually. Very handy reference for observing. Lots of tidbits of information useful to amateurs and professionals.

Burnham, Robert, Jr., *Burnham's Celestial Handbook*. 3 vol. New York: Dover, 1978. Comprehensive work on the contents of outer space, as we knew them a few years ago—plenty on the lore of the sky, too.

Dance of the Planets Loveland, Colorado: Arc Science Simulations, 1992. Solar system and night sky simulator for PCs running DOS or Windows.

Ferris, T. *Coming of Age in the Milky Way*. New York: Morrow, 1988. A book about how our perception of outer space has changed, by a popular author.

Fraknoi, Andrew *The Universe at Your Fingertips: An Astronomy Activity and Resource Notebook* Astronomical Society of the Pacific, 1995.

Goldman, S. J., "Astronomy on the Internet." *Sky & Telescope* (August, 1995). An excellent and up-to-date review of astronomical information available through the Internet. Includes addresses for mailing lists, newsgroups, FTP sites, and World Wide Web.

Powers of Ten (The films of Charles and Ray Eames). Santa Monica, CA: Pyramid Film and video, 1978. A classic video to aid visualizing the scale of the universe. 21 minutes.

Ridpath, Ian Ed., *Norton's 2000.0* New York: John Wiley & Sons Inc., 1990. A new version of a favored old standard. Contains easy to use star atlas and other reference material.

Robbins R. R., and Hemenway, M. K. *Modern Astronomy: An Activities Approach*. Austin: University of Texas Press, 1982. Chapters include "The Principles of Measurement: Using a Cross-Staff and a Quadrant," "Mapping the Night Sky and Its Motions," and "The Motions of the Planets."

The Sky GSC (2.0) Golden, CO: Software Bisque, 1994. A sky simulator for PCs using Windows and a CD-ROM.

Tirion, Wil *Sky Atlas 2000.0*. Sky Publishing Corp.. Twenty-six charts covering the entire sky, showing 43,000 stars and 2,500 deep-sky objects. In various formats.

Sky Catalogue 2000.0, Vol. 1 and 2. Sky Publishing Corp. Catalogs to complement *Sky Atlas 2000.0*, giving information on stars, double stars, variable stars, and nonstellar objects.

Van Helden, A. *Measuring the Universe—Cosmic Dimensions from Aristarchus to Halley*. Chicago: University of Chicago Press, 1985. Contains information on Aristarchus, Ptolemy, Copernicus, Kepler, Galileo, Eratosthenes.

Voyager II 2.0: San Ramon, CA: Carina Software, 1994. Dynamic sky simulator for the Macintosh. This version requires System 7 and CD-ROM.

There are two excellent magazines for beginning astronomers. One discusses astronomy mainly from the amateur, or hobbyist, point of view. Nice pictures. Monthly sky columns and charts. Twelve issues per year for $24.

Astronomy
Kalmbach Publishing
P.O. Box 1612
Waukesha, WI 53187-9950

The other astronomy magazine is read by many professionals as well as amateurs. It presents a good view of the world of astronomical research, but some articles are a little dense for most beginners. Monthly sky columns and charts. Twelve issues per year for $33.

Sky and Telescope
Sky Publishing Corporation
P.O. Box 9111
Belmont, MA 02178-9111

The following businesses have free mail order catalogs that provide access to a large variety of educational materials in astronomy.

Astronomical Society of the Pacific
Catalog Department
390 Ashton Avenue
San Francisco, CA 94112

MMI Corporation
Dept. ST-95
2950 Wyman Parkway
P.O. Box 19907
Baltimore, MD 21211

Sky Publishing Corp.
P. O. box 9111
Belmont, MA 02178-9111

CHAPTER 2

THE COPERNICAN REVOLUTION
The Birth of Modern Science

Scientific Method

The scientific method is applied to many situations in everyday life. Example: Before diving into an unknown pool of water, the diver will first exam the pool carefully from various angles, maybe drop several small objects in to test the depth, and possibly ask others if they are familiar with the pool (gather some data). The diver will then decide if the pool is safe to dive into and what part is the deepest (form a theory). The diver will then dive in and explore the pool (test that theory). People often use this same approach when purchasing a new item (spaghetti sauce, car, a new stereo). Have the students choose an example and try to identify the three steps in the method.

The scientific method is an ongoing process in science and one which is repetitive.

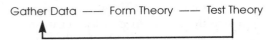

Gather Data —— Form Theory —— Test Theory

When a theory is being tested it is often for the purpose of gathering additional data to further refine the theory. Scientists build on the work of others in an ongoing process therefore, a scientist may start at any one of the three steps, the previous steps having been provided by other people.

Retrograde Motion

This is never obvious to students, and it is best to demonstrate it. First, explain that the larger the orbit, the slower the planet moves (This will be justified in Ch. 3.). Draw some stars across the entire black board. Ask for a student volunteer to play the role of an outer planet. Have the student walk slowly from the right to the left (as seen by the class). You play the role of the observer on Earth. Without moving note that the outer planet appears to move from west (right) to east (left). However, if you now walk parallel to the student (letting the student start first) and you move at a faster pace, you will appear to over-take and pass the student. This will be obvious. Now try it again but stop both of your motions before you pass and several times while passing and note the position of the student relative to the background stars on the board. If the student walks slowly enough and you fast enough, you should get a good retrograde effect. (Try this out first before going into the classroom in order to find an effective pace to use.)

Expand on this idea, showing roughly circular orbits for the planets and how retrograde motion only occurs during the "passing" of the Earth relative to the outer planet. This will always occur when the outer planet is near opposition. Ask students which planets would have retrograde motion if they were standing on Mercury or Venus. Would other objects appear in retrograde motion or only outer planets? Emphasize that the effect is not unique to viewing from Earth, nor does it only occur for planets.

Historical Developments

The interplay between the historical figures; Copernicus, Tycho, Kepler, Galileo, and Newton, are sufficiently important that providing the students with a time-line is helpful.

	Galileo	
	1564–1642	
Copernicus	Tycho	Newton
1473–1543	1546–1601	1642–1727
	Kepler	
	1571–1630	

The students can quickly grasp that Tycho, Kepler, and Galileo were contemporaries and followed the work of Copernicus. Newton then built on all this previous work ("stood upon their shoulders" as he was known to have said) in his formulation of gravity. Other people and events can be added for perspective; Leonardo Da Vinci (1452-1519), Christopher Columbus (1451-1506), and the discovery of America (1492).

Kepler's Laws

Students typically have two difficulties with the first law. The shape of the ellipse is unfamiliar to them and the position of the Sun at one focus, rather than at the center, is not "logical" to them. Although the text illustrates how an ellipse may be drawn, a quick demonstration of this is very helpful. Have the students draw their own ellipses. Using a scaling factor, such as 1 centimeter = 1 A.U., have them measure the semi-major axis, perihelion and aphelion distances, and calculate the eccentricity. Have them also label the position of the Sun. Reinforcing these ideas is necessary in order to replace the common misconception that the orbits are circular and that the Sun is at the center.

Give examples of the orbits of asteroids and comets. These orbits are often quite eccentric and the objects are usually visible only during perihelion passage. This is a graphic example of the fact that the Sun is located at the focus of the ellipse and not at the center.

In the second law, the concept of equal areas being swept out in equal times often means very little to students. Emphasize what this means in terms of the speed of the object in its orbit. The speed is the highest at perihelion and the lowest at aphelion. A computer graphic demonstrating the motion of an object in an eccentric orbit, where the velocity variations are obvious, is very helpful.

Kepler's third law has several concepts that may need additional explanation. The orbital (sidereal) period should be defined and demonstrated. A common *misconception* of students is that the period depends upon the location in the orbit it is measured, e.g. the period measured from one perihelion to the next is shorter than the period measured from one aphelion to the next. Students are often unaware that the planets all have different orbital periods and so Table 2-1 will be quite new to them.

Review the mathematical meaning of "squaring" and "cubing." Many students will confuse a^3 with $3a$. The more mathematically-aware students are often concerned that the units of the third law do not work out correctly. When it is said that the constant of proportionality is one, that does not imply that there are no units associated with the constant. In fact, the constant is 1 yrs^2/AU^3, but for convenience we rarely show it.

Newton's Laws of Motion

Most students are Aristotelian in their thinking about motion, i.e. a state of rest is normal and motion must somehow be maintained. There are a variety of demonstrations; air tracks, frictionless carts, air pucks, that can help students understand the effects of friction on motion. Demonstrate how difficult it is to make an object remain stationary; the slightest disturbance will make an object move. Thus it should be expected that in space objects will be found moving. This will help them understand the answer to the very commonly asked questions "Why is everything moving? What started everything moving?".

The concepts of velocity and acceleration are often confused. Newton's second law can also be effectively demonstrated with frictionless devices used in examining the first law. Show how an acceleration can produce either an increase or a decrease in speed.

A more difficult concept to understand is that an acceleration can also produce a change in direction without necessarily changing the speed. Show that it is necessary to use a force to change the direction of motion. Attach a string to the side of a frictionless cart. Set it moving and gently pull to the side. Ask the students if they can think of other ways to have the cart change directions. Point out to them how a force is necessary in each case. (One imaginative student suggested that if the table top was curved, like the surface of the Earth, the cart would naturally move along a curved path and not in a straight line. He, of course, had neglected the force of gravity!)

Demonstrate the third law by pushing against a wall or setting an object on a table. The wall or table push back with an equal but opposite force. Because the forces are balanced, no motion occurs. Push against the hand of one of the students to show how they have to push back with the same force that you are pushing. Suddenly increase or decrease your force and show how the hands move (accelerate) in response to the unbalanced forces (the second law).

Gravity

Ask your students if the Earth, *by itself*, has a gravitational force. Most will say it does. Ask them to explain how they know this. Typical responses will be: objects fall when let go, we have weight. Ask if the gravitational force is more or less constant on the surface of the Earth (assuming a perfectly spherical shape). Responses may vary to this question but usually are either no, it does not vary or yes, it does. Ask those who answer yes for examples. Again, typically students will say that the weight of objects vary, therefore the gravitational force varies. The results of this dialog will help the students understand Newton's law of gravity.

Emphasize the importance of the terms $m_1 m_2$ in the equation. If m_1 is the mass of the Earth and there is no other object present ($m_2 = 0$) then in fact there is no gravitational force. Gravity is a mutual force between two bodies that have mass. The gravitational force depends on the masses of the two bodies. The weight of an object is a measure of this gravitational force. Two objects with different masses will have different weights. Ask the students "If the Earth is attracting us with a force equal to our weight, do we attract the Earth, and if so, with what force?". Point out that the order of $m_1 m_2$ does not matter. We attract the Earth with the same force the Earth attracts us. What is the weight of the Earth on us is a valid question. It is the same as the weight of us on the Earth.

Why then do people often say that the Earth has stronger gravity than small objects like a person? Demonstrate how it is the acceleration due to gravity that is actually being observed.

$$a = \frac{Gm}{R^2}$$

If m represents the mass of the Earth, then the acceleration is what we experience when objects fall on Earth. If m represents a persons mass, the acceleration will be much, much less, although not zero. Demonstrate the differences in these accelerations by jumping off a chair or table. The students will agree that you were accelerated downward. Ask if they felt the Earth accelerated upward at the same time. Of course they will not because the acceleration is so small, but emphasize that it is not zero and that if you repeated the demonstration with a larger object, like the Moon, then the acceleration of *both* objects would be obvious.

Orbital Motion

It is useful to actually twirl a mass on the end of a string to demonstrate orbital motion. Let go of the string while twirling to show how an object will move in a straight line in agreement with Newton's first law. Also point out the difference between orbital motion and the mass and string demonstration. Whereas the velocity and tension can be varied at will in the demonstration, in orbits gravity sets the tension, so there is only one possible velocity (for circular orbits).

Ask your students whether it is possible to throw an object into orbit. If they have read the text before coming to lecture they will probably answer "no" because orbital velocity is about 18,000 mph around the Earth. Next, bet them that you can actually throw an object into orbit and will even demonstrate it in class (brag a little about your fast pitch!). After they express their doubts, throw an object across the room so they can easily see the curve of the projectile path. Tell them that the object was in orbit but ran into the Earth! Objects orbit around the center of mass and for all practical purposes this is the center of the Earth in this case. Draw on the chalk board what the orbit would have been if the object had not run into the Earth. By throwing the object harder and harder it goes farther. If thrown fast enough (orbital velocity) it will curve (fall) around the Earth at the same rate the Earth itself curves.

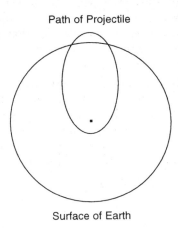

Path of Projectile

Surface of Earth

Center of Mass

Here is an interesting demonstration of the Earth-Moon system and the position of their center of mass. The ratio of Earth-to-Moon masses is about 100:1. Take a meter stick and hang a 1000 gram mass from one end. Balance it on a sharp edge so that the weight of the meter stick balances the 1000 gram mass. (When I do this the balance occurs at about 6 cm from the mass.) Now add a 10 gram

mass to the other end and find the new balance position. It should balance about 1 cm farther (7 cm in my case). One centimeter is 1/100 of the distance between the two mass and therefore is 1/100 of the distance between the Earth and Moon, as measured from the center of the Earth. This is approximately 4,000 km or about 3/4 of the Earth's radius. Although this example can be done purely numerically, it is much more effective when demonstrated. It also graphically demonstrates the meaning of center of mass.

Escape Velocity

Throw an object vertically at different speeds. The higher the initial speed, the greater the height the object reaches. If thrown fast enough, it should escape the Earth's gravity. Using the formula for the escape velocity, estimate the escape velocity from the Moon. Notice that the escape velocity depends on the square root of the mass divided by the radius of the object. Since the Moon is about 1/100 the mass and 1/4 the radius of the Earth, it is easy. The smaller mass should decrease the velocity by 10 but the smaller size should increase it by 2. Therefore, the escape velocity is about 1/5 of the Earth's escape velocity or 8,000 km/hr (5,000 mph). Give examples for other objects and distances.

If you want to explore the concept of escape velocity further, pose the question of escaping from the Sun's gravity at the distance of the Earth from the Sun. There is an easy way and a hard way of doing this. First, calculate the escape velocity using $\sqrt{2}$ of the orbital velocity. (The Earth's orbit is very nearly circular and has an average velocity of 30 km/s or 67,000 mph.) Thus the escape velocity from the Sun, at the distance of the Earth, is 42.4 km/s or about 95,000 mph.

This escape velocity sounds really high, and it is, so, is there an easy way to go this fast? In a sense, yes. Since the Earth is already traveling at 30 km/s, an object only has to be given an additional 12.4 km/s, *in the direction the Earth is moving in its orbit*, in order to escape the Sun; this is only 1.2 km/s more than it takes to escape the gravity of the Earth. This is the easy way.

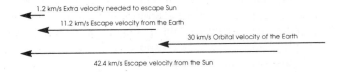

The hard way is to choose a direction different from this; the worst case being in the opposite direction the Earth is moving.

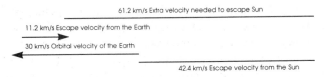

Then you have to have 30 km/s just to become stationary relative to the Sun and an additional 42.4 km/s to escape, for a total of 72.4 km relative to the Earth, to escape the Sun! This is 5.8 times the other escape velocity or 34 times as much energy (fuel) needed. Obviously, NASA chooses carefully the direction its probes take to outer planets and uses the orbital motion of the Earth (and the rotational motion too) as a significant boost in the right direction. This entire discussion is a useful example of the addition of velocities without having to get into the concept of vectors.

ANSWERS TO CHAPTER 2 REVIEW QUESTIONS

1. Islamic astronomers preserved the discoveries of the ancient Greeks. They developed many methods in trigonometry. Most common stars have names given to them by Islamic astronomers. Chinese astrologers kept careful records of comets and "new" stars, extending back many centuries.

2. The geocentric model of Aristotle has the objects of the solar system revolving around the Earth. (See Figure 2.5.) The planets moved in small circles called epicycles and the center of these circles moved around the Earth in circles called deferents. Ptolemy needed 80 circles, however, to fully describe the motions of the 5 visible planets, the Moon, and the Sun.

3. The basic flaw in the Ptolemaic model is the Earth is not at the center of the solar system, let alone the entire universe. Another flaw, which is equally valid, is that the Ptolemaic model did not attempt to explain why the motions are the way they are observed to be. There was no physical reason given for the complex model of Ptolemy. Today we would require any such explanation to be based on fundamental physical laws.

4. Copernicus re-introduced the heliocentric model for explaining the motions of the visible bodies of the solar system. In so doing he realized that the rather complex observed motions of these bodies could be explained in a simpler way.

5. Copernicus's ideas were finally published in the year of his death, 1543. By the beginning of the next century, around 1600, both Galileo Galilei and Johannes Kepler had fully embraced the Copernican heliocentric theory. It was not until the 19th and 20th centuries that the heliocentric theory could actually be proved.

6. The Copernican principle states that the Earth does not have a central position with respect to the solar system or any other part of the universe. It has been expanded upon to include the Sun not having a central position in the Galaxy and the Galaxy not having a central position in the universe.

7. Galileo discovered the phases and size changes of Venus. He also found the sizes and phases were related

and could be explained using the heliocentric model. Other discoveries such as the moons of Jupiter showed that objects could move around a body other than the Earth.

8. First Law: the orbits of planets are in the shape of an ellipse with the Sun at one focus. Second Law: a line connecting the Sun and a planet sweeps out equal areas in equal intervals of time. Third Law: the square of the orbital period is proportional to the cube of the semi-major axis.

9. The Astronomical Unit, defined as the semi-major axis of the Earth's orbit, was used to describe the distances to other planets but the size of the A.U. was not known. Using radar, which allows distances to be determined directly in units such as kilometers, the distance to Venus could be measured. With the distance to Venus known in both A.U. and kilometers, the length of the Astronomical Unit could be determined and thus the distance between the Earth and the Sun.

10. Kepler's three laws resulted from the analysis of observational data. Kepler's laws describe the motions of planets around the Sun but they do not explain why the planets move as they do. Newton's laws were derived from a mathematical model. They represent a deeper understanding of the way in which all objects move and interact with one another.

11. The first modification was to Kepler's first law. The planet and Sun move in elliptical orbits round a common center of mass, located at the focus of the ellipse. The second modification was to Kepler's third law. The period squared is not only proportional to the semi-major axis cubed, it is also inversely proportional to the sum of the masses.

12. In fact, the Earth also moves in response to the baseball but its motion is not noticeable because it is so slight. Newton's second law states that the acceleration, produced by a force, is inversely proportional to the mass of the object being moved. The baseball has little mass and displays a large acceleration. The Earth is very massive and has so little acceleration in response to the baseball that it can not be measured. If the baseball were as massive as the Moon, the motion of the Earth would be obvious, as indeed it is to astronomers who can measure the motion of the Earth due to the Moon.

13. The height to which a baseball can be thrown is dependent on the force of gravity pulling it back down (and also on how fast you initially throw it). All else being equal, because the Moon's gravity is about one sixth of the Earth's, the ball can be thrown much higher. Note also that the lack of air friction on the

surface of the Moon (it has no atmosphere) also contributes significantly to the increased height to which the ball can be thrown.

14. Escape velocity is the velocity necessary to escape the gravitational pull of a body. A velocity less than this will result in an object eventually falling back to the body. A velocity greater than the escape velocity will result in an object never returning to the body.

15. Geometry allows astronomers to determine distances to the nearest astronomical bodies. It is particularly important for distances within the solar system and for distances to the nearest stars.

16. There are more scientists thinking about more problems, so the climate for new ideas is certainly better in that sense. But scientists are still human and often appear closed-minded to new theories that challenge their own theories. The scientific method, if applied properly, allows new theories to be tested and to challenge existing theories. The high rate of communication present today also encourages the development of new ideas.

17. If the Sun's gravity suddenly stopped, Earth would continue to move at its current velocity but in a straight line path. The gravitational pull between the Earth and Sun accelerates the Earth in the direction of the Sun, changing this straight-line path to one that is curved.

ANSWERS TO PROBLEMS

1. 1 AU is about 150 million kilometers. 0.3 AU is 45 million kilometers. Since the speed of light and radar is 300,000 kilometers per second, and a round trip to Venus is 0.6 AU, or 90 million kilometers, 90,000,000 km / 300,000 km/sec = 300 seconds (which equals 5 minutes).
$\sqrt[3]{30.06^2}$, P = 164.8 (accurate to 4 significant digits)

2. Call the distance between the focus and center of an ellipse "c." The eccentricity of an orbit is just e = c/a, where a is the semi-major axis. The perihelion distance will be a - c = a - ae or a(1-e). For Pluto this gives 39.53(1-0.248) = 29.7 A.U. which is smaller than 30.06, which is the semi-major axis of Neptune's orbit.

3. The modified version of Kepler's Third Law is in Earth and solar units; P must be in years, a must be in AU, and the mass will be in units of the mass of the Sun. 1.9 million km = 0.0127 A.U., 16.7 days = 0.0457 year. Solving the Third Law for the mass gives M = a^3/P^2. Using these values for a and P gives M = 0.000981 solar masses. The Sun's mass is 1.99×10^{30} kg, so the mass of Jupiter should be about 1.86 ×

10^{27}kg. (Jupiter's mass is known to be 1.90×10^{27}kg, so our estimate is good.)

4. Assume your mass is 55 kg. Using Newton's law of gravity;

$$F = \frac{6.67 \times 10^{-11} \times 5.97 \times 10^{24} \times 55}{(6.378 \times 10^6)^2}$$

F = 538 N

F = 121 lbs, that is, your **weight**!

SUGGESTED READING

Aveni, A. F. (ed.), *Native American Astronomy*. Austin: University of Texas Press, 1975. Specialists in archaeology, astronomy, architecture, art history, mathematics, solar physics, and anthropology explore the astronomical knowledge and beliefs of pre-Columbian peoples in the Americas.

Blumenberg, H., *The Genesis of the Copernican World*. Cambridge, MA: Massachusetts Institute of Technology, 1987. Major work by a German philosopher on the significance of the Copernican revolution for our understanding of modern thought. Presents a new account of the history of philosophical interpretations of the significance of the heavens for human beings.

Carlson, J. B. "America's Ancient Skywatchers." *National Geographic* (March 1990). Descriptions of the cosmologies of the Maya, Navajo, Inca and other American civilizations.

Christianson, G. E., "Newton's Principia: A Retrospective." *Sky and Telescope* (July 1987). Written in honor of the 300th anniversary of one of the most influential books in the history of science.

Gillies, G. T. and Sanders, A. J. "Getting the Measure of Gravity." *Sky & Telescope* (April, 1993.)

Gingerich, O. "Astronomy in the Age of Columbus." *Scientific American* (December, 1992.)

_ *The Great Copernicus Chase* . Massachusetts: Cambridge University Press, 1992. A collection of 36 essays written by the author on a variety of historical topics in astronomy. Also available through Sky Publishing Corp.

Krupp, E. C. *Echoes of the Ancient Skies* . New York: Harper and Row, 1983. Excellent discussion of archaeoastronomy.

Ley, W. *Watchers of the Skies*. New York: The Viking Press, 1969. Willie Ley was a famous rocket scientist, but he also had a wonderful ability to tell a story. Good reading!

Mohlenbrock, R. H. "Medicine Mountain, Wyoming." *Natural History* (January 1990). Interesting story about Wyoming's Big Horn Medicine Wheel, thought to have been used centuries ago as an astronomical observatory.

Pannekoek, A., *A History of Astronomy*. New York: Dover, 1961. Classic, scholarly history of astronomy from ancient times to the middle of the 20th century. Translated into English in 1961, it was hailed as the best history of astronomy written in over half a century. 521 pages.

Waters, T., "Gravity Under Siege." *Discover* (April 1989). Tests of Newton's theory of gravity performed in Greenland and elsewhere. Lively discussion about the possibility that gravity may be more than Newton or even Einstein knew.

Whitlock, G., "Digging into Science." *Mercury* (July-August, 1995). Archaeoastronomy in a multicultural science curriculum is used as a bridge between the humanities and the physical sciences.

Chapter 3

RADIATION
Information from the Cosmos

The Wave Nature of Light

Demonstrate wave motion using a rope, cord, or slinky. Have the students note the speed of the waves. Vary the wavelength and frequency so they can see the relationship between the two for a given velocity. If time permits, measure the velocity, wavelength, and frequency using a stop watch and a meter stick.

Use a laser to demonstrate diffraction and interference. Mount a mirror in the back of the classroom so that a laser can be set up in the front and the image projected on to a screen also in the front. This will also provide for a long path length. A 1 mW laser is usually sufficiently powerful and safe for demonstrations. Use a knife-edge to demonstrate diffraction. To demonstrate interference by showing a diffraction pattern, use a smooth metal or plastic ruler ruled in millimeters as a grating. (The diffracting grating spacing is therefore one millimeter.) Let the beam skim the surface of the ruler. For a He-Ne laser (633 μm wavelength), projected over 12.5 meters, I obtained an interference spacing from zeroth-to-second order of 1.6 cm. You can measure this spacing in the demo and actually calculate the wavelength of light using a simple ruler and laser light. A true diffraction grating works much better but is often not understood by the students. Use pin holes, a hair, single and multiple slits, and various gratings to show other patterns.

Electromagnetic Waves and Spectrum

Simple electrostatics demonstrations are good at showing action at a distance for charges. A charged pith ball suspended by a thread will move when a charged wand is moved near it. Show how the interaction depends on the distance. The same may be done to demonstrate magnetic interactions but in this case use two strong magnets.

The demonstrate the visible continuous spectrum, use a slide projector or any strong source of light. Place a slit in front of it and direct towards a screen. (Do not tape a slit to the front on the projector. The heat build-up can easily crack the lens or otherwise damage the projector.) Use a good prism or diffraction grating that is slightly larger than the slit to form the spectrum. If a prism is used, a second prism may be used to reverse the spectrum back into white light.

Review the various major types of radiation as given in Figure 4.9. Help the students relate to each type by identify everyday examples.

infrared: although we can not see it, we do feel it. We have infrared (heat) sensitive cells in our skin that allow us to locate sources of infrared. Notice how warm a light bulb is when it is on. It is producing a lot of infrared, along with visible light.

ultraviolet: the danger of sunburn increases with elevation because there is decreasing protection from the Earth's atmospheric absorption of ultraviolet.

microwaves: in an oven they are "tuned" to vibrate water molecules. Water, which makes up at least 80% of most foods, becomes hot and heats the other molecules. Notice the screen in the front of the oven. Its holes are large enough to allow light to pass through but small enough to block microwaves.

am radio: 540 - 1600 kHz on the radio dial. Convert these frequencies into wavelengths (556 m - 188 m). Because of their long lengths, few objects, like buildings and hills, are large enough to block them.

fm radio: 88 - 108 MHz on the radio dial. Again, convert these to wavelengths (3.4 m - 2.8 m). These wavelengths are sufficiently short as to be blocked by buildings and hills. Diffraction helps some, but you get the best reception with a direct line-of-sight to the transmitter.

Kelvin Temperature Scale

It is always informative to demonstrate temperatures and to show the Kelvin scale. A large demonstration digital thermometer with a probe is good to use. Measure the temperatures of various objects such as boiling water, tap water, ice water, dry ice, room temperature, body temperature, and liquid nitrogen. Demonstrate the effects of cold temperatures on common materials. Cool in liquid nitrogen a piece of rubber tubing, a green leaf, and a small inflated balloon. Show how the rubber and leaf become brittle and the balloon seems to deflate, only to reinflate as it warms.

Planck Curve

Connect a filament light bulb (without the frosted glass) to a variac. Allow the students to observe the light (and infrared) produced by the bulb at various levels of power. Relate this qualitatively to temperature. As power is increased, the filament first glows a dull red, then orange, yellow, and white. Have a student hold a hand up to the bulb and comment on the amount of infrared coming from the bulb. At low temperatures (low power), most of the energy comes out in the form of infrared and very little as visible light. As power is increased, not only is more visible light produced, more infrared is produced. Establish the two ideas that at higher temperature, an object produces more radiation and at higher frequencies than at lower temperatures.

There are filament light bulbs available with a straight filament. Have students observed the filament using a diffraction grating and note the changes in the appearance of the continuous spectrum as the temperature of the filament is increased (Wien's Law). I have yet to find a good way to do this as a lecture demonstration. Students normally have to be close to the bulb to see a sufficiently bright spectrum.

The Doppler Effect

An easy demonstration of the Doppler Effect is tying a toy whistle or buzzer (battery operated) to the end of a string and twirling it over head. The variation in frequency is easily heard. Repeat the demonstration but this time twirl it vertically. Their should be little, if any, variation heard. Thus the motion must be towards or away from the observer to produce the Doppler Effect.

Make recordings of race cars as they rush by the microphone (easily done from a televised race) or from a friend driving by the recorder and blowing the car's horn. First record the car's horn when it is stationary, then again as it approaches and moves away. From the moving car, record a friend (who is stationary) blowing a horn or whistle. It does not matter whether it is the object or the observer who is moving; the Doppler Effect still occurs.

ANSWERS TO CHAPTER 3 REVIEW QUESTIONS

1. The wave period is a measurement of the amount of time needed for a wave to repeat itself at some point in space. The wavelength is the distance between any two consecutive positions in the wave, such as from peak to peak. The amplitude is the maximum height or depth of the wave above or below the undisturbed state. The wave frequency is the number of waves that pass a point per unit of time, usually waves per second.

2. The longer the wavelength, the lower the frequency; the shorter the wavelength, the higher the frequency. Wavelength and frequency are inversely related.

3. Diffraction is the ability of waves to bend around corners. A sharp -edged gap in a wall produces a fuzzy shadow due to diffraction. Diffraction would not occur if light strictly made of particles.

4. The speed of light is symbolized by the letter c. The speed of light is actually the speed of all electromagnetic radiation in a vacuum and is a constant.

5. The electric force is similar to the gravitational force in that it drops off by the inverse square of the distance. It is different in that it can be either attractive or repulsive; dislike charges attract and like charges repel. If the number of positive and negative charges are equal in an object, it appears to be neutral and have no electric force. Gravity is always present and is never neutralized.

6. A star contains many charged particles that are moving. This motion creates waves in the electric fields of the charged particles and these waves propagate or move outward and away from the star. Traveling at the speed of light, a few of these waves will finally reach a person's eye, which also contains charged particles. The waves make the charged particles move, and this motion is sensed by nerves and transmitted to the brain as an image of the star.

7. White light is made up of the colors violet, blue, green, yellow, orange, and red. The colors are simply waves of different wavelengths. Actually, white light is made up of all wavelengths of light between red and violet, a continuous spectrum. This spectrum is perceived by the eye as being made up of these 6 colors.

8. Radio waves, infrared radiation, visible light, ultraviolet radiation, x-rays, and gamma rays are all electromagnetic radiation and move at the speed of light in a vacuum. They differ only by their wavelengths (or frequencies), from longest wavelength (radio waves) to shortest wavelength (gamma rays).

9. The parts of the electromagnetic spectrum for which the Earth's atmosphere is transparent are the visible (when it isn't cloudy!), parts of the infrared, and radio waves between about one centimeter to ten meters.

10. A black body is an idealized object that absorbs all radiation falling on it. It also reemits all this radiation. The radiation emitted occurs at all wavelengths but peaks at a wavelength that depends on the temperature of the black body. The hotter the temperature, the shorter the wavelength of the peak radiation.

11. Wien's Law states that the wavelength at which a body emits the peak amount of radiation in its black-body curve depends inversely on the temperature of the body; no other factors are involved. By observing the wavelength at which this peak radiation occurs, the temperature of a star can be determined.

12. Stefan's Law relates the amount of radiation emitted by a black body to its temperature. The amount depends upon the fourth power of the temperature.

13. A star emits its radiation in all directions. A sphere surrounding a star at a given distance has its surface illuminated by the star. But the area of the sphere depends on its radius (distance from the star) squared. The larger the distance, the larger the area of the sphere and the more diluted the radiation falling on it. The radiation falling on any unit area of the sphere depends inversely on the square of the distance to the star.

14. The Doppler effect is the observed change in the wavelength (or frequency) of a wave due to the motion of the emitter, observer, or both, towards or away from each other. If the motion is towards each other, the observed wavelength appears shorter than the wave emitted. If the motion is away from each other, the observed wavelength appears longer than the wave emitted.

15. Even with clouds, the day-night cycle is quite evident. The lunar cycle would be evident from the light given off by the Moon, although it might not be clear what the object is that causes the lunar cycle. Radio radiation easily penetrates clouds. Little would be known about stars because their radiation is mostly at visible wavelengths.

16. As the coal cools off, its temperature decreases. According to Wien's Law, more and more of its radiation will be emitted at longer and longer wavelengths. According to Stefan's Law, it will emit less and less radiation as it cools. The net result is that it gets fainter and redder with time.

ANSWERS TO PROBLEMS

1. The relationship between frequency, wavelength, and wave velocity is $\lambda f = v$. The frequency is 100 MHz or 10^8/sec and $v = 3 \times 10^8$ m/sec. $\lambda = 3$ m.

2. Wien's Law states that the peak wavelength is inversely proportional to the temperature. Comparing 200 to 650 nm gives a factor of 3.25, therefore the object with a peak wavelength of 200 nm must be 3.25 times hotter than the object that peaks at 650 nm.
   Stefan's Law states that the energy radiated is proportional to T^4. If the hotter object is 3.25 hotter than the cooler object, it must radiate $(3.25)^4 = 112$ times as much energy as the cooler object.

3. $37 + 273 = 310$ K
   Using Wien's Law, $\lambda_{max} = 0.29/T$, with T in Kelvins and the wavelength in centimeters. For 310 K this gives $\lambda_{max} = 0.00094$ cm $= 9.4$ μm. This is in the infrared.

4. Using Wien's Law again, $\lambda_{max} = 0.29/1000$ gives $\lambda_{max} = 0.00029$ cm or 2.9 μm.

5. Since the shift is to a lower frequency, the wavelength is shifted to a longer wavelength. Thus the motion of the spacecraft must be away from the transmitter. To solve for the speed, the frequencies must be converted to wavelengths. The wavelengths are, respectively, $300.3/300 = 1 + v/c$. Solving for v gives $v = 10^5$ m/s or 300 km/s.

SUGGESTED READING

Cowen, R. "Heavenly Bodies Make Their UV Film Debut." *Science News* (January 26, 1991). Results from NASA's Ultraviolet Imaging Telescope.

Davies, J. K. "The Extreme Ultraviolet: A Promising New Window on the Universe." *Astronomy* (July 1987). The latest on using the extreme ultraviolet, or EUV, to understand the universe.

Englert, B-G. et al., "The Duality in Matter and Light." *Scientific American* (December, 1994).

Field, G. B. and Chaisson, E. J. *The Invisible Universe*. New York: Vintage Books, 1987. The universe as revealed by modern studies across the electromagnetic spectrum.

Griffin, R. "The Radial-Velocity Revolution." *Sky and Telescope* (September 1989). How increasingly sensitive radial velocity measurements are used in studies of possible binary systems and in the search for distant solar systems.

Minnaert, M. *Light and Color in the Outdoors*. New York: Springer-Verlag, 1993. A classic for half a century, this book explains the simple physics behind hundreds of everyday light phenomena.

Morris, R. *Light*. Indianapolis, New York: The Bobbs, Merrill Company, 1979. Off-beat but interesting history of man's thinking about light. Chapters include "Lasers" and "Light in Painting."

Vershuur, G. *The Invisible Universe Revealed*. New York: Springer Verlag, 1987. The story of modern radio astronomy.

Chapter 4
SPECTROSCOPY
The Inner Workings of Atoms

Spectral Lines

It is very traditional to allow students to observe the spectra of various gases. Use a gas discharge tube and power supply and give each student a grating to look through. For classroom demonstrations neon, sodium, and mercury usually produce the brightest spectra. For the laboratory environment, hydrogen and helium are very useful. If it is not possible to do this demonstration in a large lecture environment, allow the students to check out a grating and observe various light sources such as neon lights, street lamps (incandescent, mercury, or sodium), and fluorescent lights. Have them note which colors occur for each of these. There are excellent yet cheap student gratings available from Learning Technologies Inc.

In a laboratory environment or as a demonstration measure the wavelengths of the first three Balmer lines (in the red, green, and violet). Use the following wavelengths and colors for approximate measurements.

violet	blue	green	yellow	orange	red
4100	4600	5000	5700	6000	6500 Å

Determine the approximate wavelengths of the first 3 Balmer lines and calculate the energies of the third, fourth, and fifth energy levels (use 10.2 eV for the energy of the second level, the level from which the Balmer lines originate). Use the following formulae provided earlier in the text.

$$\lambda f = V \ \text{ and } \ E = hf$$

For example, the first line of hydrogen is seen in the red, so λ is estimated to be 6500Å.

$$f = 4.6 \times 10^{14} \ \text{sec}^{-1}$$
$$E = 3.1 \times 10^{-12} \ \text{erg}$$
$$E = 1.9 \ \text{eV}$$
$$E_3 = 10.2 + 1.9$$
$$E_3 = 12.1 \ \text{eV}$$

The wavelengths for these three lines are 6563, 4861, and 4340 Å. $E_4 = 12.75$ eV and $E_5 = 13.06$ eV. By setting the first energy level at zero eV and drawing the energy levels to scale in the usual way, the structure and convergence of the energy levels becomes quite apparent.

Energy Levels

The most important concepts to develop are that it requires energy to move up to a higher energy level and the energy levels are quantized. Attach two rubber balls to each other with a rubber string. Use a larger ball to represent the nucleus and a smaller ball for the electron. The lowest energy state is represented by the balls pulled apart but without the string being stretched. Holding the balls vertically, show that energy (work, actually) must be added to the electron in order for it to be in a higher energy level. When released from that higher energy level it freely gives up that energy. Continue the demonstration using the concepts of the absorption and emission of light.

Quantization, of course, does not occur on the macroscopic scale and is therefore more difficult to understand. A very simple idea is to use a meter stick with pegs inserted into holes drilled at various positions. Attach a large rubber band to one end of the stick and attack the other end to one of the pegs. The pegs represent the quantized levels of the atom. Stretching the rubber band to a higher level requires the input of energy. Just the correct amount of energy is needed to stretch it to a specific peg; more energy or less will make it miss the peg.

Absorption Line Identification

An excellent laboratory exercise, which may also be done in a limited fashion as a classroom demo, involves identifying absorption lines in the solar spectrum. Obtain a detailed copy of the solar spectrum. These are available from various sources in the form of an atlas, series of slides, or on a laser disc. I have used the latter because it is so easy to display on a screen and the spectrum is nicely enlarged. The spectrum should be marked with a wavelength scale for comparison. Again, the laser disc shows the spectrum marked every 100 Å. Establish a wavelength scale appropriate for the particular display being used and determine the wavelengths of various lines in the spectrum. Look up the wavelengths in *A Multiplet Table of Astrophysical Interest* by Charlotte E. Moore. Often there will be several different possibilities for the line identification. If well-planned in advance, common lines expected to be found in the spectrum can be assigned for measurement and identification. A special project can involve trying to identify the weaker lines.

The above experiment can be reversed by asking whether specific lines of specific elements are present in the spectrum. The exact location of a wavelength can be identified on the spectrum and it can be seen whether an absorption line occurs at that location.

ANSWERS TO CHAPTER 4 REVIEW QUESTIONS

1. Spectroscopy is the observation and study of spectra. Since light is about the only information received from

astronomical objects, this light is the source of all the information about those objects. Spectroscopy is the detailed study of this light and allows many properties of objects to be determined.

2. A simple spectroscope is made up of a slit, a prism, and an eyepiece or screen. The slit defines a narrow beam of light. The prism spreads the light out into its various wavelengths or colors. The eyepiece or screen allows the spectrum to be observed.

3. The spectrum emitted by a black body is known as a continuous spectrum. Light is emitted at all wavelengths but the amount of light emitted at each wavelength varies and depends on the temperature of the black body. An absorption spectrum appears like a continuous spectrum but with specific wavelengths missing. Dark vertical lines or bands, which can be quite narrow or very broad, are found throughout the spectrum.

4. Gamma rays carry much more energy in every photon than radio waves. They carry enough energy to harm living tissue. In passing through cells, gamma rays can break up important molecules, such as DNA, and also ionize atoms which then cause further cellular damage.

5. Color is usually related to wavelength; red is the longest wavelength and violet the shortest wavelength. Since wavelength and frequency are inversely proportional, red has the lowest frequency and energy; violet has the highest frequency and energy.

6. The hydrogen atom has one proton in its nucleus and one electron moving around it. The electron is found in one of many possible energy levels or orbitals.

7. The normal condition for atoms is one in which the number of electrons equals the number of protons in the nucleus. The electrons are in their lowest energy level. When an atom is excited an electron is found in a higher energy orbital. The precisely defined energy states or energy levels are referred to as orbitals. They are the regions occupied by electrons surround the nucleus.

8. In order for a photon to be absorbed, it must have an energy that is precisely equal to the energy difference between two energy levels, the lower level which is occupied by an electron. The electron absorbs the photon and moves to the higher energy level. Very quickly thereafter the electron moves back down to the lower energy level by emitting a photon of equal energy to the energy difference the two levels.

9. A star produces a continuous spectrum. However, this light passes through a cooler layer of gas surround the star. Specific wavelengths are absorbed by this gas and the resulting spectrum appears as an absorption spectrum, a continuous spectrum with specific wavelengths missing. Emission lines are not normally found in a stellar spectrum because they are produced in a hot, low density gas. Most stars have a layer of a cool, low density gas forming an absorption spectrum. However, in some cases such a hot, low density layer can form or can be found in clouds of gas between stars and an emission spectrum is seen.

Information about the composition and temperature of the cool gas, along with its motions, can be determined from the absorption lines.

10. According to Kirchhoff's first law, a luminous solid liquid or dense gas will emit light of all wavelengths and produce a continuous spectrum.

11. The H-alpha absorption line of hydrogen results from electrons jumping from the second to the third atomic orbital. Because the Sun's lower atmosphere is rather cool, relatively few atoms have electrons in the second orbital; most are in the ground state. Hence, in the Sun, the H-alpha line is weak.

12. Molecules can rotate and they can vibrate. These two motions have quantized energy levels just like the electrons in an atom. Changes in the rotational or vibrational state of a molecule will produce specific spectral lines unique to each molecule.

13. The intensity of a spectral line depends primarily on two factors, the number of atoms of a particular element and the number of those atoms that are able to make the necessary transition between orbitals to produce that spectral line. The first factor gives information on the existence and abundance of an element. The second factor depends on the temperature of the gas. Astronomers are thus able to determine the abundance of an element and temperature of the gas from line intensity.

14. When an atom produces a spectral line, the wavelength observed depends on the motion of the atom. The Doppler effect tells us that an atom moving towards us will produce a line that is observed to be shifted to shorter wavelengths; an atom moving away will produce an observed wavelength that is longer. In any hot gas there are atoms moving in all directions; the hotter the gas the faster they move. The net result is a broadening of the spectral line. Mass motions of the gas and stellar rotation will also produce broadening of the line in much the same way.

15. Radial velocity of the star, elemental abundance, temperature, rotation, turbulence, magnetic field, atmospheric pressure.

16. The emission lines will provide information about the abundance of the gas, density, temperature, and motion of the cloud.

ANSWERS TO PROBLEMS

1. $c = f\lambda$. 3×10^8 m/s $= f \times 600 \times 10^{-9}$ m. $f = 5 \times 10^{14}$ Hz

2. $E = hf$, so energy is proportional to frequency. A 1 nm gamma ray has a frequency of 3×10^8 m/s $= f \times 1 \times 10^{-9}$ m; $f = 3 \times 10^{17}$ Hz. The 10 MHz radio photon has a frequency of 10^7 Hz. The ratio of these two frequencies is 3×10^{17} Hz $/ 10^7$ Hz $= 3 \times 10^{10}$.

3. Because the energy of the two levels are so similar, the calculation needs to be carried out to more decimal places. $E_{100} = 13.59864$ eV, $E_{99} = 13.598612$ eV. The difference is 2.76×10^{-5} eV or 4.416×10^{-24} J. 4.416×10^{-24} J $= 6.63 \times 10^{-34}$ J s $\times$ f. $f = 6.66 \times 10^9$ Hz. This is 6660 MHz which is in the radio range. Its wavelength is 3×10^8 m/s $= 6.66 \times 10^9$ Hz $\times \lambda$. $\lambda = 0.045$ m or 4.5 cm.

4. $3 \rightarrow 2$, $2 \rightarrow 1$, $3 \rightarrow 1$ are the only possible combinations, so there are different photons that can be emitted. From the fourth level there are $4 \rightarrow 3$, $3 \rightarrow 2$, $2 \rightarrow 1$, or $3 \rightarrow 1$, $4 \rightarrow 2$, $2 \rightarrow 1$, $4 \rightarrow 1$ for a total of 7.

5. The H-α line has a wavelength of 656.3 nm. Using the Doppler formula from chapter 3 gives $655/656.3 = 1 + V/3 \times 10^8$ m/s. $V = -5.94 \times 10^5$ m/s or -594 km/s.

SUGGESTED READING

Achinstein, P. *Particles and Waves: Historical Essays in the Philosophy of Science.* New York, Oxford University Press, 1991. Contains historical background and more on the wave-particle debate about the nature of light.

Goldberg, L., "Atomic Spectroscopy and Astrophysics." *Physics Today* (August 1988). A personal retrospective on the importance of atomic physics to astronomy.

Griffin, R. "The Radial-Velocity Revolution." *Sky and Telescope* (September 1989). How increasingly sensitive radial velocity measurements are used in studies of possible binary systems and in the search for distant solar systems.

Hearnshaw, J. B., *The Analysis of Starlight.* Cambridge: Cambridge University Press, 1986. Subtitled "One Hundred and Fifty Years of Astronomical Spectroscopy."

Kaler, J. B., "Origins of the Spectral Sequence." *Sky and Telescope* (February 1986). How astronomers classify and interpret spectra.

Kaler, J. B., "Extraordinary Spectral Types." *Sky and Telescope* (February 1988). Objects that defy classification under the standard systems.

Chapter 5

TELESCOPES
The Tools of Astronomy

Telescope Optics

Use a large demonstration convex lens to show how light is focused and images produced by the optics of a telescope. A plain light bulb can serve as the object. Mark a large black × on the bulb to aid students in seeing the image. Also try using a bright colored bulb, such as green, to emphasize that optics are not "black and white" (a common misconception), but in color. Image the object onto a screen. Vary the object distance to demonstrate how the image distance depends on the object distance. Show how, as the object distance gets larger, the image distance varies less and less and is eventually at the focal length for very distant objects.

Chromatic aberration of the lens may be seen by using two differently colored bulbs, e.g. green and red, and showing that the image distances are different for the two. This is best demonstrated using a large diameter, short focal length lens.

A similar set of demonstrations may be done using a large, concave mirror. The setup is a little more difficult. These mirrors are often spherical, so image quality will not be that good. A paraboloid mirror is the best to use, if available. Use a small, bright bulb for better image quality. Use a small, white card to locate the image and serve as the screen. Slant the apparatus diagonally across the front of the classroom so that students can see the image. Again, demonstrate the dependence of image distance on object distance and the meaning of the focal length of the mirror.

When initially demonstrating the mirror, walk between the light source and the mirror in an attempt to find the image. Totally block the light to the mirror and point out the problem this makes in telescope design. Show how the small screen being used does not actually produce a dark spot in the middle of the image (another common misconception). Use larger and larger cards for a screen and show how the image brightness is reduced. A small, flat secondary mirror may be used to demonstrate the Newtonian focus design.

Different colored light bulbs may again be used to demonstrate the lack of chromatic aberration in mirrors. Reduced image quality some times makes this difficult to show, though.

An interesting variation of the above demonstrations involves using a strong source of infrared radiation, e.g. a hot, glowing stove filament or a heat lamp bulb. For imaging use a digital thermometer with a dark-colored probe with sufficient surface area. Show how the lens passes little, if any, infrared. The mirror is quite effective at collecting and focusing infrared. A very impressive demonstration using a strong source of infrared radiation and a match placed at the image distance. When the match ignites (it may take a few seconds), students are impressed and convinced the infrared is being focused!

Telescope Design

Many departments have old, unused refractors and Newtonians. Take one of each into class and disassemble in front of the class. For the refractor, first remove the eyepiece and the focusing rack and pinion and explain the purpose of the eyepiece. (It is only necessary for visual observations. The telescope works fine without one.) Next, remove the primary lens and show how it looks just like the demonstration lenses used earlier. Next, turn the tube vertically and drop something through it like a pencil. The tube is empty! The lens is really the telescope and the tube just helps support it and keeps the eyepiece aligned with the lens. The tube can also keep stay light from entering the telescope. Demonstrate the Newtonian in a similar fashion. Emphasize the basic simplicity of telescopes and the simplicity of their purpose: to collect large amounts of radiation (i.e. light, infrared, radio, etc.) and concentrate (focus) it into a usable image. That's about it!

Satellite dishes are commonly seen on campuses and at homes. Have students look at one and note the similarities in design to optical reflectors. Are they Newtonian, Cassegrain, or prime focus. Usually, one of the latter two.

Resolving Power

It is often difficult for students to see how the diffraction pattern demonstrated using a laser and a pin hole relates to the diffraction-limited optics of telescopes. Telescopes are about 1,000 bigger than pin holes and therefore the diffraction pattern will be 1,000 times smaller. But the image quality produced by a telescope allows the pattern to be seen.

Remind the students what the "size" of an arc second is. It is the breadth of a thin hair (0.05 mm) viewed from a distance of 10 m or a penny viewed from 2.5 miles.

Try the following demonstration which tests the resolving power of the human eye. On a plain sheet of white paper, draw two black dots 0.5 cm in diameter and separated by 1 cm. It should look something like this.

● ●

Now hold this pattern at a distance from a student so that they can just distinguish the two dots as two dots and not blurred together as one. Use the following table to give the resolving power (in arc minutes) at various distances. Humans with perfect vision have a resolving power of about 1 or 2 arc minutes; most classrooms will not be big enough for a person with good vision to see the two dots blur together. So try this experiment with students who have vision that is less than perfect! Have them remove their glasses and test their resolving power.

Distance (ft)	Resolving Power (arc minutes)
110	1
55	2
40	3
30	4
20	5
10	10
6	20
4	30
3	40

Have the students notice how their resolving power improves when they wear their glasses. Point out that this is analogous to the repair of the Hubble Space Telescope; it had less than good vision until corrective optics (glasses!) were installed. Its resolving power has now dramatically improved.

Telescope Mounts

The equatorial and alt-azimuth designs are the most important. A commercially produced Schmidt-Cassegrain (S-C) telescope can be used to demonstrate both designs. Without the wedge mount, the (S-C) is alt-azimuth. With the wedge, it is equatorial. Make sure the wedge is clamped down or mounted to a tripod, otherwise the telescope will not be stable. Use a globe of the Earth tilted so that your latitude appears horizontally on top of the globe. Show how the mount is tilted parallel to the Earth's axis. As the Earth rotates west to east, the objects appear to move east to west. The mount tracks accordingly. I prefer doing this entire demonstration outside during a night lab session, but this is not always possible.

Detectors

Show a photographic plate to the students. They will be unfamiliar with plates. Set it on an overhead projector so that the images (which are very small in most cases) can be seen. Although the photographic plate is not efficient in using light (quantum efficiencies of less than 1% are common), a plate records many images. Typical for an astrographic or Schmidt plate may 100,000 to over 1 million star images per plate.

If a plate is not available, select a slide of a very rich star field and project it onto a large screen. Estimate the number of stars in the field by counting the number of stars in a small region and multiplying by the number of regions in the picture.

Demonstrate a photodetector. Particularly useful are those with a digital display. These are commonly available at low cost. Show how the signal strength varies with light intensity. Although photodetectors are much more efficient (typically around 15%) than plates, they measure only the light from one star at a time. They also measure the light much more accurately than does a plate. Astronomers use to have to choose which they wanted, lots of star images with low quality information on each or high quality information on single stars.

Although the CCD can not be effectively demonstrated in class, describe how they allow astronomers to combine the best qualities of the plate and photodetector. They are very efficient (about 75%), they record a field of stars, and they allow accurate determinations of the brightness of each star or object in the field.

For decades, astronomers did not build larger and larger telescopes because they knew their detectors were wasting most of the light the telescopes were collecting. Emphasis was placed on building new and more efficient detectors instead of larger telescopes. With the availability of CCDs, the emphasis is now on larger telescopes because the CCD is utilizing most of the light collected by the telescope.

Demonstrate how a Geiger counter works. Set the audio level high enough for the students to hear. Hide a small radioactive source ahead of time and find it with the Geiger counter. Place the Geiger tube at the end of a pipe, preferably lead. The angular resolution of the detector can be increased in this way. Sweep across the source in a series of scans to show how an "image" of the source might be produced by a similar detector in space. Although this is the old way of imaging x-ray and gamma ray sources, it does demonstrate how this radiation has to dealt with differently from other forms of electromagnetic radiation because of the higher energies.

ANSWERS TO CHAPTER 5 REVIEW QUESTIONS

1. The two reasons why larger telescopes are better than smaller telescopes are greater collecting area and better angular resolution. The primary purpose of a telescope is to make faint objects bright enough to detect. Larger telescope mirrors collect more light and bring it to a focus. It is also necessary to see detail in the image formed by the telescope, to resolve two objects that appear close to each other. Larger telescope mirrors produce less diffraction, which blurs an image and limits resolution.

Currently, there seems to be a sudden interest in building large telescopes. The last large telescope was built in 1948, the Palomar Observatory 5 meter telescope. For about 4 decades astronomers did not seem interested in building larger telescopes. Why did this suddenly change? The answer is that the detectors of light used by astronomers were very inefficient; they wasted most of the light received by the telescope. A photographic emulsion is no better than 5% efficient, 95% of the light is wasted. Other detectors were not much better than 10% efficient. Astronomers were not limited by the size of their telescopes but by the inefficiencies of their detectors. When CCD detectors became available, astronomers could use up to 75% of the light, so little light was wasted. Now, to see fainter objects, they had to start building bigger telescopes.

2. The largest telescopes are reflecting telescopes primarily because of 3 distinct disadvantages of the refracting telescope. When light passes through a lens, light of different wavelengths focus at slightly different places. This is known as chromatic aberration and can produce seriously out of focus images. It is not easy to correct when making large lenses. Note, however, that camera lenses are quite successful in correcting this aberration, else wise all your color photos would be rather blurry. A second problem is the glass lens absorbs certain wavelengths of light that the astronomers needs to observe. In the infrared, for instance, glass is not transparent like it is for visible light. In the infrared, the glass lens blocks light from entering the telescope. Lastly, it is difficult to keep a lens bigger than about one meter from bending in its support. Glass is flexible and lenses can only be supported around their edge. When a large glass lens bends due to its own weight, its curvature changes and so does the focus, thus ruining the image.

3. The Earth's atmosphere smears out images seen in telescopes. "Seeing" is the blurring in the image of an object, such as a star, as its light passes through the Earth's atmosphere. Instead of the star image being very small, limited by the diffraction of the telescope, the image is blurred to many times this size. The atmosphere of the Earth is not homogeneous; it is turbulent and contains layers of varying temperatures and density. Light passing through these layers are refracted into many slightly different paths. Fortunately for astronomers, the Earth's atmosphere is really rather thin and so the images are not completely blurred to uselessness.

4. The Hubble Space Telescope is not affected by seeing because it orbits above the Earth's atmosphere. It can also observe at wavelengths that are absorbed by the Earth's atmosphere. It's disadvantages are several; it is a very complex telescope to use and astronomers must use it remotely. If something goes wrong, they can not easily fix it. Since it orbits close to the Earth, half the sky is blocked by the Earth. Because it orbits quickly around the Earth, objects may be observable for only part of the time; the rest of the time they are blocked by the Earth.

5. A CCD is a charge-coupled device. It has thousands of individual detectors arranged in a grid, each much more sensitive than a photographic plate. The light level of each detector is read out by computer. A CCD's primary advantages are its high sensitivity to light, its linear response to light (twice as much light produces twice as much signal, unlike a photographic plate which is highly non-linear), and the ease with which the image can be processed by computer software.

6. CCDs produce an electronic picture that is in digital form. The image is stored as a series of numbers in the memory of a computer. The raw data, however, can contain flaws produced by imperfections in the CCD chip, optical defects in the telescope, and unwanted light entering the CCD camera. Computer programs can remove most of these effects and produce clean images. This process is known as image processing.

7. The Hubble Space Telescope compensates for atmospheric blurring by orbiting the Earth outside the atmosphere. On the surface of the Earth adaptive optics are just now being developed that change the shape of mirrors in the telescope in order to compensate for atmospheric distortions.

8. The resolution of a telescope depends on the wavelength of the light observed; the longer the wavelength, the lower the resolution. Radio waves are very long relative to visible light. Since larger telescopes produce higher resolution, radio telescopes must be very large, compared to optical telescopes, in order to have a useful resolving power.

9. Conditions in some objects produce radio waves but little or no visible light. Some objects produce both but by different mechanisms. Radio astronomy allows all these objects to be studied. The radio emissions reveal a great deal of information about the objects that could not be learned by observations in visible light.

10. Interferometry is a technique that uses two or more separate telescopes to synthesize a larger telescope, equivalent in size to the telescopes' separation. Although the collecting area of this array of telescopes is not as large as one telescope the size of their separation, angular resolution is obtained equivalent to a telescope of such a size. Using telescopes that are widely separated, radio astronomers are able to obtain resolutions are very high, far better than in the optical.

11. Even large radio telescopes have poor resolution when compared to optical telescopes. To improve their resolution would require radio telescopes of enormous size; at least kilometers in diameter. The technique of interferometry synthesizes a telescope of this size by separating several radio telescopes by this distance and simultaneously observing the same object. Using some rather complex computer processing, the individual images are combined to synthesize what would have been observed by a telescope the size of the separation between the telescopes. Radio interferometry can now reach resolutions that are far better than optical telescopes.

12. Infrared observations must be conducted above much of the Earth's atmosphere because it absorbs much of the infrared radiation coming from space. Because anything that is warm emits strongly in the infrared, the telescopes and instruments must be cooled to low temperatures to reduce the amount of interference from them. Infrared observations are best done from space.

13. Many objects emit their peak amount of radiation at wavelengths other than visible. When the universe is observed at new wavelengths, these different objects suddenly become visible and astronomers are then able to study them.

14. With one degree resolution, the smallest objects visible to the eye would have to be about 60 times bigger than they are now. Reading or any close work would be very difficult or impossible. If we could only see in the infrared, many things would look very different than they do now. Instead of seeing some objects by reflected light, we would see them by the infrared light that they emitted, due to their warmth. This question is open-ended and much more could be added to this response.

ANSWERS TO PROBLEMS

1. The amount of light collected by a telescope depends on the area of the mirror; the area depends on the square of the diameter. A 6-m telescope is 3 times bigger in diameter than a 2-m telescope but it has $3^2 = 9$ times the light gathering power. The larger telescope will gather light 9 times faster than the smaller telescope, so what the 2-m telescope can accomplish in 1 hour, the 6-m can accomplish in 1/9 hour or about 7 minutes.

2. The angular resolution of a telescope is inversely pro-

portional to the wavelength. (a) 3.5 μm = 3,500 nm. 3,500/700 = 5, so the wavelength is 5 times longer. The resolution should be 5 times poorer or $0.05'' \times 5 = 0.25''$. (b) Similarly, 140 nm/700nm = 0.2 and $0.05'' \times 0.2 = 0.01''$.

3. The CCD records 75/5 = 15 times as much light as a photographic plate. If it took 1 hour to photograph an object, it should take the CCD 1/15 as long or $60^m/15 = 4^m$. (In practice, the CCD will likely record this light even faster than this. This is because the photographic process does not have a constant efficiency. If it is 5% efficient at the start of the exposure, it will be much less efficient by the end of the hour. But CCDs have an efficiency that remains constant. This can result in the CCD being more like 100 times better than the photographic plate.)

4. Set up a ratio of the angle to 360° is equal to the distance at Andromeda to the circumference of a circle at Andromeda's distance. Change degrees to arc seconds.

$$\frac{d}{2\pi \times 700,000} = \frac{0.05''}{360° \times 3600''/°}$$
$$d = 0.17 \text{ pc.}$$

At a resolution of 0.001" the radio interferometer has 50 times the resolution and so should be able to see a distance 50 times smaller than HST. This is 0.15 pc / 50 = 0.0034 pc or 700A.U.

5. Area is proportional to diameter squared. $6 \times (4 \text{ m})^2 = 96 \text{ m}^2$. Taking the square root of this to get the diameter of a single mirror of equivalent area gives 9.8 m.

SUGGESTED READING

Balick, B. "Astrophysics at Apache Point." *Sky and Telescope* (August 1988). A fully automatic 3.5-meter telescope in New Mexico. Accompanying article describes Roger's Angel's technique for making "spin-cast" telescope mirrors.

Bowyer, S., "Extreme Ultraviolet Astronomy." *Scientific American* (August, 1994). The sky is now being explored in one of the least accessible parts of the spectrum.

Bunge, R., "Big Scopes: Dawn of a New Era." *Astronomy* (August, 1993).

Fugate, R. Q., and Wild, W. J. "Untwinkling the Stars—Part I." *Sky and Telescope* (May 1994). How adaptive optics is changing the way astronomers think about ground-based astronomy.

Wild, W. J., and Fugate, R.Q. "Untwinkling the Stars—Part II." *Sky and Telescope* (June 1994).

Gatley, I., "An Infrared View of Our Universe." *Astronomy* (April, 1994).

Gehrels, N. et al., "The Compton Gamma Ray Observatory." *Scientific American* (December, 1993).

Hardy, J. W., "Adaptive Optics." *Scientific American* (June, 1994). Removing the effects of atmospheric distortion in stellar images.

"*Hubble's* Agony and Ecstasy." *Sky and Telescope* (January 1991). Early results from the *Hubble Space Telescope.*

Jelley, J. V. and Weekes, T. C., "Ground-based Gamma-ray Astronomy." *Sky & Telescope* (September, 1995) Excellent review of the topic and the mechanisms that produce the observed radiation.

Krisciunas, K., "Science with the Keck Telescope." *Sky & Telescope* (September, 1994).

Kristian, J., and M. Blanke, "Charge-coupled Devices in Astronomy." *Scientific American* (October 1982). Tiny television sensors that have enabled astronomers to obtain a new, vastly more detailed look at the heavens.

Learner, R. "The Legacy of the 200-Inch." *Sky and Telescope* (April 1986). How the successful design of the Palomar 200-inch telescope suppressed fresh ideas about ways to build large telescopes for four decades.

MacRobert, A. "Stunning Planet Images from Earth." *Sky and Telescope* (June 1991). High-resolution images of solar system objects, obtained using CCDs at the Pic du Midi Observatory.

McLean, I. S., "Infrared Arrays: The Next Generation." *Sky & Telescope* (June, 1995). CCDs are now in used in the infrared, for imaging and spectroscopy.

Ratcliffe, M. "Remote Astronomy: Bringing Mount Wilson to you." *Sky and telescope* (July 1994). Increasingly, astronomers are able to observe the heavens through major telescopes from long distance, without ever visiting the instruments they use.

Strom, S. "New Frontiers in Ground-based Optical Astronomy." *Sky and Telescope* (July 1991). What some proposed and existing ground-based telescopes are expected to reveal about the universe.

Tresch-Fienberg, R. "*HST:* Astronomy's Discovery Machine." *Sky and Telescope* (July 1990). Deployment into space of the *Hubble Space Telescope.* Includes general information about the telescope.

Tresch-Fienberg, R. "Hubble's Image Restored." *Sky and Telescope* (April 1994). The *Hubble* repair mission, along with some remarkable examples of the telescope's corrected optics.

Tucker, W., and K. Tucker. *The Cosmic Inquirers.* Cambridge, MA: Harvard University Press, 1986. Based on a series of interviews, this book reveals how and why prominent astronomers accomplished their goals of building and operating large observatories.

Chapter 6

THE SOLAR SYSTEM
An Introduction to Comparative Planetology

Scale of the Solar System

Figure 6.5 shows the planetary orbits drawn to scale. It is very helpful to reproduce this on the chalk board. Use a scale of 1 AU = 10 or 20 cm, which ever fits the board, and the data from Table 6-1 for the construction. Place the Sun on the far left or right; Pluto will be on the other end. The terrestrial planets will be a bit crowded together, but this is okay since it emphasizes the real situation. Note to the students that the size of the Sun, on this scale, is 1 or 2 millimeters, depending on which scale is used. The planets are like chalk dust; the Earth would be 100 times too small to be seen with the eye, even the orbit of the Moon would be too small to see. It is also appropriate to note at this time that the nearest star, Alpha Centauri, would be 29 km (18 miles) away on the scale of 1 AU = 10 cm.

Under each planet give the mass (in Earth masses), number of moons, escape velocity, temperature, and density. (I prefer to use gm/cm^3 for density.) Note the differences between the Terrestrial and Jovian planets. Pluto is always an exception! Using the density, anticipate some of the expected differences that will be found among the planets, e.g. the Jovian planets are lower in density so their composition must be of lower density material.

Sizes of Planets and Moons

Figure 6.7 shows the relative sizes quite nicely. The transparency of this figure is very useful in discussing this in class. It is not so important for students to know the numerical properties of the planets as it is for them to understand the comparative properties. This chapter emphasizes the importance of this approach. Note that when the sizes of planets are being discussed it is almost impossible to also discuss their distances or compare sizes to distances; the scales are just too different. The Astronomical Unit is 11,600 times bigger than the Earth's diameter. In class I often use a 12-inch globe of the Earth and a 3-inch ball for the Moon; I can scale the Earth-Moon system by size and distance within the confines of the classroom. But the Sun would be over 2 miles away at this scale.

In Figure 6.7, if the Earth and Moon were separated by their true (scaled) distance, the Moon would have to be placed where Neptune appears. The Earth-Moon distance would seem to make for another useful comparison, e.g. Jupiter's diameter is over one third this distance. However, most people do not have a good intuitive feeling for the distance to the Moon, i.e. it is much farther away than it

appears, and so this type of comparison does not work particularly well.

For a more hands-on approach cut out scale models of the planets and the largest moons (the Moon, Io, Europa, Ganymede, Callisto, Titan, and Triton). Use white cardboard. A convenient scale to use is one Earth diameter = 5 cm. Use the relative sizes given in Table 6-1 for the planets. Using this scale for the Earth, the Sun would be 5.4 m in diameter (draw it approximately on the chalk board or project a slide of the Sun to that size. A large circle on an overhead transparency will also work well.), the Earth-Moon distance is 1.5 m, and an Astronomical Unit would be 600 m or about the length of 6 football fields. Compare the sizes of the largest moons to the terrestrial planets. When discussing individual planets later, these models can be used again to demonstrate the relative sizes of the moons and their orbits. Planetary rings can also be added, if desired.

Escape Velocity

Once the escape velocity from the Earth is calculated (11.2 km/s), it is very easy to calculate for other objects using the formula given in the *More Precisely* feature on p. 136. This also gives students the opportunity to calculate escape velocities for other interesting objects.

$$\text{Escape Velocity} = 11.2 km/s \sqrt{\frac{mass}{radius}}$$

Mass and radius must be in Earth units, as found in Table 6-1.

On what size object could a person pitch a ball at escape velocity? A person can pitch a ball at a speed of 50 mph (80 km/hr). Convert this to 0.022 km/sec and apply the above formula. The mass isn't known but density can be substituted for mass, so that the formula now looks like the following.

$$11.2\sqrt{\rho R} = 0.022$$

For a density of about 0.5 Earth's density, this gives R = 0.0028 Earth diameter or about 20 miles in diameter. A person could pitch a ball at escape velocity on a typical asteroid!

Planetary Atmospheres

Using the information and examples provided in the *More Precisely* feature on p. 136, make predictions as to whether the various objects in Table 6-1 will have atmospheres and whether they can hold hydrogen in their atmosphere.

Remember, for molecules of the same type, the average molecular velocity is proportional to √temperature.

Hydrogen in Earth's Atmosphere
Hydrogen molecules move at 2 km/s
2 × 6 = 12 km/s > 11.2 km/s
So Hydrogen has escaped from Earth

Atmosphere of Pluto
At a temperature of 50 K it has lower molecular velocities

$$\sqrt{\frac{50}{300}} = 0.41$$

0.41 × 0.5 × 6 = 1.2 km/s ~ 1.3 km/s
It might just barely keep an atmosphere like Earth's,
but what about an atmosphere of methane?
Oxygen is twice as heavy as methane so methane will have speeds of
$\sqrt{2}$ = 1.4 times that of oxygen (0.5) = 0.7 km/s
Repeating the above calculation gives
0.41 × 0.7 × 6 = 1.7 km/s < 1.3 km/s
Mercury will lose methane
Hydrogen in Jupiter
The temperature is about 100 K by

$$\sqrt{\frac{100}{300}} = 0.58$$

But hydrogen will move 4 times faster than 2 km/s, therefore
0.58 × 2 × 6 = 7 km/s > 60 km/s
Jupiter can easily hold hydrogen in its atmosphere

Now I come to the most important aspect of this chapter; it is a marvel, and typical of science, what has been discovered in this chapter about the planets from just a bit of information and some physics.

We have gone from examining some very fundamental properties of the planets to making some very important predictions about the compositions of their atmospheres. Each step has combined observation and theory to lead us to new information. Observation of lunar periods, combined with Kepler's Third Law, allows a planetary mass to be determined. We started the chapter looking for similarities and differences among the planets and have ended with an understanding of the fundamental differences between the Jovian and Terrestrial planets. This process will be repeated again and again, it is the Scientific Method.

ANSWERS TO CHAPTER 6 REVIEW QUESTIONS

1. In our solar system there are 1 Sun, 9 planets, 61 (known) moons, asteroids, meteoroids, comets, and interplanetary dust. There are at least two basic types of planet, terrestrial and Jovian, found in the inner and outer parts of the solar system. The terrestrial planets are all found close to the Sun, within 1.5 A.U. The Jovian planets are scattered out at much greater distances, from about 5 to 30 A.U. Pluto, which is neither a Jovian or Terrestrial planet, is at about 40 A.U. The space between these objects is a better vacuum (space void of matter) than can be produced on Earth, although it contains much more material in the form of dust and gas than found between the stars.

2. Mercury, Venus, Earth, Mars, Jupiter, Saturn, Uranus, Neptune, Pluto.

3. Comparative planetology contrasts and compares the properties of objects throughout the solar system. Typical examples are the comparison of Mars and Venus to the Earth or Mercury to the Moon. By looking for similarities, new objects can be understood; by looking for differences, new processes are revealed.

   By understanding the similarities and differences among the bodies of the solar system, it will be possible to understand its origin and evolution. In the end, we might hope to understand the Earth much better than we do now. By seeing how other bodies formed and developed we may be able to understand how Earth developed its environment that has been so supportive of life. It is not clear at this time that other bodies have done this nor is it understood why they have or have not.

4. Over the last several centuries, telescopes have revealed many of the objects of the solar system that are invisible to the naked eye. Often, little but the existence and motion of these bodies could be observed. But space probes, during the last few decades, have revealed what these objects really look like. Instruments on board the probes also tell us much about other properties, such as the magnetic fields and compositions, that would be impossible to observe from Earth.

5. The Titius-Bode "Law" is an approximate formula for calculating the distances between the Sun and the planets. Described in *Interlude 6-1*, the rule says to take Mercury's distance and add to it 0.3 doubled for each subsequent planet. It actually does not say anything about Mercury's orbit, predicts a planet between Mars and Jupiter, and incorrectly predicts the positions of Neptune and Pluto. It is not a true scientific law because it is not accurate and is not based on any fundamental principles. Some use it as an easy way of remembering the distances of the planets from the Sun; others would argue it is simply easier to remember the actual distances than to use the Titius-Bode law and its exceptions!

6. Using the Titius-Bode Law, as given in Interlude 6-1 gives the positions as 38.8, 77.2, and 154.0 A.U. for the ninth, tenth, and eleventh planets.

7. The terrestrial planets are Mercury, Venus, Earth, and Mars. They are called terrestrial because they are simi-

lar to the Earth in their physical and chemical properties. The Jovian planets are Jupiter, Saturn, Uranus, and Neptune. Jovian means Jupiter-like; the Jovian planets have Jupiter-like properties.

8. Three differences between Jovian and Terrestrial planets: (1) location in the solar system, (2) size of the planets, (3) density. The Terrestrial planets are in the inner 1.5 A.U. of the solar system; the Jovian planets are scattered from 5 to 30 A.U. The Jovian planets are much larger than the Terrestrial planets. Terrestrial planets have a much higher density than the Jovian planets, which indicates a fundamental difference in composition. Terrestrial planets are rocky, Jovian planets are made up of light elements.

9. Pluto is not a Jovian planet, nor a terrestrial planet, because it is small and icy and has properties of neither type of planet.

10. Gravity holds the atmosphere to the planet, heat opposes gravity and determines the thickness of the atmosphere. Gravity determines the escape velocity from the planet. The velocity of the atoms or molecules of the gas due to its temperature must be generally lower than the escape velocity in order for the planet to have an atmosphere. But the composition of the gas is also quite important. At any temperature, light molecules move fast and heavy molecules move slowly. So, the planet's gravity is able to retain gases of certain types and this is related to the temperature of the atmosphere.

   If a planet's temperature increased or if its mass decreased, gases made of lower weight molecules could now escape because they would be able to move faster than the escape velocity.

11. Asteroids and meteoroids are important because they often contain material that has undergone little change since the solar system was formed. The surface material of the Earth and Moon, for instance, has changed greatly over time, thus little is known about the original conditions under which they were formed.

12. The ices that make up a comet become gaseous as the comet nears the Sun. These gases emit light which can be analyzed. Comets also release dusty particles which reflect sunlight and reveal information about their size and composition.

13. Rocket engines are sometimes insufficient to propel spacecraft to the needed speeds to reach the outer planets. Gravity assists allow a spacecraft to "rob" a planet of a tiny bit of its orbital energy to boost its speed. This method is also a cheap solution to this sort of problem.

14. All planets have been visited by spacecraft with the exception of Pluto. Spacecraft have landed only on Venus and Mars.

ANSWERS TO PROBLEMS

1. To do this problem, the Earth's mass, radius, and density must be known. Looking these up in the Appendix, Table 3 gives, respectively 5.97×10^{24} kg, 6.378×10^6 m, and 5520 kg/m^3. Assume a spherical shape for a planet and density is mass divided by volume. Example for Mercury:

$$\text{Density} = \frac{0.06 \times 5.97 \times 10^{24}\, kg}{4/3\pi (0.4 \times 6.378 \times 10^6\, m)^3}$$

Density = 5150 kg/m^3 or 0.93 the density of the Earth.

2. The distance between Earth (1.0 A.U. from the Sun) and Jupiter (5.2 A.U. from the Sun), at closest approach is 4.2 A.U. 1 A.U. is about 150 million km, so 4.2 A.U. is about 6.3×10^8 km. Light (and radio waves) travel at 300,000 km/s and so will travel the Earth-Jupiter distance in 6.3×10^8 km / 300,000 km/s = 2100 s or 35 minutes. The round trip takes 70 minutes or 1 hour and 10 minutes. Mission Control on Earth can not maneuver spacecraft in real time because it would take over an hour for a command to be sent and a response returned; the delay is too long for maneuvering a high-speed spacecraft.

3. If the mass and radius of a body are given in Earth units, then the escape velocity is given as

$$\text{Escape Velocity} = 11.2\, km/s \sqrt{\frac{\text{mass of object}}{\text{radius of object}}}$$

For Mercury, using the values for its mass and radius from Interlude 6-2 gives

$$\text{Escape Velocity} = 11.2\, km/s \sqrt{\frac{0.055}{0.38}}$$

Escape Velocity = 4.3 km/s, as given in the table.

4. The total mass of all asteroids would be 6000×10^{17} kg = 6×10^{20} kg. The average mass of a Terrestrial planet is about 0.5 Earth masses or 3×10^{24} kg. Comparing these, 3×10^{24} kg / 6×10^{20} kg = 5,000. Thus, an average Terrestrial planet has 5,000 times more mass than all the asteroids combined. As we see them today, the asteroids would not make up much of a planet!

5. The Earth is at 1 A.U. and Mars is at 1.52 A.U. (using its semi-major axis as an average distance). The major axis of the orbit must be the sum of these or 2.52 A.U. The semi-major axis of the orbit is half this or 1.26 A.U. The distance between the Sun and the center of the orbit is the semi-major axis minus the perihelion distance or 1.26 - 1 = 0.26 A.U. Eccentricity is this latter distance divided by the semi-major axis; 0.26 / 1.26 = 0.21. Using Kepler's third law to determine the orbital period gives $P^2 = 1.26^3$. P = 1.4 yrs.

6. From Interlude 6-2 we know that Jupiter's escape velocity is 60 km/s. One sixth of this is 10 km/s; the velocity that molecules must have to escape. Jupiter's current molecular velocity is 1.2 km/s for its temperature of 100 K. This velocity must increase by a factor of 8 to reach 10 km/s. The average molecular velocity is proportional to the square root of the temperature; the temperature is therefore proportional to the square of the molecular velocity. 8^2 x 100 K = 6400 K, which is a little more than the surface temperature of the Sun!

SUGGESTED READING

Beatty, J. K., and A. Chaikin, eds. *The New Solar System.* 3d ed. Cambridge, MA: Cambridge University Press and Sky Publishing, 1990. An authoritative synthesis of planetary exploration, by 26 scientists in the field.

Hartley, K. "Solar System Chaos." *Astronomy* (May 1990). The dynamics of the solar system in light of modern chaos theory.

Littmann, M. *Planets Beyond: Discovering the Outer Solar System.* New York: John Wiley & Sons, 1988. Tales of Uranus, Neptune, and Pluto. Includes descriptions of what modern spacecraft have found.

Lovi, G. "The Solar System Seen from Outside." *Sky and Telescope* (August 1986). Excellent for showing how our viewpoint on a moving planet determines the way we see other members of our solar system.

Miller, R., and W. K. Hartmann, *The Grand Tour: A Traveler's Guide to the Solar System.* New York: Workman Publishing, 1981. Imaginative guide to the solar system, with many photos and paintings by the authors.

Sheehan, W. *Planets and Perception: Telescopic Views and Interpretations 1609—1909.* Tucson: University of Arizona Press, 1988.

"Were Titius and Bode Right?" *Sky and Telescope* (News Notes, April 1987). A mechanism by modern theorists that explains how the orbits of the planets came to be where they are.

Chapter 7

THE EARTH
Our Home in Space

Earth's Structure; Density, Buoyancy, and Differentiation

The Earth is not mostly made up of water! Obvious? Well, not to many students; actually this is a common misconception. If you have not yet demonstrated density, as suggested in Chapter 5, this is a good time to do so. Make sure you determine the density of two objects, one denser and one less dense than water.

Buoyancy is a concept related directly to density and of importance in the study of planetary structure. When the density of an object is greater than a fluid, that object will sink in that fluid. A common rock has a density in the range of 2000-3000 kg/m^3 and will sink in water, which has a density of 1000 kg/m^3. The continents, made up of this rock can not float on an interior of the Earth made of water; they would sink! The average density of the Earth (5500 kg/m^3) implies an interior with a higher density than the crust and therefore the crust actually "floats" on the higher density material of the mantle (which is semi-fluid). Now show the transparency of Figure 7.1 and have the students see not only the structure of the Earth but how its layers depend upon density variation, from a high in the core of about 12000 kg/m^3 to about 5000 kg/m^3 in the mantle to about 3000 kg/m^3 in the crust. The oceans with a density of 1000 kg/m^3 float on the crust and the atmosphere with a density of 1 kg/m^3 float above the continents and oceans.

Since solid rock is rather difficult to move through, the question arises as to how did the crust get to the top and the high density rock to the core? The answer is differentiation. The Earth had to be molten when it was very young.

Tidal Force

The tides are unfamiliar to many students who do not live near coastal areas. Even for those students who regularly experience tides, they are usually at a loss to explain how there can be two high and two low tides each day. If the concept of the Moon pulling the tide on the Earth is known at all by students, it usually results in them saying there must be one high tide (pointing to the Moon) and one low tide (on the opposite side of the Earth). Various demonstrations, using rubber rings (dog toys) and small inflated inner tubes, have been used to show the effects of tides. The rings or tubes are pulled on one side and become elliptically shaped like the tidal pattern. But students often find these unconvincing because they want to know who or what is holding the other side of the Earth to stretch it into this shape! It is a good question.

The tidal force is simply a *differential* gravitational force, i.e. it results from differences in the gravitational pull of the Moon from one side of the Earth to the other *relative to the pull at the center of the Earth*. The tidal pull can easily be shown using a little calculus and Newton's law of gravity. With greater difficulty the same result can be obtained using algebra. Although mathematical explanations may not be as satisfying to some students, it is none-the-less another approach to helping them understand the reason for the two high and two low tides. First the calculus approach.

$$F = -\frac{GMm}{r^2}$$

$$\frac{dF}{dr} = \frac{2GMm}{r^3}$$

$$\frac{dF}{F} = \frac{2dr}{r}$$

The algebra takes a bit more work but will (must!) give the same basic result. For a small change in r, Δr, there is a small change in F, ΔF. As r gets larger, F gets smaller, which explains the signs in the starting equation.

$$F + \Delta F = -\frac{GMm}{(r + \Delta r^2)}$$

Solve for ΔF, factor out F, and place everything over a common denominator,

$$\Delta F = F\left[\frac{1 - 1 - 2\dfrac{\Delta r}{r} - \dfrac{\Delta r^2}{r^2}}{1 + 2\dfrac{\Delta r}{r} + \dfrac{\Delta r^2}{r^2}}\right]$$

Although this looks very messy, it quickly reduces to the answer. If Δr is the radius of the Earth and r is the Earth-Moon distance, then $\Delta r/r$ is about 0.017, which is < 1. The squared terms in $\Delta r/r$ are completely insignificant and the one term of $\Delta r/r$ in the denominator is also small compared to the 1. In the numerator the $\Delta r/r$ can not be set to zero or else the whole expression is zero. Finally one obtains,

$$\frac{\Delta F}{F} = -\frac{2\Delta r}{r}$$

which is the same as the result from calculus. Now a physical interpretation can be obtained from either of these expressions.

The Earth-Moon distance, r, is measured from the Moon to the center of the Earth. Δr is going to be ± radius of the Earth. Thus, the tidal force appears to be the same on both sides of the Earth (towards or away from the Moon). The size of the tidal force, $\Delta F/F$, is about 0.034 or 3% as stated in the text.

The above calculation seems to have a significant limitation in that it calculates the tidal force for only two points on the Earth. To derive the force at other locations can be done approximately from these results.

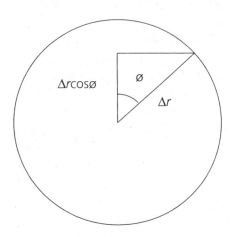

As cosø varies from 0 to 90 degrees, the tidal force varies. At 90 degrees there is no force, i.e. low tide. The elliptical shape of the tidal bulge can thus be plotted out.

Atmospheric Structure

Use a meter stick to model the atmosphere (1 cm = 1 km). The Earth would be larger than a football field at this scale. Use the following to demonstrate the various levels. Also refer to Figure 7.4.

5 cm	Half the atmosphere lies below this level.
8 cm	The tallest mountain, Mt. Everest.
9-12cm	Cruising altitude of jet airliners.
10 cm	90% of the atmosphere is below this level.
15cm	Top of the troposphere, most of the weather occurs below this level.
24cm	Altitude record for a jet, set by SR-71
30cm	99% of the atmosphere is below this level.
15-50cm	Stratosphere
20-50cm	Location of the ozone layer.
50-90cm	Mesosphere
90-250cm	Thermosphere
200cm	Low Earth Orbit satellites and Space Shuttle

ANSWERS TO CHAPTER 7 REVIEW QUESTIONS

1. The density of water is 1000 kg/m³ and the density of rock is typically 3000 kg/m³. Since the average density of the Earth is 5500 kg/m³ then the interior of the Earth must be made up of high density material.

2. Rayleigh scattering is the effect by which particles selectively scatter waves, depending on the waves' wavelengths. Particles tend to scatter waves whose wavelengths are about equal to or smaller than the particle size. Rayleigh scattering accounts for the blue sky of Earth and red sunrises and sunsets.

3. The magnetosphere is that region around a planet that is most influenced by the planet's magnetic field. The magnetic field can trap charged particles. Very early satellites detected fast moving particles that were trapped in our magnetic field. The regions in which the particles were found are called the Van Allen Belts.

4. Both P-waves and S-waves are seismic waves that move outward from the site of an earthquake. P-waves are the first to arrive; these pressure waves alternately expand and compress the material through which they move, just as sound waves do. They move through both liquids and solids. S-waves are shear waves and are like waves on the surface of water. They move more slowly than P-waves and move only through solids. These waves carry information about the earthquake that produces them and also about the material through which they have traveled.

5. Without earthquakes to produce seismic waves and volcanos to bring material from the mantle to the surface, we would know almost nothing about the interior below a depth of a few kilometers.

6. A dynamo needs both liquid metal and reasonably rapid rotation. The dynamo in Earth's interior is believed to create the planet's magnetic field.

7. Certain types of seismic waves can not travel through liquid rock. It has been known for decades that these waves, produced by earthquakes, do not travel through certain parts of the Earth's interior. This region is now mapped out as being the outer core. The inner core appears to be solid.

8. The fact that the Earth is differentiated, structured in layers decreasing density towards the surface, suggests the Earth must have been molten in its past. If it was molten then high density material could slowly sink to the interior while lower density material would float to the surface. This is what is observed today.

9. Convection is the rising of hot material through cooler material. (a) In the Earth's atmosphere it transports heat from the surface into the atmosphere and is responsible for many of the weather patterns. (b) In the Earth's interior it helped for the crust, mantle, and core of the Earth. It currently is responsible for volcanism and plate tectonics.

10. Certain kinds of elements, such as uranium, are inherently unstable. The nuclei achieve greater stability by disintegrating into lighter nuclei. A half-life is the time required for half of the original nuclei to disintegrate.

During this radioactive decay, subatomic particles are produced that move away very rapidly. When the particles collide with surrounding matter, their kinetic energy is converted into heat. Rock is such a good insulator that much of this heat remains in the interior of the Earth. Radioactive heating of the Earth still has not ended because there are still some radioactive elements remaining. But it is occurring at a much reduced rate than when the Earth was young.

11. Plate tectonics is the cause of mountains, trenches, and most other surface features of the Earth's surface. Mountains are often caused by plates colliding with each other, pushing up parts of one plate into mountains. When plates pull apart, they form trenches that allow new crustal material to rise.

12. Quasars are so far away that they never show any measurable motion on the sky because of their own motion in space. Thus any apparent change in their position can be interpreted as being due to the motion of the telescope or of the tectonic plate on which it is located.

13. Hot mantle material, as it cools on the surface of the crust, freezes in the orientation of the magnetic field. Material of different ages show different orientations. Reversals of the Earth's magnetic field occur every 500,000 to one million years. Absence of the magnetosphere, during a reversal, would allow high-energy particles from space to reach the surface of the Earth. Although not fatal to life, it could induce evolutionary changes through reproductive mutations.

14. The Moon would experience stronger tides than on Earth because the Earth, which produces the tides, is much more massive than the Moon, which produces the tides on the Earth. A compensating factor is the Moon's smaller size, which reduces this effect somewhat. Since the Moon rotates once during each orbit, the tidal bulges would not appear to move relative to the surface of the Moon.

15. The greenhouse effect keeps the temperature of the Earth mostly above the freezing point of water and quite likely helps make life possible. In this sense it is quite helpful. An enhanced greenhouse effect could potentially raise the temperature of the Earth to the point of being detrimental to life. A higher temperature would melt the ice caps, flood most coastal regions, and significantly change the weather on Earth in, as yet, an unpredictable way.

ANSWERS TO PROBLEMS

1. The volume of the atmosphere is the surface area of the Earth times the thickness of the atmosphere. $4\pi(6.378 \times 10^6 \text{ m})^2 \times 10^4 \text{ m} = 5.1 \times 10^{18} \text{ m}^3$. This volume multiplied by the density will give the total mass of the atmosphere. $5.1 \times 10^{18} \text{ m}^3 \times 1.2 \text{ kg/m}^3 = 6.1 \times 10^{18} \text{ kg}$.

The mass of the Earth is 5.97×10^{24} kg; dividing this into the mass of the atmosphere gives 10^{-6} or one millionth the mass of the Earth.

2. From the Instructor's edition, the tidal force, dF, is proportional to the mass of the body producing the tide and inversely proportional to the cube of its distance. It is easiest to answer this question by comparing Jupiter's tidal effect to that of the Moon. This allows lunar units to be used, i.e. Jupiter's mass in Moon masses and 4.2 A.U. in lunar distances. Jupiter's mass is 318 Earth masses and the Moon is about 80 Earth masses, so Jupiter is 25,400 Moon masses. The Moon's distance from the Earth is about 1/400 A.U. so 4.2 A.U. will be 1680 lunar distances. Jupiter's tidal effect is $= 25,400 / (1680)^3 = 5.4 \times 10^{-6}$ or about 5 millionth that of the Moon's tidal effect on Earth.

3. 6000 km $\times$ 1000 m/km $\times$ 100 cm/m $= 6 \times 10^8$ cm. At a rate of 2 cm/yr, this will give 6×10^8 cm/2 cm/yr $= 3 \times 10^8$ yr or 300 million years.

4. The diameter of the Earth is 2×6378 km $= 12,756$ km. At 5 km/s the time it will take is 12,756 km/5 km/s $= 2551$ s or 42.4 minutes.

SUGGESTED READING

Badash, L. "The Age-of-the-Earth Debate." *Scientific American* (August 1989). The controversy that has "aged" the Earth 4.5 billion years in the past three centuries. It embroiled Archbishop Usher, James Hutton, Lord Kelvin, Ernest Rutherford, and others.

Evans, D. L. et al., "Earth From Sky." *Scientific American* (December, 1994).

Gallant, R. A., "Journey to Tunguska." *Sky & Telescope* (June, 1994). Thorough review of the 1908 impact in Siberia.

Kirshner, R. P., "The Earth's Elements." *Scientific American* (October, 1994).

Macdonald, K., and P. Fox. "The Mid-Ocean Ridge." *Scientific American* (June 1990). How a planet-girdling undersea mountain range is created by magma welling up from below as tectonic plates pull apart.

"Managing Planet Earth." *Scientific American* (Special issue, September 1989).

Monastersky, R. "Clouds without a Silver Lining." *Science News* (October 15, 1988). The role of clouds in global warming.

"Planet Earth." *The Planetary Report* (Special issue, January/February 1990).

The editors of *Astronomy* magazine are now publishing a magazine called *Earth*. You can get six issues per year for $14.95.

Kalmbach Publishing Co.
21027 Crossroads Circle
P.O. Box 1612
Waukesha, WI 53187
(414) 796-8776

The American Geophysical Union publishes a wonderful magazine called *Earth in Space*. There are nine issues per year for $10.

American Geophysical Union
2000 Florida Ave. N.W.
Washington, D.C. 20009
1 (800) 966-2481
1 (202) 462-6900

Chapter 8

THE MOON AND MERCURY
Scorched and Battered Worlds

Surface Temperature

For many of the solar system objects to be studied, a range in surface temperatures (if there is a surface!) is usually stated. These, of course, vary greatly throughout the solar system. Design a large picture of a thermometer that can show a range from 0 K to at least 700 K. Have two adjustable markers for HIGH and LOW to indicate the high and low temperatures at the surface. This can also be done by making a transparency of the thermometer and a second overlay transparency that shows the specific high and low for the object. As each object is discussed, have the thermometer displayed and discuss the reasons for the temperature range. For the Earth set the high and low to 320 K and 210 K; for the Moon set the high and low to 400 K and 100 K. Note that for a planet with an atmosphere, the temperature varies widely with elevation, so we generally use the temperature at the surface.

Lunar Structure

Show the transparency of Figure 8.25, the cross-sectional view of the Moon and contrast it with Figure 7.1. Use comparative planetology to point out the similarities and differences between the Earth and Moon. Of course the Moon has a smaller size, but it is structured in a similar way as the Earth. Again, this is due to density variations. The Moon's crust is much thicker than the Earth's and its mantle is relatively thicker (about 80% of the radius for the Moon compared to about 45% for the Earth).

Synchronous Orbit

Students often do not know that the same side of the Moon faces the Earth. Show pictures of the Moon at various phases and indicate examples of features that are constantly in view. With this concept established, ask whether this means the Moon rotates, and if so, at what rate. A very common response is that the Moon does not rotate. Change the students' frame of reference to outside the Earth-Moon system. Place a globe on a table and play the part of the Moon by facing the Earth. Have the students agree ahead of time that in order for you *not* to rotate, you must face them at all times while orbiting around the Earth. Start moving around the Earth and at about half way, ask what the Earth is seeing of you. They will realize that the Earth's view of the you (the Moon) has changed. Go back to your original starting point and try again, but this time make sure you face the Earth at all times. Have the students note how much you are turning your body while moving around the Earth. It becomes obvious that you must turn once for each orbit, i.e., the orbit must be synchronous.

Lunar Surface Features

With a resolution of 1 arc second, features as small as about 2 km can be seen on the Moon from Earth. Under the best of conditions, 1 km sized objects can be seen (about the size of the Barringer Meteorite Crater in northern Arizona). Use a large projected picture of the Moon and a meter stick to measure the diameters of various maria and craters. Measure the diameter of the Moon and determine the sizes of the maria and craters by scaling their sizes to the diameter. Use 3500 km (or 3476 km) for the diameter of the Moon. Note the number of craters larger than 100 km and larger than 10 km. Show that there are significantly more smaller craters than larger craters.

From Section 8.4, relate the sizes of the meteoroids to the sizes and depths of the craters. An impact velocity of 10 km/s, given in the example in that section, may actually be on the low side. (For comparison, note that a rifle bullet typically has a velocity of 0.5 km/s; 20 times slower than the meteoroid in this example. Cars travel no faster than 0.03 km/s on the freeway; 10 km/s is not so slow on the hu-

man scale!) Velocities of 50 or 60 km/s are quite possible in head-on collisions. The Earth (or Moon) moving in its orbit at 30 km/s around the Sun might be struck by an object head-on having a similar velocity. The energy released by any collisions depends on the square of the velocity; at 50 km/s 25 times as much energy is released as in a 10 km/s collision. That is equivalent to 250 kg of TNT for a 1 kg meteoroid.

Alternate pictures from the far side and the near side of the Moon. Use these to contrast the differences, particularly in terms of the apparent lack of maria on the far side (due to the thicker crust). Relate this directly to the synchronous orbit and the way in which the Earth "protects" the near side of the Moon from meteorite impacts. Since we know the maria were formed when the Moon was relatively young, ask the students whether we can tell how long the Moon has been in synchronous orbit. The synchronous orbit must have been established when the Moon was young because otherwise the maria we see on the near side would have been exposed to more meteorite impacts.

Lunar Exploration

I believe there is significant value in showing our students as much as possible about our space program. The *Apollo* program ended well over 20 years ago and will be viewed by most students as history. NASA produced films on each of the *Apollo* missions; I like to show two of them, *Apollo* 11 and *Apollo* 17. There is a tremendous difference between these two missions. In the first, everything is done with such caution and determination. It is a significant historical event. In *Apollo* 17 the astronauts are so confident; it almost seems routine. Notice too the improvement in technology in terms of the quality of transmissions, now even the launch from the lunar surface can be viewed. These films are now available on video tape and laser disc.

Mercury

Albedo

Discuss examples of objects with differing albedo. We often think an object is reflecting a lot of light when in fact it is not. Water ice, depending on the form it takes, has an albedo from 0.5 to about 0.9 (or 50% - 90%). An ice cube does not look as bright as fresh snow. Some objects reflect little light, although enough to be seen. Carbon black or graphite may reflect on about 1%. The Moon, with an albedo of only 0.07 may be thought of as being quite dark. Yet it appears bright in the sky. Why is that? It is seen in contrast with the sky, which is quite dark, and so the Moon appears relatively bright. Mercury, with an albedo of 0.106, is actually not as dark as the surface of the Moon.

Density

A planet may be thought of as composed of X% high density material and Y% low density material. The Earth's interior is under enormous pressures, producing high densities. Mercury, being much less massive, has significantly lower pressures in its interior. But the × and Y percentages must be about the same for Earth and Mercury because the mean density of both are very similar. Thus the composition of the high density material in Mercury must be a substance that has a high density without necessarily being under high pressures. Iron, and probably nickel, are the most probable substances.

Surface Temperature

Set the high and low at 675 K and 100 K. Note that the low is the same as for the Moon and the reasons for it (long night, no atmosphere, rocky surface). The high is higher than the Moon's high because of the closeness of Mercury to the Sun.

Spin-Orbit Resonance

By far one of the most unique features of Mercury, and one of the most difficult to explain, is the 3:2 spin-orbit resonance. There are three problems involved with explaining this concept. First is the 3 rotations in 2 revolutions. Second is how this is related to the elliptical shape of the orbit. Third is how or why the 3:2 was "chosen" by Mercury. A demonstration of Figure 8.13 is almost essential for better understanding.

The demonstration is rather simple: all that is needed is the Sun (a bright yellow ball works well) and Mercury. For Mercury I prefer an oblong object that emphasizes the tidal distortion produced by the Sun. A balloon that is a bit elongated works well. A rugby ball, if available, is my personal favorite because of its size and ellipsoidal shape.

Start the demo with one end of the balloon or ball pointing towards the Sun. Make the orbit vertical so that students can better view the changing orientation of Mercury. Suspend the Sun from the ceiling or place in on a ring stand. The 3:2 motion is not hard to produce if it is remembered that the ball must be turned 180° for each third of the orbit. At the completion of one orbit, the end of the ball that was initially pointing towards the Sun should be pointing away from the Sun (for one and a half rotations). Repeating the orbit again fully demonstrates the 3 rotations per 2 orbits. The length of the day can also be described during this demo.

Repeat the demo but now making the orbit in the shape of an exaggerated ellipse. The balloon must be tidally aligned at perihelion; high tide must point towards the Sun. Using a balloon is easier for this demo because as Mercury progresses through its orbit it can be pushed into a more spherical shape. Note that the greatest tidal effect occurs at perihelion. If you are very proficient with this demo, try varying the speed in the orbit, fastest at perihelion and slowest at aphelion. It is not easy to do, but the students will enjoy seeing you try! Now show how a 1:1 is not possible because the variation in the speed does not allow the tidal bulge to continue to point towards the Sun. (This requires turning the ball or balloon at a constant rate of one rotation per revolution while varying the orbital speed!) Remind the students that the rotational speed can not vary like the orbital motion can. The planet can not spin up or down but must maintain a constant rotation.

In the third part of the demonstration, show that during the brief time around perihelion, Mercury appears to mimic synchronous (1:1) rotation when it is in a 3:2 resonance. (The key phrases in the text are: "Tidal forces always act to try to synchronize the rotation rate with the *instantaneous orbital speed.*" and "Mercury's orbital and rotational motion are almost exactly *synchronous at perihelion.*") This means that the tidal bulge tries to continue to point towards the Sun during its closest approach. You are now ready to prove mathematically this will occur for only the 3:2 resonance.

For the orbital and rotational motion to be synchronous at perihelion means the orbital angular velocity must equal the rotational angular velocity at the time of perihelion. Orbital velocity is given by

$$v = \sqrt{G(m_1 + m_2)}\sqrt{\frac{2}{a} - \frac{1}{r}} \ cm/sec$$

where a is the semi-major axis, m_1 is the mass of the Sun, m_2 is the mass of Mercury, and r will be, in this case, the perihelion distance

$$r = a(1 - e) \ cm$$

For Mercury, a = 5.7895×10^{12} cm, e = 0.206, and its rotational period is 58.646 days (remember to convert this into seconds). Mercury's mass, compared to the Sun's mass, is insignificant, so m_2 can be zero. Calculate the orbital velocity at perihelion

$$v = 5.90 \times 10^6 \ cm/sec.$$

Angular velocity is given by

$$\Omega = \frac{v}{r} \ sec^{-1}$$

where Ω is the angular velocity. This gives

$$\Omega = 1.284 \times 10^{-6} \ sec^{-1} \ \text{(orbital)}$$

For the rotational angular velocity Ω is more easily calculated by

$$\Omega = \frac{2\pi}{P}$$

where P is the rotational period. This gives

$$\Omega = 1.240 \times 10^{-6} \ sec^{-1} \ \text{(rotational)}$$

These two angular velocities are very close to being the same! Indeed, the planet Mercury does try to be in synchronous rotation during perihelion. Notice also, as stated in the text, the rotational angular velocity is a little slower than the orbital angular velocity at perihelion. Thus the Sun exhibits retrograde motion around the time of perihelion.

These calculations may or may not be appropriate for the level of course being taught. What is significant is that by using some very simple physics and mathematics the 3:2 spin-orbit resonance can be completely understood!

ANSWERS TO CHAPTER 8 REVIEW QUESTIONS

1. Currently, the easiest method by which the distance to the Moon is measured is by radar. By timing how long it takes a radar signal to travel to the Moon and back, 2.56 seconds, and knowing the speed of light, the calculation is simple. $2.56 \times 300,000 / 2 = 384,000$ km. The division by two is necessary because the time is for the round trip.

2. Mercury is one of the brightest objects in the nighttime sky, but, as the closest planet to the Sun, it is never seen very far from the Sun. As a result, Mercury is always seen near the horizon just before sunrise or just after sunset. It is rarely high enough above the horizon to be easily seen.

3. The Moon's equatorial diameter is nearly 4 km larger than the polar diameter. Given its slow rotation, one would expect the equatorial bulge to be on the order of 0.1 km. The extra bulge may mean that the Moon rotated more rapidly long ago. If the Moon became solid during that time, it might have retained some of its early bulge. Also, the distance from Earth to the Moon is believed to have been much less in the past. Earth's tidal force on the Moon would have been much greater. The resulting distortion would have set when the Moon solidified.

4. Both the Moon and Mercury have low masses and low escape velocities. Yet both objects are in the inner solar system and experience high daytime temperatures. All gases, at these temperatures, will exceed the escape velocity. Neither object, then, has been able to hold an atmosphere.

5. Mercury's rotation is not synchronous in a 1 to 1 ratio but in a 3 to 2 ratio. It rotates 3 times for every two orbits. This was the result of Mercury's eccentric orbit and allows the same side of Mercury to face the Sun every other orbit at perihelion. It is at perihelion that the tidal forces are the strongest on Mercury and this locked it into the 3 to 2 ratio.

6. Both Mercury and the Moon are heavily cratered. The crater walls on Mercury are generally not as high as on the Moon, however, and material ejected by striking meteorites landed closer to the impact site, just as you would expect on a world whose gravity is stronger than

that of the Moon. Also, Mercury lacks extensive lava flow regions akin to the lunar maria.

7. A scarp is a cliff formed when Mercury's surface wrinkled due to cooling. Scarps are found crossing craters indicating they are younger than the craters.

8. On the opposite side of Mercury from the Caloris basin, there is a region of oddly rippled and wavy surface features that is usually referred to as "weird (or jumbled) Terrain.": It is thought to have formed when seismic waves produced in the Caloris impact traveled around the planet and converged on the diametrically opposite point, causing a large scale disruption of the surface.

9. The primary source of erosion on the Moon is cratering. There is no water or wind erosion and no erosion due to plate tectonics because none of these exist on the Moon. But they do exist on the Earth and therefore the rate of erosion on the Earth is much higher than on the Moon.

10. First, it is quite apparent that the lunar highlands are more heavily cratered. The maria were resurfaced by lava flows and all the old craters were covered over but the highlands remained untouched. Samples of highland and maria material were brought back by the Apollo program and age-dated. The highland material was shown to be much older than the maria material.

11. Lunar soil, called regolith, contains no organic matter as earthly soil does. There are no fossils embedded in the lunar soil. All lunar soil samples returned to Earth were completely dry. The samples lack even embedded water, which is almost always found in earthly soil. Lunar soil contains fairly large numbers of glass beads, produced in the high temperatures of meteorite impacts.

12. The extreme temperature variations of Mercury are, in part, due to its lack of an atmosphere. An atmosphere helps to insulate the surface of a planet from cooling at night. Mercury's very long day (slow rotational period) also plays a role. The Sun is up for a long period, allowing the rock to heat up. With an equally long night, there is ample time to cool down to a low temperature. Earth, in contrast to Mercury, rotates rapidly and has less time to heat up to high temperatures or cool down to low temperatures.

13. Mercury, for its small size, has a high density. This indicates it has a relatively large metallic core. The fact that Mercury has a small magnetic field lends further evidence that this core, which was differentiated when Mercury was young and molten, is relatively large.

14. Mercury is composed of higher density material, on average, than is the Moon. Both differentiated when young, however, the Moon has at best a small core and Mercury has a large core. The Moon cooled faster

than Mercury which may account for the Moon having visible maria. These impacts had to have occurred when the Moon was rather young, with a thin crust. Both the Moon and Mercury, though, show similar histories of cratering although Mercury does not appear as heavily cratered. Many of its oldest craters have been covered over by lava flows, more extensive than those that formed the maria on the Moon. It is unclear why this is the case.

15. The favored theory for the formation of the Moon is that a large body, maybe Mars-sized, struck the Earth a glancing blow. Material thrown off could have then coalesced into forming the Moon. This theory explains two major features of the Moon. If the Earth was young but already differentiated enough to have a iron core and rocky mantle, the Moon would have formed primarily out of mantle material. This is consistent with the Moon being composed of rock very similar to the Earth's mantle and explains why the Moon appears to have no iron core.

16. First, the Earth would change due to its own rotation. With an orbital inclination of just over five degrees to the ecliptic, the Earth would appear to move higher and lower in the sky, as seen from a location on the Moon. Finally, because the Moon's orbit is eccentric, the distance between the Earth and Moon changes. At times the Earth would appear larger than at other times.

17. The best place on the Moon to look with a telescope is along the terminator line, which separates day from night on the lunar surface. There the Sun is low in the sky, casting long shadows that let an observer distinguish small surface details. If you looked at the Moon through a telescope, you would see lunar mountains, low plains called maria, and numerous craters. If standing on the lunar terminator, the Sun would be on the horizon (or just slightly above it). The same is true for Earth's terminator; you would be viewing either sunrise or sunset.

18. The far side of the Moon would be best for astronomical observations. The bright Earth would never interfere with observations. The surface of the Moon has no atmosphere, so the resolution of telescopes would be at their maximum. With no atmosphere, the sky is always dark, even when the Sun is out. Radio astronomy would benefit from shielding by the Moon of man-made radio transmissions.

19. Mercury is the closest planet to the Sun and is always seen near the Sun. At midnight, the Sun is opposite of overhead and Mercury is not far away.

20. When the lunar material differentiated, Earth's gravity played an important role. Denser mantle material settled closer to the Earth; lighter crustal material settled farther away. The large impacts that were to form the maria fractured the crust on the near-Earth side sufficiently for lunar mantle basalts to flow to the surface. On the far side of the Moon the crust was sufficiently thick to endure the impacts and prevent any basaltic flows from occurring.

21. The definition of a planet does not specifically depend on size. A planet must be a relatively large body that orbits the Sun. Mercury is much larger than the largest asteroid or comet. Moons, by definition, are bodies of any size that orbit a planet.

ANSWERS TO PROBLEMS

1. Mercury has a semi-major axis of 0.39 A.U., so on average and at its closest, it would be 0.61 A.U. from Earth. This is equivalent to 91.5 million km. Dividing by the speed of light gives 305 s one way or 10 minutes and 10 seconds round-trip.

2. The Sun appears to be about half a degree from Earth. Mercury is at 0.4 A.U. from the Sun and therefore $1/0.4 = 2.5$ times closer than the Earth. The Sun should appear 2.5 times larger than it does from Earth or $0.5 \times 2.5 = 1.25$ degrees.

3. From the text, a 10 km crater is formed every 10 million years. Such a crater has an area of 78.5 km². The surface area of the Moon, assuming a spherical shape, is $4\pi (1738 \text{ km})^2 = 3.8 \times 10^7$ km². Dividing this area by the area of a 10 km crater gives the number of such craters needed to cover the entire surface; 3.8×10^7 km² / 78.5 km² $= 4.8 \times 10^5$. Multiplying this result by 10 million years gives 4.8 trillion years; about 1,000 times longer than the age of the solar system.

   The cratering rate for 10 km craters would have to be approximately 1,000 times what it is today in order to have cratered the Moon in the 4.6 billion years since its formation. This would be one 10 km crater every 10,000 years. That's rather often!

4. From Interlude 2-2 Newton's law of gravity states that the gravitational force is proportional to the product of the masses and inversely proportional to the square of the distance to the center, in this case the radius of the Moon. With 1/4 Earth radius, the Moon's gravity will be $1/(1/4)^2$ times larger or 16 times. But the Moon's mass is 80 times less than the Earth's. The result is $16/80 = 0.2$. The Moon's gravity is one fifth the gravity of the Earth.

   A kilogram on Earth weighs about 2.2 pounds; 150 kg × 2.2 lbs/kg = 330 lbs. This is the weight on Earth of the astronaut plus backpack and spacesuit. On the Moon the astronaut would weight 1/5 of this or 66 lbs.

5. Set up a ratio of the angle to 360° is equal to the dis-

tance at the Moon to the circumference of a circle at the Moon's distance. Change degrees to arc seconds.

$$\frac{d}{2\pi \times 384,000 km} = \frac{0.05''}{360° \times 3600''/°}$$

$$d = 0.093 \text{ km or } 93 \text{ m}.$$

SUGGESTED READING

Beatty, J. K. "The Making of a Better Moon." *Sky and Telescope* (December 1986). An explanation of what is currently the best theory on the origin of the Moon.

Bruning, D., "Clementine Maps the Moon." *Astronomy* (July, 1994).

Burnham, R. "How *Apollo* Changed the Moon." *Astronomy* (July 1989). On the twentieth anniversary of the first manned lunar landing.

Burns, J. O., N. Duric, G. J. Taylor, and S. W. Johnson. "Observatories on the Moon." *Scientific American* (March 1990). The authors propose plans for establishing high-resolution optical, radio, infrared, gamma-ray, and X-ray observatories on the Moon.

Cameron, W. S. "Lunar Transient Phenomena." *Sky and Telescope* (March 1991). On the claim that something unusual, perhaps associated with volcanic or other activity, is still happening on the Moon.

Chaikin, A., "The Moon Voyagers." *Astronomy* (July, 1994). The Apollo missions to the Moon.

Chapman, C. R. "Mercury's Heart of Iron." *Astronomy* (November 1988). An article about Mercury's large iron core and possible violent origin.

Cordell, B. M. "Mercury: The World Closest to the Sun." *Mercury* (September/October 1984). A comprehensive look at the innermost planet, by a planetary scientist.

____, "Search for the Lost Lunar Lakes." *Astronomy* (March, 1993). Frozen lakes at the Moon's poles.

Cowen, R. "Icy Clues Gleaned from Mercury's Other Half." *Science News* (November 9, 1991). The discovery of a polar ice cap on Mercury.

Goldman, S. J. "Clementine Maps the Moon." *Sky & Telescope* (August, 1994).

Kitt, M. T. "Eight Lunar Wonders." *Astronomy* (March 1989). Using a small telescope to investigate eight geological oddities on the Moon.

———. "One Day at Copernicus Crater." *Astronomy* (September 1988). Using a small telescope to explore sights of a large lunar crater in the course of the long lunar day.

Logsdon, J. M. and Dupas, A., "Was the Race to the Moon Real?" *Scientific American* (June, 1994). New insights into the "race for space."

Ryder, G., "Apollo's Gift: The Moon." *Astronomy* (July, 1994). The geology of the Moon learned from the Apollo missions.

Strom, R. G. *Mercury, the Elusive Planet.* Cambridge: Cambridge University Press, 1987. Short, excellent book on many aspects of the planet Mercury.

Taylor, G. J., "Apollo, The Scientific Legacy." *Scientific American* (July, 1994). The science learned from the Apollo missions 25 years later.

Thomsen, D. E. "Man in the Moon." *Science News* (March 8, 1986). Discussion of the future possibility of a lunar colony.

Vilas, F., C. R. Chapman, and M. S. Mathews, eds. *Mercury.* Tucson: University of Arizona Press, 1988. Forty-seven contributors give a comprehensive picture of the planet Mercury.

Chapter 9

VENUS
Earth's Sister Planet

Surface Temperature

Set both the high and low temperatures at 750 K. Venus has much more atmosphere than Earth, which insulates the surface and prevents large temperature variations from day to night, polar to equatorial regions. Venus has the highest *average* surface temperature of any planet.

Phases

Both Venus and Mercury are observed to go through phases just like the Moon. For historical reasons the phases of Venus are the most important. Galileo first noted the changes of phase with his telescope. But the real importance of this was the phases were correlated with the brightness changes in Venus and the apparent size of Venus. At inferior conjunction Venus is both bright and large (as noted in the text, Venus is brightest just before and after inferior conjunction) and is seen as a thin crescent. At superior conjunction Venus appears faint and small and is in the full phase. Galileo became convinced that the correlation of phase with brightness and size was due to Venus orbiting the Sun, thus supporting the Copernican Theory.

Demonstrate the changing phases of Venus (or Mercury) as seen from Earth using a light bulb for the Sun and a plain sphere for Venus. Photographs taken of Venus at various phases are an excellent way of showing what is actually seen and that it is not a subtle effect.

Atmosphere

Most people take the atmospheric pressure on Earth for granted and do not think about it except when it varies due to weather conditions. They do not realize that the atmosphere is pressing on them with a force of 14.5 pounds for each square inch. (Sometimes it seems appropriate to regress to English units in order to make a point. I prefer not doing this too often.) Ask students why they are not particularly aware of this pressure, which adds up to quite a force over the area of our bodies. Fluid pressure inside our bodies is pressing outward with an equal and opposite force. We are in equilibrium. On the surface of Venus the atmospheric pressure is 90 times that of the Earth's atmosphere. The pressure would be about 1,300 pounds per square inch, which is truly a crushing force.

Model the venerian atmosphere in the same way as was done for the Earth's atmosphere (1 cm = 1 km). Contrast the differences between Earth and Venus.

1 - 30 cm	Atmosphere is clear.
30 - 50 cm	Layer of haze.
50 cm	90% of the atmosphere is below
50 - 70 cm	Cloud layers composed of sulfuric acid
70 cm	Jet stream clouds moving at 300 - 400 km/hr.
100 cm	Top of troposhere
200 cm	Top of mesosphere

Greenhouse Effect

The runaway greenhouse effect can be explained in more detail. Emphasize the importance of water being liquid on Earth in controlling the greenhouse effect here. Carbon dioxide dissolves fairly easily in water. Chemical reactions and the presence of life in the water bound the carbon dioxide into rock formations. More carbon dioxide would then be removed from the atmosphere and dissolved in the water and so forth.

On Venus, both water and carbon dioxide were in the atmosphere as gases. With an ever increasing greenhouse effect, the temperature rose. Any water that may have been in the crustal rocks and carbon dioxide that was chemical bound in rock is "cooked" out of the surface rocks and into the atmosphere. The water is eventually destroyed and the carbon dioxide remains.

Asking the Right Question

The abundance of carbon dioxide and absence of water in the venerian atmosphere, and the reasons for this, are excellent examples of why scientists have to make sure they are asking the right question. One can not really answer the question "Why does Venus have so much carbon dioxide in its atmosphere?" The correct question is "Where is all the carbon dioxide that should be in the Earth's atmosphere?" Similarly one should not ask "Why does Earth have so much water" but "What happened to the water on Venus?"

Science can not find the right answers if the original question is wrong! Progress is often made when a scientist gains new insight to a problem and finds a new way of stating a question that can then be answered.

ANSWERS TO CHAPTER 9 REVIEW QUESTIONS

1. Venus is the third brightest object in the sky, after the Sun and Moon. It is completely covered by very reflective clouds so that much of the sunlight received by Venus is reflected back into space. Venus also is one of the closest planets to the Earth, depending on where it is in its orbit. This also helps make Venus appear bright. Its brightness depends on its phase and distance from the Earth.

2. Since Venus is an inner planet, it will never be found too far from the Sun. However, it is much easier to see than Mercury, having an orbit almost twice the size of Mercury's.

3. Technically, you could not see Earth from the surface of Venus because of all the cloud cover of Venus. If you could see Earth, it would appear slightly larger than does Venus from Earth, a bit darker because of its lower albedo, and there would certainly be visible the blue, browns, and whites of the oceans, continents, and clouds and ice regions. Earth would not go through phases like Venus because it would be seen as an outer planet.

4. When Venus is at a given distance from Earth, its angular diameter is measured. Knowing the distance to Venus easily gives the diameter.

5. At one time, Venus was thought to have a warm, tropical environment. In the 1950s, radio observations of Venus measured its thermal emission. The radiation emitted by Venus has a Planck curve spectrum characteristic of a temperature near 600 K. It was hardly a tropical, habitable planet.

6. The surface atmospheric pressure on Venus is about 90

bars, or 90 times that at sea level on Earth. The temperature is around 750 K hot enough to melt lead.

7. The ultraviolet images revealed fast moving upper layers of clouds. These clouds had velocities of up to 400 km/hr.

8. The atmosphere of Venus has a total mass about 90 times greater than that of Earth. It extends to a much greater altitude—90 percent of the Earth's atmosphere lies within about 10 km of the surface, compared with 50 km on Venus. The surface temperature and pressure of Venus's atmosphere are much grater than Earth's.

9. The dominant component of the atmosphere of Venus is carbon dioxide. It accounts for 96.5 percent of the atmosphere by volume. Almost all of the remaining 3.5 percent is nitrogen. Trace amounts of other gases, such as water vapor, carbon monoxide, sulfur dioxide, and argon are also found. The clouds are made of sulfuric acid.

10. Venus has both a very thick atmosphere and one mostly composed of carbon dioxide. Carbon dioxide is a very effective greenhouse gas, trapping infrared light within the atmosphere and raising the temperature. This, in combination with the largeness of the atmosphere, has produced a very large greenhouse effect and a resulting high temperature.

11. On Earth, almost all of the water vapor and carbon dioxide present in the planet's early atmosphere quickly became part of the surface of the planet, in the oceans or in the surface rocks. On Venus, the temperature may have been so high that no oceans condensed, in which case water vapor and carbon dioxide remained in the atmosphere. The carbon dioxide was never incorporated in the crust of Venus. The water was slowly broken down by solar ultraviolet light in to hydrogen and oxygen. The hydrogen escaped into space and the oxygen formed oxides of sulfur and carbon.

12. The runaway greenhouse effect is a process by which an increased atmospheric temperature increases greenhouse gases, which in turn increase the atmospheric temperature even more. Water and carbon dioxide are both greenhouse gases. When Venus was young, even with some liquid water, its higher temperature, due to its closeness to the Sun increased atmospheric water and raised its temperature. This did not allow carbon dioxide to remain dissolved in the oceans, forcing it out into the atmosphere and further increasing the greenhouse effect and the temperature.

13. Its climate might be similar to Earth's. An important point to remember, however, is that Venus is a smaller planet with a lower surface gravity. It might not have been able to hold on to as much of an atmosphere as the Earth.

14. The continents of Venus make up only 8% of its surface, as compared to the 25% of the Earth's surface. They are not tectonically produced but do show extensive lava flows. The mountains are of similar height but are produced by upward convective flows and not the tectonic activity found on Earth.

15. There is a strong deficiency in small impact craters on Venus, due to its atmosphere destroying meteoroids smaller than about 1 km. The smaller impact craters show evidence of the meteoroid being shattered prior to impact. There is also a deficiency in larger craters, but this is likely due to the surface of Venus being resurfaced by volcanic activity.

16. Volcanic craters are very common on the surface of Venus. The largest features are the coronae, formed from upwelling mantle material. The deficiency in large impact craters suggests significant resurfacing by lava flows.

17. The level of sulfur dioxide above Venus's clouds show large and fairly frequent fluctuations which may be the result of volcanic eruptions. The *Pioneer* and the *Venera* orbiter observed bursts of radio energy from the Beta and Aphrodite regions, similar to those produced by lightning discharges that often occur in the plumes of erupting volcanos on Earth.

18. What would have to be found are before and after changes in the vicinity of suspected active volcanos. The actual eruptions can not be imaged by radar but changes in the caldera and extent of lava flows would show up.

19. The dynamo model for the production of planetary magnetic fields requires both an iron-rich core and a relatively rapid rate of rotation. Venus lacks the rapid rotation and therefore does not appear to produce a magnetic field. Actually, the fact that is does not have a magnetic field strongly suggests that the dynamo model is correct.

20. The greenhouse effect and the distance from the Sun. The Earth, with a modest greenhouse effect, is sufficiently warmed to sustain life. Venus, with its massive atmosphere of carbon dioxide, has a large greenhouse effect which has raised its temperature well beyond the comfort zone for life. But more fundamentally, Venus is closer to the Sun, was originally warmer than the Earth, and possibly never had liquid water on its surface. Water and carbon dioxide in the atmosphere would produce a powerful greenhouse effect. In addition, the carbon dioxide would remain in the atmosphere and not become locked away in the crust as is the case with the Earth. With a large quantity of liquid water on Earth, carbon dioxide remained dissolved and could be chemically incorporated into the crust. With

little water or carbon dioxide in its atmosphere, the Earth has maintained a modest greenhouse effect over time.

21. Life on Venus appears to be impossible due to its very high temperature. This temperature is sufficient to break down virtually any important molecules that would be necessary for life. In addition, the environment of sulfuric acid would be very destructive to these same molecules. The absence of water does not help either!

ANSWERS TO PROBLEMS

1. The volume of the atmosphere is the surface area of Venus times the thickness of the atmosphere. $4 \pi (6.051 \times 10^6 \text{ m})^2 \times 5 \times 10^4 \text{ m} = 2.3 \times 10^{19} \text{ m}^3$. This volume multiplied by the density will give the total mass of the atmosphere. $2.3 \times 10^{19} \text{ m}^3 \times 21 \text{kg/m}^3 = 4.8 \times 10^{20}$ kg.

   From Problem **1.** in Chapter 7, the Earth's atmosphere is 6.1×10^{18} kg. Dividing this in the mass of Venus's atmosphere gives 79.

   The mass of Venus is 4.87×10^{24} kg; dividing this into the mass of the atmosphere gives 10^{-4} or one ten thousandth the mass of Venus.

2. Angular size is inversely proportional to the distance. At inferior conjunction, Venus has an angular diameter of 64"; its distance is 0.28 A.U. At superior conjunction its distance is 1.72 (its orbit is virtually circular).

$$\frac{\theta}{64''} = \frac{0.28 A.U.}{1.72 A.U.}$$

$$\theta = 10''$$

3. The circumference of Venus is $2 \pi \, 6{,}051$ km = 38,020 km. This distance covered in 4 days or 96 hours gives 400 km/hr. A kilometer is about 5/8 of a mile, so this is about 250 miles per hour.

4. The amount of radiation emitted per square meter is proportional to the fourth power of the temperature. $(750/300)^4 = 39$, so Venus radiates 39 times more than the Earth.

5. Set up Kepler's third law in the form of a ratio with Venus on top and Earth on the bottom. This eliminates having to deal with constants that complicate the calculation. Remember that "a" is the distance from the spacecraft to the center of the planet. For HST and Earth this will be 6378 + 600 = 6978 km; for *Magellan* and Venus this will be 6050 + 4370 = 10,420 km.

$$P^2 = \frac{a^3}{M}$$

The mass of Venus is 0.82 the mass of the Earth, so

$$\left(\frac{P}{95}\right)^2 = \left(\frac{10{,}420}{6978}\right)^3 \times \frac{1}{0.82}$$

P = 191 minutes

SUGGESTED READING

Allen, D. A. "Laying Bare Venus' Dark Secrets." *Sky and Telescope* (October 1987). A cloud layer deep within the atmosphere of Venus, revealed by infrared measurements.

Beatty, J. K. "*Magellan* at Venus: First Results." *Sky and Telescope* (December 1990). Early results from a space mission to obtain sophisticated radar images of the surface of Venus.

————. "A New Look at Old Worlds." *Sky and Telescope* (March 1991). What the *Galileo* spacecraft found on its detour through the inner solar system.

Brazilevskiy, A. T. "The Planet Next Door." *Sky and Telescope* (April 1989). Comprehensive article on what was known about Venus shortly before the *Magellan* mission.

Burnham, R., "What Makes Venus Go?" *Astronomy* (January, 1993). The history of Venus revealed by Magellan's radar.

Cole, S. "Rediscovering Venus and Jupiter." *Astronomy* (January 1989). On the *Galileo* and *Magellan* missions to Jupiter and Venus.

Eicher, David J. "Ashen Light on Venus." *Astronomy* (August 1988). Modern attempts to see this mysterious glow on the night hemisphere of Venus.

Kaula, W. M. "Venus: A Contrast in Evolution to Earth." *Science* (March 9, 1990). Differences in the atmosphere, origin, evolution, geology, and so on of Earth and Venus.

Lemonick, M. "A Restless Venus Unveiled." *Time* (October 8, 1990). Popular article about the *Magellan*'s look at the hidden surface of Venus.

Luhmann, J. G. et al., "The Pioneer Mission to Venus." *Scientific American* (April, 1994).

Powell, C. S. "Venus Revealed." *Scientific American* (January 1992). Striking *Magellan* spacecraft radar images of the cloud-covered planet.

Robinson, C., "Magellan Reveals Venus." *Astronomy* (February, 1995).

Saunders, R. S. "The Surface of Venus." *Scientific American* (December 1990). A portfolio of vivid radar images sent back from Venus by the *Magellan* spacecraft. The accompanying article is written by the mission's project scientist.

Chapter 10

MARS
A Near Miss for Life?

Orbital Properties

Since Mars is the first planet to be encountered whose orbit lies outside of the Earth's orbit, this is a good opportunity to demonstrate how these planets are viewed from Earth. Set up the Sun (a light bulb) and two spheres for Earth and Mars. Remember that the Martian orbit is about 1.5 times the size of the Earth's orbit. Show how Mars appears in a full phase most of the time; this will be true for all the rest of the planets. Next demonstrate the arrangement for opposition. Although this is our closest approach to Mars, we are still farther away than we are from Venus at its closest approach (inferior conjunction). Ask the students which planet would be best or most easily viewed; Mars at opposition or Venus at inferior conjunction. Although Venus is closer and larger, it is also in seen in the glare of the Sun and appears as a thin crescent. Mars is seen full and will be the highest in the sky around midnight (because it is "opposite" the Sun). Astronomers usually try to observe most of the outer objects in the solar system during their respective oppositions.

The eccentricity of the Martian orbit is best demonstrated with respect to favorable oppositions. Using a scale of 1 m = 1 AU, show that compared to the position of the Earth, Mars will be at 1.38 AU (favorable opposition occurring at perihelion) or 1.66 AU (unfavorable opposition occurring at aphelion). The difference of 28 cm in the position should be easily seen. Ask how a favorable opposition might depend on the orbit of the Earth and its eccentricity. Since this eccentricity is low, 0.017, the Earth will vary by only ±1.7 cm on this scale between its perihelion and aphelion. This effect produces a maximum of 12% variation in quality of the opposition, which is sufficiently large to be important.

Viewing Mars from Earth

As noted in the text, Mars at opposition, appears about 25 arc seconds in diameter. Under the best viewing conditions on Earth, telescopes can view detail down to about half and arc second. Therefore, astronomers should be able to see objects on Mars down to a size of about 1/50th its size, or 135 km (rounded off to 100 km in the text). When Percival Lowell thought he saw canals on Mars they would have had a minimum *width* of over 100 km to be seen! These are rather wide canals for such an arid planet! Often, simple arguments such as these can be used to recognize the fallacies of such reports.

Knowing the sizes of the polar ice caps or the volcano Olympus Mons, will these objects be visible from Earth?

Will the caldera of Olympus Mons be visible, large craters, canyons, ancient rivers? For the most part, all these latter features can not be resolved because of the limitations of the Earth's atmosphere.

Surface Temperature

As measured at the Viking landing sites, set the thermometer high at 244 K (-20° F) during the summer and set the nighttime low at 187 K. Temperatures at the poles certainly reach 146 K, which is the freezing point of carbon dioxide. Note that soil temperatures can exceed the freezing point of water, 273 K, as it is warmed by the summer sun. Equatorial regions may also record higher temperatures than found at the Viking sites.

Volcanoes

The large volcanoes of Mars are among some of the most interesting surface features of the planets. There is a common misconception that volcanoes are very steep-sided. Although some are, shield volcanoes have very gentle slopes. Model Olympus Mons using a meter stick for the base of the volcano. Attach a string slightly longer than a meter to both ends of the meter stick. Lift the string in the middle 3.5 cm above the meter stick and make a flat top 11 cm in length. This is a model of Olympus Mons. For comparison, Mauna Loa in Hawaii would be 17 cm at its base and 1.3 cm high. Note how Mauna Loa has a steeper rise to it than Olympus Mons. Instead of making these models, the same dimensions may be used in drawing a model on the chalk board.

Water on Mars

Most students do not realize that the boiling point of water depends on temperature *and* atmospheric pressure. Use a vacuum pump and bell jar to demonstrate boiling water at room temperature. Fill a small beaker with tap water and have a student check the temperature by putting a finger in the water; no need to use hot water. Put the beaker under the bell jar and start the vacuum pump, making sure you have a good seal around the base of the bell jar. It should take no more than 2-3 minutes, depending on the quality of the pump, to start the water boiling. After the pump is turned off and air is released into the bell jar, have a student check the temperature of the water again to show that it has not changed and become hot. This is important because there is also an additional misconception that evacuating the air somehow raises the temperature and that the water boils for this reason. This demonstration is an excellent way of showing that liquid water can not be present on the surface of Mars with its current atmosphere and that the atmosphere must have been much larger in the past in order to allow liquid water to exist.

ANSWERS TO CHAPTER 10 REVIEW QUESTIONS

1. Mars's orbit is fairly elliptical, with an eccentricity of 0.09. Mars is best viewed from Earth at opposition, when it is directly opposite the Sun. But because of its orbital eccentricity the view at opposition may or may not be favorable. The ideal situation is when Mars is at perihelion when it is also at opposition. It is then the closest to Earth as it can ever get.

2. River and stream channels are certain evidence that water once flowed on the surface of Mars. The same might be said for similar features in some of Earth's most arid deserts, where water may flow for only a matter of hours during an entire year. But the water flow on Mars is not seasonal as it is on Earth.

3. Liquid water can not exist on Mars today because the atmospheric pressure is too low; the water would immediately boil into a gas and would be evident in the atmosphere of Mars. But this is not observed; Mars has little water in its atmosphere. Frozen water does exist in the polar ice caps and, potentially, there still may be large amounts of water present in the crust of Mars, below the surface.

4. The canals were just figments of the imagination of those who believed they had to exist. Percival Lowell mistakenly believed canals had been discovered by Italian astronomers and jumped to the conclusion that there was life on Mars. He built and funded the operation of an entire observatory dedicated to their study and further discovery. Any canal that might have existed was known by astronomers to be impossible to see from Earth; it would have to be enormous is size and contrary to the fact that there was little evidence of water on Mars. All this has had a happy ending, though. The Lowell Observatory in Flagstaff Arizona became an important research facility for astronomy and has been productive for many years.

5. The northern hemisphere is made up largely of rolling volcanic plains, not unlike the lunar maria. The southern hemisphere, by contrast, consists of heavily cratered highlands lying several kilometers above the level of the lowland north. Most of the dark regions visible from Earth are in the south. these extensive northern lava plains—much larger than on earth or the Moon—were presumably caused by eruption involving great volumes of lava It's usually assumed that the southern terrain represents the original crust of the planet.

6. Temperatures would sometimes rise above freezing, but dust storms are common. Strong winds at the surface sweep up the dry dust, carry it aloft, and eventually deposit it elsewhere on the planet. Such storms are far worse than any dust storm on Earth.

7. The two polar caps are actually composed of two separate caps each, the seasonal cap and the residual cap. The seasonal cap has a composition of frozen carbon dioxide. they grow during the winter and diminish during the summer. The southern residual cap has a composition of frozen carbon dioxide, with some frozen water. The northern residual cap is almost 3 times larger than the southern residual cap and is composed mostly of frozen water.

8. The soil of Mars has a large amount of iron oxide in it, i.e. rust. This gives Mars its red or rust color.

9. There's not much to breathe on Mars! Its atmosphere is less than a hundredth that of the Earth's atmosphere. Even if you could breathe such a thin atmosphere it wouldn't do you much good; it is composed mostly of carbon dioxide. Note, though, that this is not necessarily true for some simple plants, which absorb carbon dioxide (as all plants do) and might be able to survive in this thin atmosphere.

10. Gravity on Mars is only 40 percent of what it is on Earth. The height to which a shield volcano grows depends on its ability to support it own weight. With lower gravity, the volcanoes grow correspondingly higher.

11. The *Viking* orbiters measured the gravitational effects of both moons and estimated their masses. Their densities are about 2 g/cm^3, which is rather low for rocky bodies and suggest that they were captured by Mars and did not form along with Mars.

12. Mars has no current volcanic activity. It lacks any significant magnetic field. It has a relatively low density and high abundance of iron on its surface. All these facts suggest that Mars never melted as extensively as did Earth.

13. Mars, at its closest approach to Earth, is just slightly farther away than is Venus at its closest approach. So Earth would look quite similar to the circumstances described in the answer to question 3. in Chapter 9. The one important difference is that Earth would be seen as an inner planet from Mars and would appear to go through phases. At closest approach (Mars in opposition and perihelion) Earth would look quite dark because its night side would be facing Mars.

14. Water might be obtained from the ice caps of Mars or from subsurface deposits. Air to breathe would be more

difficult to come by. Oxygen could be extracted from the oxides in the surface soils but nitrogen would be rare and have to be imported. Carbon dioxide for growing plants could be collected and concentrated from the atmosphere. Energy would have to come from sunlight but Mars receives less than half the sunlight Earth receives, per square meter. There are many other environmental factors that could be discussed here.

15. There is plenty of carbon dioxide to create a greenhouse effect, just no significant atmosphere to be warmed by it. The atmosphere of Mars is less than one percent that of the Earth and produces little insulation to keep the surface warm.

16. All three planets had their secondary atmospheres produced by outgassing of their volcanoes. Abundant quantities of water and carbon dioxide were likely produced in all three cases. Now, however, the evolution of these atmospheres depend on the planet's distance from the Sun. Really, it is just the story of the three bears; one that was too hot, one that was too cold, and one that was just right. Venus, at the closest distance, was warmer and very likely never had liquid water on its surface. Both water and carbon dioxide are efficient greenhouse gases, so Venus warmed up quickly to a high temperature. Its atmospheric water was subsequently destroyed by solar ultraviolet light.

Mars, being the farthest from the Sun of these three planets, likely had liquid water in which carbon dioxide could dissolve. This allowed the carbon dioxide to become bound into the crustal rocks of Mars. Now, the greenhouse effect, which had kept Mars modestly warm, lessened and the surface temperature of Mars dropped. Water eventually froze out, further reducing the greenhouse effect and made Mars even cooler. The remaining atmosphere has been continually reduced by the effects of solar ultraviolet light.

Earth developed similarly to Mars. Temperatures did not rise, like in the case of Venus, because the carbon dioxide become dissolved in the oceans and subsequently incorporated into Earth's crust. But being closer to the Sun, Earth's temperature did not drop so low as to freeze out water. The small amount of carbon dioxide and water vapor in Earth's atmosphere has maintained a modest greenhouse effect that has kept the environment at a relatively constant, comfortable temperature. It's just right for life! Of course life has altered Earth's atmosphere and produced a significant amount of oxygen (from plant life). Animal life continues to exhale carbon dioxide and inhale oxygen. Now a new balance exists. Life on Earth has both created this balance and depends on it for its own existence.

ANSWERS TO PROBLEMS

1. Surface gravity is proportional to mass divided by the radius squared. In Earth units, the mass of Mars is 0.11 and the radius is 0.53, so $0.11/(0.53)^2 = 0.39$.

2. This can be solved graphically or by using simple trigonometry. If θ is the angle of greatest elongation, then $\sin(\theta) = 1/1.5$ and $\theta = 42°$.

3. The amount of sunlight received by a planet depends on inversely on the square of its distance from the Sun. At twice the distance from the Sun as the Earth, a planet would receive 4 times less light. Mars is 1.5 A.U. from the Sun and receives

$$\frac{1}{1.5^2} = 0.44$$

times the light received by the Earth.

Angular size is inversely proportional to the distance. At 1 A.U. the Sun has an angular size of 30'. Mars, at 1.5 A.U., will see the Sun with a size of 30' / 1.5 = 20'.

4. The amount of parallax depends directly on the size of the baseline. Increasing the baseline from 1 A.U. to 1.5 A.U. will increase all parallaxes by 1.5, so the parallax of this specific star will be 0.15".

SUGGESTED READING

Beatty, J. K. "Images: A New Perspective on Mars." *Sky and Telescope* (June 1987). Stunning mosaic image, constructed from 102 separate pictures of Mars taken from 20,000 miles up by the *Viking* orbiters.

Benningfield, D., "The Odd Little Moons of Mars." *Astronomy* (December, 1993).

Chaiken, Andrew. "Four Faces of Mars," *Sky and Telescope* (July 1992). Exciting composite images from the U.S. Geological Survey.

Cowen, R., "Mars meteorite poses puzzling questions." *Science News* (March 25, 1995).

Goldman, S. J. "The Legacy of *Phobos 2*." *Sky and Telescope* (February 1990). Scientific bounty from the Soviet *Phobos* mission to Mars.

Haberle, R. M. "The Climate of Mars." *Scientific American* (May 1986). The past and present climate of the planet next door.

Hartmann, W. K. "What's New on Mars?" *Sky and Telescope* (May 1989). Report from an extremely favorable opposition of Mars, plus new looks at old spacecraft data.

Hoyt, W. G. *Lowell and Mars*. Tucson: University of Arizona Press, 1976. A good look at the process of science from a time earlier in this century and a wonderful tale about Mars.

Kargel, J. S. and Strom, R. G., "Iced Ages of Mars." *Astronomy* (December, 1992).

Kasting, J. F., O. B. Toon, and J. B. Pollack. "How Climate Evolved on the Terrestrial Planets." *Scientific American* (February 1988). Why Mars is too cold, Venus is too hot, and Earth is just right.

Robinson, M. "Exploring Small Volcanos on Mars." *Astronomy* (April, 1994).

_ and Wadhwa, M., "Messengers from Mars." *Astronomy* (August, 1995). Meteorites from Mars.

Zakharov, A. V. "Close Encounters with Phobos." *Sky and Telescope* (July 1988). Prelaunch report on the Soviet *Phobos* mission to Mars.

Chapter 11

JUPITER
The Giant of the Solar System

Appearance from Space

Use the scale models from Chapter 6 for Jupiter, the four Galilean moons, and the Earth and Moon for comparison. Set up a scale model of the jovian system and compare it to the Earth-Moon system. If a scale of one Earth diameter = 5 cm has been used, place Io, Europa, Ganymede, and Callisto at 1.68 m, 2.69 m, 4.27 m, and 7.42 m from the center of Jupiter. Jupiter's ring is only 48 cm from the center and about 1.3 cm wide. A ring of paper can be cut out to represent the ring. Note that the thickness of the ring, on this scale, is 3 times thinner than the paper. The Moon, for comparison, is 1.5 m from Earth and only 1.3 cm in diameter.

Mass of Jupiter

It is interesting to note, from the above model, that Io is just a little farther away from Jupiter than is the Moon from Earth. But the orbital period of Io is 1.769 days compared to 27.322 days for the Moon. Ask the students why a moon such as Io, which appears to be similar in size to the Moon and has a similar size orbit, should have a faster orbital period. The answer is that it is orbiting a much more massive planet. To calculate Jupiter's mass (in Earth masses), all that is needed is the orbital size and period of one of its moons and Newton's form of Kepler's third law.

$$P^2 = \frac{a^3}{M}$$

Inserting appropriate values for the Moon's orbit and Io's orbit gives

$$\left(\frac{27.322}{1.769}\right)^2 = \left(\frac{384,000}{422,000}\right)^3 \times \frac{M}{1}$$

$$M = 317 \text{ Earth masses}$$

The answer is very close to 318, the actual value. The mass, M, is actually the total mass of Jupiter and Io. If Io's mass is small relative to Jupiter, then M is the mass of Jupiter alone. How do we know that Io's mass is actually insignificant compared to Jupiter's mass? It is always good to check our assumptions! Notice that Io has a diameter about 3.5 times smaller than the Earth. This gives a volume about 40 times smaller (volume goes by the cube of the diameter or radius). So even if Io has the same density as the Earth, its mass would only be 0.02 Earth masses, i.e., quite insignificant compared to Jupiter's mass.

Numerical examples are often avoided in descriptive science courses, but the previous example can show students the power in being able to apply a little math (arithmetic, really) to a problem. Kepler's third law is the physical principle, the period and size of Io's orbit are the needed observations (along with the same for the Moon's orbit). With very little effort we find Jupiter's mass. This method can also be applied to any planet with at least one small moon. Science is a process; I believe it is much more important for students to understand how the mass of a distant planet can be determined than to memorize all their masses. When we discuss in a later chapters the masses of stars and entire galaxies, this same method will be available as an easily-applied tool.

Rotation Rate

How can the equatorial regions of Jupiter rotate *faster* than the entire planet? If winds are blowing clouds in the same direction as the rotation, then the rotation will appear faster than it actually is. This may be easily demonstrated using any large globe or ball. Mark a point on the equator and another point to which it will move due to wind during one rotation. Rotate the globe once and show that the second mark shows up "early" and gives the mistaken impression of a faster rotation rate. Since the equatorial radius is 71,400 km and the circumference is 2π times the radius, in 9^h50^m the speed is 45,600 km/hr. For 9^h56^m, which is the true rotational period, the speed is 45,200 km/hr. The difference in these two speeds, about 400 km/hr is about the speed of the winds, blowing to the east, given later in the chapter.

Temperature

Set the thermometer at 125 K for a low and roughly 300 K for a high. Since the high depends strictly on the depth, this is given approximately for the lowest cloud layer, about 80-100 km in depth. 300 K is the temperature of a warm day on Earth. For the most part, Jupiter is a very warm (hot!) planet. This is not due to warming from solar radiation but due to internal sources of heat.

For the outer planets solar heating is often less important in determining the planet's temperature than other sources of heating. By examining the temperature of their cloud tops, we realize that 3 out of 4 of them emit more energy than they receive from the Sun. The following figure demonstrates this by showing their measured temperatures as a bar graph and an arrow pointing to the temperature they would have if it were due only to the Sun's energy they receive. For convenience and comparison, the graph is shown here for all 4 jovian planets.

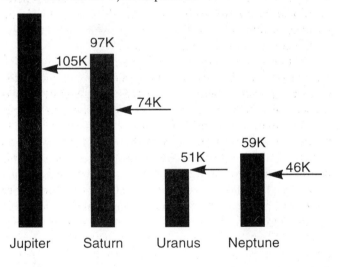

Internal Structure

For the terrestrial planets, a meter stick model of the atmosphere has been used. Here, a meter stick model of the entire planet is helpful. Jupiter will scale at about 714 km / cm. In the following example, zero centimeters marks the center of Jupiter.

99.9 - 100 cm	Cloud layers in the upper atmosphere
93 - 100 cm	Gaseous atmosphere
71 - 93 cm	Hydrogen is liquid
14 - 71 cm	Hydrogen is liquid metal
0 - 14 cm	Rocky, high density planetary core

What we see of Jupiter is really the very thin outer layer of its atmosphere and not representative of most of the planet. This layer makes up the outer 1/1000 of the planet. However, the atmosphere of the Earth and the region within which life exists on Earth also makes up about the same fraction. We are often the most interested in the smallest parts of a planet!

A liquid metal is sometimes a difficult concept to imagine. Bring to class a flask of mercury and show that at room temperature and pressure it is a liquid but under different conditions it would be solid. Mercury may be frozen (at -39° C) using dry ice or liquid nitrogen. *Remember, mercury is a hazardous substance and must be properly handled.*

Galilean Moons

These four moons are relatively close to Jupiter and so Jupiter, seen from the surfaces of these moons, would appear large. The following are the angular sizes of Jupiter from the distance of each moon.

Io	20°
Europa	12°
Ganymede	8°
Callisto	4°

Jupiter, from Io, would appear about as large as your fist when your arm is fully extended. Even from Callisto, Jupiter would be over 8 times larger than the full moon. (From Metis, the closest of the Jovian moons, Jupiter would be 68° across, reaching across over one third of the sky. Quite a view!)

Io's volcanos are spewing material at velocities of 1-2 km/sec. The altitude to which the material should rise can easily be calculated. From simple motion laws in physics and Newton's law of gravity we know

$$v^2 = v_0^2 + 2gs$$

$$g = \frac{GM}{r^2}$$

where g is the acceleration due to gravity on Io and is calculated from its mass and size and s is the distance to which material with an initial velocity of v_0 will rise. The final velocity, v, is zero. For an initial velocity of 1 km/sec, s = 280 km; for an initial velocity of 2 km/sec, s = 1100 km. Note that the escape velocity from Io can also be easily calculated and is about 2.5 km/sec. If some of the material ejected from a volcano is very hot, and much of it is, when raised to a high elevation, some of it can escape. Due to temperature, some of the molecular velocities may exceed escape velocity. Io's orange color makes it a rather unique object in the solar system. The color is attributed to sulfur and sulfur compounds. Sulfur usually appears yellow or pale yellow. A very impressive demonstration can be easily done to show how sulfur can appear orange. In a test tube or beaker place some powered sulfur. Heat it slowly over a Bunsen burner or on a hot plate. Be careful not to ignite it! Since its melting point is about 113°C it can safely be heated in boiling water and then "finished" over the flame. When melted the sulfur will turn an orange or orange/brown color. The color compares nicely to the usual pictures of Io.

ANSWERS TO CHAPTER 11 REVIEW QUESTIONS

1. The two most massive bodies in the solar system are the Sun and Jupiter. Although Jupiter is 1000 times less massive than the Sun, it contains more mass than the rest of the solar system objects combined. In terms of the gravitational force on other bodies, these two objects dominate.

2. The equatorial regions of Jupiter appear to rotate faster than the polar regions. This is known as differential rotation. It is the first indication that Jupiter is not solid. The faster motion of the atmosphere at the equator gives rise to a wind moving at about 300 km/h relative to the overall rotation of Jupiter's interior.

3. Most of the data presented in these chapters on the outer planets came from the *Voyagers*. They made it possible to obtain accurate measurements of the amount of helium in Jupiter's atmosphere. The showed the Great Red Spot to be characterized by swirling circulations much like a whirlpool or a terrestrial hurricane. The *Voyagers* made it possible for us to recognize the full extent of Jupiter's magnetosphere. They showed that the plasma torus surrounding Jupiter is created as the planet's magnetic field sweeps past the Galilean moon Io. They discovered small moons orbiting closer to Jupiter than Io. they sent back some remarkably detailed photographs allowing us to see fine detail on the surface of the Galilean moons and revealing that these moons are very different not only from Earth's moon but also from each other. They made possible the discovery of active volcanos on Io. They found that Jupiter is surrounded by a ring.

4. The Great Red Spot is a reddish colored spot in Jupiter's atmosphere that has been seen for over 300 years. It is a region of swirling, circulating winds like a whirlpool or a terrestrial hurricane. It is about twice the Earth's diameter in length. The source of its energy appears to come from the zonal atmospheric flows to its north and south. However, there are still some uncertainties as to how it continues to be maintained.

5. The colors indicate clouds with various compositions. The highest clouds are white and composed of ammonia ice. The yellows, reds, and browns are found in lower clouds which contain ammonium hydrosulfide ice. It is possible that sulfur, phosphorus, or their com-

pounds contribute to these clouds. Even organic compounds are a possibility. Below these clouds are bluish clouds of water ice.

6. The weather on Jupiter is generally windy and stormy. Due to its large atmosphere and rapid rotation, its winds are very fast near the equator, around 300 km/h. Elsewhere storm systems, similar to hurricanes, of varying size are found. Many of these storms last for years and frequently produce lightening. The weather is less violent near the poles, where the winds have much lower speeds and fewer storms are found. Temperatures at the cloud tops is a rather cool 125-150 K. However, warmer temperatures occur with increasing depth, so descend to the temperature of your choice.

7. Jupiter has retained most or all of its original atmosphere for two reasons. It is a massive planet, and as such, has sufficiently strong gravity to hold an atmosphere of hydrogen and helium. Second, it is located in the outer part of the solar system where temperatures are low. The atoms and molecules of gas can not attain a high enough velocity to escape the planet's gravity.

8. When Jupiter formed, gravity compressed its gases, causing the temperature to rise. The atmosphere has allowed this energy to slowly leak out of Jupiter, causing it to continue to emit more energy than it receives from the Sun.

9. The cloud layers of Jupiter are relatively thin, a few hundred kilometers thick at most. Below this layer, the atmosphere of hydrogen and helium becomes denser and denser with depth. At a few thousand kilometers hydrogen is compressed into a liquid. At about 20,000 kilometers the hydrogen changes to a liquid metallic hydrogen. Finally, there is a small, dense core made of rocky material similar to Earth. Although a little larger than Earth, it has a mass about 15 Earth masses.

Our understanding of the interior of Jupiter, and the other jovian planets, comes from a combination of theoretical modeling and observation of the bulk properties. The model must be consistent with the mass, radius, composition, rotation, temperature, flattening, and so on, observed for Jupiter.

10. Magnetic fields, in general, are produced by rapid rotation and some sort of conducting material in the interior of the object. In the case of Jupiter, it has a rotation rate of just under 10 hours and a larger amount of liquid metallic hydrogen in its interior that apparently produce its magnetic field.

11. Although Jupiter has the composition of a star, mostly hydrogen and helium, it has far too little mass to have ever even come close to being a star. When it was very young, it did radiate a lot of energy in the form of light, which would have made it much brighter than our Moon in the Earth's sky.

12. The Galilean moons appear like a small solar system around Jupiter. They have relatively circular orbit in the equatorial plane, they all orbit in the same direction, their densities decrease with increasing distance from Jupiter, and they are all significantly smaller than Jupiter. These moons also have well-defined surfaces and are at least composed of some rocky material. Jupiter and its Galilean moons can therefore be likened to the Sun and the terrestrial planets.

13. The densities vary from high to low, corresponding to the position of the moons. Io is high with a density of 3.6 g/cm³. The other densities are 3.0, 1.9, and 1.9. The decline in the densities appears to be related to an increase in the amount of water that makes up each moon.

14. Io's interior must be very hot in order to support the volcanic activity observed. The source of the energy needed to keep it hot is the gravitational pull and tug from Jupiter and Europa. It is not allowed to have a simple synchronous rotation, with a tidal bulge always pointing towards Jupiter, Europa keeps Io in a slightly noncircular orbit. The twisting of Io in side of its tidal bulge keeps it heated.

15. Io has no impact craters because its volcanism continually resurfaces it. Europa has very few impact craters; its icy surface is also subject to resurfacing. Ganymede and Callisto both show significant cratering, with Callisto showing the most. Again, this appears to be related to how frequently the surfaces are resurfaced.

16. Europa appears to be covered by an ocean of water that is frozen on top. If this is true, its ocean might be suitable for supporting life.

17. There is a lot of water among the moons of Jupiter and measurable amounts in Jupiter itself. The cooler temperatures of this part of the solar system inevitably made it possible for water to remain in solid form and participate in the formation of these many objects.

ANSWERS TO PROBLEMS

1. The force of gravity is proportional to the mass and inversely proportional to the square of the radius. The force of gravity for Jupiter can easily be compared to the Earth's by noting how much more massive and larger it is than the Earth. Jupiter is 318 times more massive and 11.2 times larger than Earth.

$$\frac{318}{11.2^2} = 2.54$$

Jupiter's gravity is 2.54 times that of the Earth's gravity.

2. Using the information in Table 11-1, the Galilean moons have a total mass of 5.36 Moon masses or 4.0×10^{23} kg. Jupiter has a mass of 1.9×10^{27} kg, so the ratio is 4750; Jupiter is this many time more massive than the combined mass of its four major moons. For the Earth-Moon system, this ratio is 80. For a planet of its mass, the Earth has a rather large moon.

3. Use Kepler's third law in ratio form, comparing the unknown orbit to that of Io's orbit.

$$\left(\frac{10}{42}\right)^2 = \left(\frac{R}{6}\right)^3$$

R = 2.3 radii

R = 164,000 km

4. The angular size of the Sun is the easiest to calculate. Since Jupiter is 5.2 A.U. from the Sun, the Sun will appear 5.2 times smaller than it does from Earth. The Sun is about one half degree is diameter from Earth or 30 arc minutes, so from Jupiter it will be 30/5.2 = 5.8 arc minutes.

To calculate the angular diameter of each of the Galilean moons as seen from the top of Jupiter's clouds, it is necessary to subtract one Jupiter radius, 71,400 km, from the distances to each moon, as given in Table 11-1. Thus, from cloud top to Io is 422,000 - 71,400 = 350,600.

The angular diameter for Io is

$$\frac{3630}{2\pi \times 350600} = \frac{\theta}{360°}$$

$$\theta = 0.59° = 35.6 \text{ arc minutes}$$

For Europa

$$\frac{3140}{2\pi \times 399600} = \frac{\theta}{360°}$$

$$\theta = 0.30° = 18 \text{ arc minutes}$$

For Ganymede

$$\frac{5260}{2\pi \times 998600} = \frac{\theta}{360°}$$

$$\theta = 0.30° = 18 \text{ arc minutes}$$

For Callisto

$$\frac{4800}{2\pi \times 1808600} = \frac{\theta}{360°}$$

$$\theta = 0.152° = 9.1 \text{ arc minutes}$$

Since all four moons have angular sizes smaller than the Sun's angular size, all of them can produce solar eclipses.

SUGGESTED READING

Astronomy (May 1979). Special issue on *Voyager* at Jupiter.

Beatty, J. K. "The Far-Out Worlds of *Voyager 1*: 1." *Sky and Telescope* (May 1979). One of the early articles expressing the amazing things found at Jupiter by *Voyager 1*.

Beebe, R. F. "Queen of the Giant Storms." *Sky and Telescope* (October 1990). A detailed look at Jupiter's Great Red Spot.

Bennett, G. L. "Return to Jupiter." *Astronomy* (January 1987). On the *Galileo* mission to Jupiter.

Levy, D. et al. "Comet Shoemaker-Levy 9 Meets Jupiter." *Scientific American* (August, 1995). Results of the comet impact and events leading up to the event.

Morrison, D. "The Enigma Called Io." *Sky and Telescope* (March 1985). The most dynamic of the four galilean satellites of Jupiter.

_ "Four New Worlds." *Astronomy* (September 1980). The largest moons of Jupiter, the galilean satellites, as seen by the *Voyager* spacecraft.

Schenk, P. M., "The Mountains of Io." *Astronomy* (January, 1995).

Soderblom, L. A. "The Galilean Moons of Jupiter." *Scientific American* (January 1980). The Galilean worlds as Earth-like bodies that can be compared with one another to gain insight into how they evolved.

Talcott, R., "Violent Volcanos of Io." *Astronomy* (May, 1993).

Waldrop, M. M. "Can Galileo Take the Heat?" *Science* (September 22, 1989). Can *Galileo* survive its circuitous route to Jupiter?

Weissman, P., "Making Sense of Shoemaker-Levy 9." *Astronomy* (May, 1995).

Chapter 12

SATURN
Spectacular Rings and Mysterious Moons

Appearance from Space

Use the scale models of Saturn and Titan made in Chapter 6; Titan will be 4.8 m away from Saturn on this scale. Also make a model of the ring system. The rings will extend from 29 cm to 55 cm from the center of Saturn. The thinness of the rings cannot be represented on this scale or any other scale suitable for the classroom. They are less than 100 m thick but about 70,000 km wide. If the ring system were as wide as a football field the thickness would be that of a hair!

Temperature

Similar to Jupiter, the low temperature is measured at the top cloud layer and is about 97 K; the high is at what ever depth is desired. Methane is a liquid; ammonia and carbon dioxide are both a solids at 97 K.

Rotation

Saturn is the most oblate of the planets. The rapid rotation has the effect of "pulling" the equator away from the planet. Although the effect is not easily calculated, a simple demonstration may suffice. Take a simple spring (typical spring constant of 20 n/m) with closed loops on both ends. Attach a small mass, e.g. 100 gm, to one end and insert a small rod through the other loop. Twirl the mass and spring, showing that as the period of rotation increases, the mass moves outward.

Once again, the equatorial velocity of the clouds may be determined by comparing the two velocities calculated from the cloud rotation rate and the planetary rotation rate. Using a radius of 60,000 km and calculating a circumference of 377,000 km, for a period of 10^h14^m for clouds at the equator gives a velocity of 36,800 km/hr. The true rotation rate of 10^h40^m gives 35,300 km/hr. The difference is a wind and cloud velocity of 1,500 km/hr towards the east. This is exactly the velocity given later in the section on weather. Note that the winds must again in the eastward direction

Internal Structure

Continuing the meter stick model of the interior of Jupiter; model Saturn in a similar way. However, continue to let Jupiter's radius be one meter. This will help show Saturn in proportion and the real differences in the thickness of the some of the layers.

84 cm	Top of cloud layer
83.7 - 84.0 cm	Cloud layers in the upper atmosphere
32 - 83.7 cm	Hydrogen is liquid
14 - 32 cm	Hydrogen is liquid metal
0 - 14 cm	Rocky, high density planetary core

Notice that although the rocky cores are the same in the size, the layer of liquid metallic hydrogen is over 3 times thinner in Saturn than in Jupiter.

The Roche Limit

In Chapter 7 we determined the form for the tidal force to be

$$\frac{\Delta F}{F} = \frac{2\Delta r}{r}$$

where ΔF is the tidal force across an object whose radius is Δr and F is the gravitational force between this object and another body at a distance r. A simple approach to the Roche limit is to think of the two halves of a moon being pulled apart by this tidal force, produced by a planet of mass M and radius R. What tries to keep the moon together is the moon's own gravitational force. Again, thinking simply as if the two halves of the moon are attracting each other, the force of attraction will be

$$= \frac{G\dfrac{mm}{22}}{\Delta r^2}$$

Setting this equal to the tidal force, ΔF, and using $F = \dfrac{GMm}{r^2}$ we have

$$\frac{GMm2\Delta r}{r^3} = \frac{G\dfrac{mm}{22}}{\Delta r^2}$$

Rearranging terms and multiplying the left side by R^3/R^3 gives

$$\frac{8MR^3}{r^3R^3} = \frac{m}{\Delta r^3}$$

But mass divided by radius cubed is just the density of the object (both sides can be divided by the factor of $4/3\pi$ to make the denominator look more like the volume of a sphere) and here we will assume the density of the moon and planet are the same. Taking the cube root, this reduces to

$$r = 2R$$

Because of our simplifying assumptions we get 2 instead of 2.4 for the constant. The Roche limit simply asks the question "At what distance does the tidal force tear an object apart?" and only a small amount of algebra is needed to demonstrate the principle.

Ring Model

Some of the information provided in the text allows a model of the ring environment to be calculated. The volume of the rings needs to be known first. This is easy, since the volume of a disc is just the area of a circle times its thickness. The volume of the inner part of the ring must be subtracted to obtain the ring volume. If R is the outer radius, r is the inner radius of the ring, and t is the thickness, then

$$\text{Vol. of Ring} = \pi(R^2 - r^2)t$$

which gives about $2 \times 10^{18}\, m^3$. Since the average ring particle size is estimated to be like a large snow ball, let the radius of each ring particle be 5 cm. The particles are made of water ice, so the density is 1 gm/cm^3 and the mass is calculated to be about 0.5 kg. (Use the formula for density = mass divided by the volume of a sphere.) The only question that remains is the spacing of the "snow balls" in the ring. This and the total mass of the ring material are the unknowns. Let us make a guess that each ring particle occupies of volume 1 meter in radius. The density of this volume is the mass of the particle, 0.5 kg, divided by the volume of a sphere 1 meter in radius. This will also equal mean density of the ring; the total mass of the ring divided by its volume. The result is a total mass of 2.4×10^{17} kg, or 3×10^{14} tons; very close to the 10^{15} tons noted in the text. So the ring environment is like having a lot of snow balls about two meters apart, swarming in their individual orbits around Saturn, moving at speeds from 59,000 km/hr to 81,000 km/hr. Little wonder that the Voyager space probe had to avoid the rings!

ANSWERS TO CHAPTER 12 REVIEW QUESTIONS

1. Saturn has a tilt of 27°. Because its rings are equatorial, we sometimes see them tilted by this amount; at other times we see them edge-on. During Saturn's 30 orbit around the Sun this orientation changes about every 7-8 years. First we see the rings from the north, then edge-on, then from the south, then edge-on again, and finally back to a north view.

2. Because Saturn has weaker gravity than Jupiter, due to its lower mass, its cloud layers are thicker; not as compressed as on Jupiter. Saturn is farther from the Sun and has a cooler temperature than Jupiter. This produces a thicker layer of ammonia clouds on top, which hides the more colorful cloud layers that occur deeper in the atmosphere.

3. Saturn's atmosphere is cooler than Jupiter's because of its greater distance from the Sun. Because of Saturn's weaker gravity, its atmosphere is 2.5 times thicker than Jupiter's. The cloud layers are similar to Jupiter's but thicker; the top layer of ammonia ice hides much of the cloud features below it. Saturn's atmosphere is underabundant in helium because it has precipitated out.

4. Saturn has a cloud layer 2.5 times thicker than Jupiter, due to its lower gravity. Its layer of molecular hydrogen is 30,000 km thick compared to Jupiter's 20,000 km thick molecular hydrogen layer. The metallic hydrogen layer of Saturn is only 15,000 km thick compared to 40,000 km for Jupiter. Saturn's core is 15,000 km thick compared to a 10,000 km thick core for Jupiter.

All these differences can be explained through Saturn's weaker gravity.

5. The Roche limit is the distance from a body at which that body's tidal forces can pull apart a second body, assuming the second body is held together by its own gravity. The rings of the jovian planets are always found within the Roche limit of the respective planets. Within the distance of the Roche limit a single object is pulled apart or many small objects are prevented from gravitationally attracting each other into a larger object.

6. Collisions between ring particles are predicted to destroy the ring system in a time relatively short compared to the age of the solar system. If this is the case then either the rings were recently formed or they are replenished by new material.

7. Mimas is the cause of the Cassini Division. Ring particles in the Division have an orbital period twice that of Mimas. They feel a gravitational pull from Mimas at the same place in their orbit every time they are the closest to Mimas. These particles are therefore pulled out of the orbit of the Division.

8. Voyager could not see the surface of Titan because it has a thick layer of haze in its upper atmosphere. The primary layer is from 100 to 200 km above the surface, with two thinner layers at 300 and 400 km elevation.

9. Titan is just a little smaller than Ganymede and has a mass between that of Ganymede and Callisto. Its density is the same as these two moons. Its albedo is the same as Callisto; darker than Ganymede. Its orbit is a little larger than Ganymede's orbit. So in many ways, Titan is a moon intermediate to Ganymede and Callisto, and actually rather similar to both. It differs by having a significant atmosphere, which neither Ganymede nor Callisto possess. It is also certainly colder, being much farther away from the Sun than the Galilean moons.

10. The key to Titan having an atmosphere and Ganymede and Callisto not is in its low temperature, about 94 K. The low temperature makes it difficult for an atmosphere to escape. The low temperature would also allowed Titan to have formed out of material rich in methane and ammonia, which condense or freeze at this temperature. Methane and ammonia may have formed its original atmosphere when radioactivity heat Titan's interior and released them as a gas.

11. Part of the surface of Enceladus has been erased by water that is now frozen. It may have water volcanos or geysers that spewed out water that then coated the surface. The nearby E ring contains material that may have been released by such eruptions.

12. Iapetus has a rather eccentric and inclined orbit. It has a large circular dark region, called Cassini Regio,

which resembles methane ice that has been altered by sunlight. Its origin is completely unknown.

13. The co-orbital satellites have circular orbits that are so similar, they differ in size by only 50 km, which is less than the size of the satellites. As the inner moon overtakes the outer moon, they gravitational interact and exchange orbits. This occurs about every 4 years.

14. The rising and setting of any, and all, objects would be hard to predict on Hyperion because of its chaotic rotation. Objects would not appear to move across the sky at a constant rate nor would they appear to follow the same path each time. Because of this chaotic rotation the positions and times of appearance of all astronomical bodies, viewed from Hyperion, would be unpredictable.

ANSWERS TO PROBLEMS

1. Saturn's equatorial radius is 60,000 km. Its circumference is $2\pi R$ or 377,000 km. At 1,500 km/h, it should take 377,000/1,500 = 251 hours for the flow to encircle the planet.

2. Determine first the mass of a typical ring particle of 6 cm radius = 0.06 m. The mass will be the volume times the density.

$$mass = \frac{4}{3}\pi(0.06m)^3 \times 1000 kg/m^3$$

$$mass = 0.29\ kg$$

Convert the ring mass in tons to kilograms, using 2000 lbs/ton and 1 kg/2.2 lbs. 10^{15} tons × 2000lbs/ton × 1 kg/2.2 lbs = 9.1×10^{17} kg. Dividing the particle mass into the total mass of ring material gives 3.1×10^{18} particles. This number is 3 million trillion particles. That's a lot of ice cubes (balls)!

3. From Kepler's third law, $P^2 \propto a^3$. The orbital radius for the inner part of the B ring is 92,000 km. Compare this to any given moon and its orbit. I'll us Pan as an example. Its orbital radius is 134,000 km and its period is 0.58 days. $(P/0.58)^2 = (92,000/134,000)^3$. P = 0.33 days = 7.9 hours = 28,500 s. The circumference of the inner B ring is $2\pi \times 92,000 = 578,000$ km. Dividing this distance by the period gives a velocity of 20 km/s.

Chapter 2 gave the velocity of a satellite in a low Earth orbit as 7.9 km/s. Why is a low Saturn orbit so much higher? Notice that Chapter 2 also gave a method for calculating orbital velocity. It depends on the square root of the ratio of mass to orbital radius. Although the large B ring orbit is almost 15 times bigger than the Earth orbit, and the square root of that should reduce the speed by a factor of 3.8, the mass of Saturn is 95 times that of Earth, which will increase the speed by 9.7. 9.7/3.8 = 2.56, so the orbital velocity should be 2.56 times that of a low Earth orbit. To check our result, $2.56 \times 7.9 = 20$ km/s. So its the mass of Saturn that makes a big difference in the orbital speed.

4. Titan has a mass of 1.83 Moon masses $= 1.35 \times 10^{23}$ kg. Surface gravity is proportional to m/r^2. Comparing to the Earth gives

$$\frac{1.35 \times 10^{23} / 5.97 \times 10^{24}}{5150 / 12,756^2} = 0.139$$

$1/7 = 0.143$, so this is about right.

SUGGESTED READING

Berry, R. "More Science from Saturn." *Astronomy* (March 1981). *Voyager 1*'s encounter with Saturn.

Burnham, R. "Saturn, Lord of the Rings." *Astronomy* (August 1991). Observing the ringed planet.

_ "Hubble Maps Titan's Unseen Landscape." *Astronomy* (February, 1995).

"Continents on Titan?" *Astronomy* (November 1989). Using radar to penetrate the atmosphere of Saturn's largest moon.

Cowen, R. "Saturn's White Spot: Driven by the Sun?" *Science News* (October 5, 1991). Report on the recent storm on Saturn.

_ "Saturn ring toss: Hubble finds more moons." *Science News* (August 5, 1995).

Croswell, K., "The Titan/Triton Connection." *Astronomy* (April, 1993). They are more similar than they look.

Eberhart, J. "Five-year Hunt Locates Saturn's 18th Moon." *Science News* (August 4, 1990). A tiny moon that apparently creates the Encke Division in Saturn's A ring.

Esposito, L. W. "The Changing Shape of Planetary Rings." *Astronomy* (September 1987). Evidence that planetary rings are young objects that grow and decay.

_ "Ever Decreasing Circles." *Nature* (November 14, 1991). Ideas on the origin of Saturn's rings.

"Iapetus: Saturn's Harlequin Moon." *Astronomy* (November 1989). Theories attempt to explain the dark face of Saturn's moon Iapetus.

MacRobert, A. M. "Hunting the Moons of Saturn." *Sky and Telescope* (July 1991). How to see and identify Saturn's moons through a small telescope.

Nichols, R. G. "Voyages to Worlds of Ice." *Astronomy* (December 1990). Introduction to CRAF—the Comet Rendezvous/Asteroid Flyby—and the *Cassini* mission to Saturn.

Robertson, D. F. "Cassini." *Astronomy* (September 1987). A craft to orbit Saturn and a probe of the atmosphere of its largest moon.

"*Voyager 2*'s Saturn: Still Surprising." *Science News* (August 29, 1991). More on *Voyager 2* at Saturn.

Chapter 13

URANUS, NEPTUNE, PLUTO
The Outer Worlds of the Solar System

Uranus and Neptune
Because these two planets are so similar, it is easiest to describe them at the same time. Use the models prepared in Chapter 9 to compare the sizes to Jupiter and Earth.

The 98° tilt of Uranus is worth demonstrating because it is so unusual. Although earlier, in the discussion of the Earth, it is established that the direction of the tilt does not change during the orbit, the concept applied to Uranus seems harder to accept. Demonstrate this using a globe for Uranus and another for the Sun. Voyager 2 viewed Uranus when its north pole (south, using a different convention) was almost pointing towards the Sun. Also indicate that the moons orbit equatorially. Neptune's tilt of about 30° appears rather normal in comparison.

Planets can not easily change the direction of their tilts because they are rotating. The faster the rotation, the more difficult it becomes. Demonstrate this with a spinning bicycle wheel; a common demonstration used in most physics classes. With the wheel spinning slowly it is easy to tilt, but with higher rates of spin it will not tilt but rather precess. Uranus very likely formed with this tilt. The equatorial orbits of the moons is added evidence of this. How can both Uranus and the orbits of its moons become tilted by a single collision?

Set the thermometer at 51 K and 59 K. It is difficult, at this time, to give the high temperatures. Using the meter stick model of Jupiter, Uranus will have a radius of 36 cm and Neptune 35 cm. Its rocky cores will extend out to about 11 cm, the "slushy" layer out to 22 cm, and from 22 cm on out is the molecular hydrogen, helium, and methane atmosphere.

The difference in rotation rates of the planets and their atmospheres allows equatorial wind velocities to be calculated. For Uranus, with a circumference of 160,500 km, the true rotation rate of 17.2^h gives a velocity of 9300 km/hr and the atmospheric rotation at the equator of 16.5^h gives a velocity of 9700 km/hr. Thus the cloud velocities are on the order of 400 km/hr, as noted in the text. For Neptune the same type of calculation is made. However, note that the rotation rate of the clouds is longer than the true rate so the cloud motion must in the east to west direction. For a circumference of 155,700 km and rotation rates of 16.1^h and 17.3^h gives velocities of 9700 km/hr and 9000 km/hr. The difference of 700 km/hr is not as high as that given in the text, 2000 km/hr. This is because the 17.3^h is an average rate and not correct for the fastest moving clouds.

The Moons of Uranus and Neptune

Uranus' rings and moons are nicely organized. Rings are from about 1.5 to 2.0 Uranus radii from its center, the smallest moons are from 2 to 3 radii, and the 5 medium-sized moons are from 5 to 23 radii. Using the 20 cm model of Uranus from the previous chapter, its easy enough to lay out this model. People often compare the 5 medium-size moons of Uranus to the 6 of Saturn. But there are some differences that may be important. Uranus' moons tend to have a slightly higher density and they are darker. For the most part the Uranian moons are also relatively farther away from their planet than are the Saturnian moons. Although we believe we know why they are darker, we really don't understand yet what these clues are telling us about Uranus, its moons, how they were formed, and how they have changed over time. It's just like a mystery where we have uncovered only some of the clues and we are uncertain whether that is enough to solve the mystery.

Miranda is undoubtedly the most unusual moon of Uranus that we know of (probably because Voyager 2 obtained some of its best images of Miranda). It has a cliff about 5 km high. This is particularly unusual because Miranda is so small, only 485 km is diameter. A little fun can be had by examining what would happen to an object or person who falls off this cliff. The acceleration due to gravity on Miranda is 0.085 m/sec^2. Using simple physics for a falling object, we can calculate the time it takes to fall down the 5,000 meter cliff.

$$t = \sqrt{\frac{2s}{g}}$$

The time will be 5^m43^s. Calculate the velocity using $v^2 = 2as$. The velocity will be 29.2 m/sec or 65 mph! The acceleration due to gravity is low and it takes a long time to fall to the bottom. But there is no air friction and the final velocity is unpleasantly high for landing! Imagine what happens to rocks that fall off the top of the cliff. There should be a lot of broken rubble at the base of the cliff.

Using the scale model of Neptune from the previous chapter, about 19.5 cm in diameter, Triton, Nereid, and their orbits can be scaled. The two moons will be small, 1 and 0.1 cm respectively. Triton is slightly smaller than the moon and Nereid is a mere dot. Triton's orbit is 136 cm from Neptune's center, tilted 20 ° and retrograde in direction. Nereid will vary from 54 to 370 cm in its very elliptical orbit. Also on this scale, the ring of Neptune can be shown from 17 to 20 cm from the center. The 6 small, inner moons orbit between 19 and 46 cm from Neptune's center.

Triton's orbit is getting smaller and it will slowly spiral into Neptune in about 100 million years. This is caused by its retrograde motion and its tidal interaction with Neptune. Imagine the series of catastrophes that will occur when Triton approaches the inner small moons and then is finally torn apart by Neptune's gravity as it approaches the location of the outer rings. In 100 million years this will be a very different-looking system of moons and rings. In light of what we learned about the rings of Saturn, I can't imagine the enormity of the ring that will be formed out of Triton.

Pluto

Using the scale we have for the other planets, Pluto and Charon end up too small for practical demonstrations. "Magnify" the model by a factor of 10. Pluto will now be 9 cm, Charon will be 5 cm, and their separation will be 77 cm. For comparison, you may want to show the Moon and/or Earth at this scale, possibly on the chalk board. The Earth will be 50 cm, the Moon will be 13 cm, and their separation will be 14 m. Although this latter model may not fit in a medium sized classroom, the point is made that Pluto and Charon are small and form a close binary-type system compared to other planet / moon systems. Indeed, the entire system fits within about one and a half Earth diameters!

With the enlarged model of Pluto and Charon the spin / orbit resonance can easily be shown. The same sides of Pluto and Charon continually point to each other. In addition, the circumstances of the eclipses can be shown. By timing the length of an eclipse of Charon (about 1.6 hours), its diameter is measured. Similarly, an eclipse of Pluto by Charon (about 2.9 hours) measures the size of Pluto. Because Charon's orbit is circular, the calculations are simple. Really! The ratio of the diameter of the moon to the circumference ($2\pi \times 19,700$ km = 124,000 km) of the orbit is equal to the ratio of the length of the eclipse 2.9hrs or 1.6hrs to the orbital period (6.4 days × 24 hrs/day = 154 hrs). So, for Pluto, its size is given by

$$\frac{2.9}{154} \times 124,000 = 2,300 km$$

For Charon, its size is given by

$$\frac{1.6}{154} \times 124,000 = 1,300 km$$

Since the size and period of the orbit must be known, Kepler's third law can also be solved for the *sum* of the masses. The value of the mass given in the text, 1.5×10^{22} kg, can easily be demonstrated. It is by assuming that Charon and Pluto have similar compositions and densities that the *individual* masses are estimated. Pluto will be more massive than Charon by the ratio of their volumes. Assuming spherical shapes, Pluto will be more massive by the ratio of the cubes of their diameters; $(2300 / 1300)^3 = 5.5$, or about 6 as given in the text.

Finally, the density can be calculated. Since both objects are assumed to have the same density, we can calculate either one. Let's do Charon. If the mass ratio is 5.5, then the total mass must be equal to 6.5 Charon masses. Charon's mass is then 1.5×10^{22} kg / 6.5 = 2.3×10^{21} kg. With a radius of 650 km = 650,000 m its volume is calculated.

$$\frac{4}{3}\pi(650,000)^3 = 1.15 \times x10^{18} m^3$$

Dividing the mass by the volume gives the density.

$$\frac{2.3 \times 10^{21}}{1.15 \times 10^{18}} = 2000 kg/m^3$$

Now it is evident that Charon and Pluto must be somewhat like Triton because they have similar sizes (Pluto being just a bit smaller than Triton) and densities. If Pluto had turned out to be a moon of some planet, it would have been the smallest of the large moons; Charon is a rather average medium-size moon.

These types of calculational demonstrations show the significance and power of some of the basic physics in the laws of gravity and orbits, as derived by Kepler and Newton.

ANSWERS TO CHAPTER 13 REVIEW QUESTIONS

1. Uranus was discovered by the British amateur astronomer William Herschel in march 1781. Herschel was engaged in charting the faint stars when he cam across an odd-looking object that he described as "a curious either nebulous star or perhaps a comet." It appeared as a disk in the Herschel;s telescope and moved relative to the stars, but too slowly to be a comet. Herschel had found the solar system;s seventh planet.

2. As astronomers observed the position of Uranus, they realized its positions were different than predicted. Using perturbation theory, an eighth planet was predicted to be affecting the orbit of Uranus. The predictions were refined and in time Neptune was discovered close to the predicted position.

3. It is the rotational axis of Uranus that is so unusual. It has a tilt of 98° relative to its orbit. At times during its orbit around the Sun, the north or south poles can actually point towards the Sun. In this regard, Uranus should have a highly exaggerated season effect.

4. The gas methane efficiently absorbs red light. Uranus and Neptune have increasing abundance of methane compared to Jupiter or Saturn. Reflected sunlight from Uranus and Neptune thus has less red light and is mostly blue. Because Uranus has less methane than Neptune, it appears more blue-green; Neptune appears quite blue.

5. Because they have lower masses than Jupiter or Saturn, Uranus and Neptune do not have liquid metallic hydrogen in their interiors. They may also have thick layers of slushy water with ammonia dissolved in it. This ionic layer could produce the magnetic fields of these planets.

6. Both Uranus and Neptune have magnetic fields that have axis that are highly tilted from their rotational axis. These tilts are 60° and 46° respectively. In addition, the magnetic fields are not centered on the planets' centers but significantly offset. Why these differences occur is not understood.

7. Miranda displays a wide range of surface terrains that seems exaggerated for its small size. There are ridges, valleys, and large faults. Apparently, Miranda has been disrupted from forces within or from without.

8. Neptune does not have a regular moon system. Triton, the large moon of Neptune, has a very unusual orbit compared to the other large moons of the solar system. It has a retrograde orbit that is tilted 20° to Neptune's equator. This suggests that Triton may have been captured or had its orbit greatly changed by some catastrophic event. Nereid has a very elliptical orbit. Proteus is Neptune's only medium-sized moon; there are 5 other small moons.

9. Over the next 100 million years Triton will spiral closer and closer to Neptune. This is caused by its tidal interaction with Neptune and its retrograde orbit. As it reaches the Roche limit of Neptune it will be torn apart, forming a very large ring.

10. Uranus has 9 distinct rings. They are dark, narrow, and widely spaced. Saturn's rings are bright, wide, and close together. Both systems of rings, however, are very thin.

11. Neptune has four dark rings, two quite narrow and two quite broad and diffuse. One of the rings is apparently "clumped" in places for unknown reasons, producing the appearance of partial ring arcs from Earth.

12. Irregularities in the orbits of Uranus and Neptune suggested a ninth planet. Percival Lowell predicted the lo-

cation of this planet but could not locate it. Finally, Clyde Tombaugh in 1930, discovered this planet and it was named Pluto. However, this discovery turned out be purely serendipitous because the irregularities in the orbits of Uranus and Neptune were not real.

13. In the 1980s, eclipses of Charon and Pluto were observed. Timing of the eclipses gives the diameters, since the size of the orbit and its circular nature is known. Kepler's third law allows the combined mass of Pluto and Charon to be determine. If their densities are assumed to be the same, then their individual masses may be determined from their volumes.

14. Pluto's size and density are more similar to the moon Triton than they are to any other object in the solar system. It is neither rocky like the terrestrial planets nor gaseous and liquid like the jovian planets. Pluto also has an icy surface like Triton.

15. No one expected nor had ever predicted that there were more planets in the solar system than those that could be seen with the naked eye. So Uranus came as quite a surprise. Perturbation theory, and observations of the planets, are now so refined that we can be certain that no new planets will be found.

16. The moon Titan is probably the most mysterious because it is shrouded in clouds that completely block viewing of it surface. The information known about its atmosphere, with various organic compounds identified, make it even more mysterious. The planet Pluto and its moon Charon are a close second, for being mysterious, because no space probe has visited them yet. HST can not image the surface of either because they are too distant.

ANSWERS TO PROBLEMS

1. The amount of sunlight received per square meter is inversely proportional to the square of the distance. Uranus should receive $1/(19.2)^2 = 0.0027$ (0.27%) as much light as the Earth. Neptune should receive $1/(30.1)^2 = 0.0011$ (0.11%) as much light as the Earth.

2. The Sun will be 30 times smaller at Neptune compared to it seen from Earth. As has been done in previous questions like this 30' / 30 = 1'. (Note: the Sun would look like a point of light to the naked eye, at the distance of Neptune. The human eye has a resolution of about 1' or more.)

To find Triton angular diameter, set up a ratio, as has been done in the past.

$$\frac{2760}{2\pi \times 354,000} = \frac{\theta}{360°}$$

$$\theta = 0.45° = 27'$$

Solar eclipses could easily occur whenever Triton crosses Neptune's orbital plane.

3. The Roche limit is 2.4 times the planet's radius. For Pluto this is $1150 \times 2.4 = 2760$ km. This is much smaller than Charon's distance of 19,700 km.

4. The round-trip distance is 2×40 A.U. $\times 150,000,000$ km/A.U. $= 1.2 \times 10^{10}$ km. Dividing this by the speed of light, 300,000 km/s gives 40,000 s or 11 hours 7 minutes. A satellite orbiting Pluto at 0.5 km/s would travel 20,000 km, or almost 3 orbits around Pluto, in a low Pluto orbit.

5. The total mass for moons of known mass equals only 0.125 Moon masses. Considering Nereid has a mass of 0.0000034 Moon masses and is 200 km in diameter, the smaller moons are negligible. Pluto is 0.2 Moon masses, so the total is about 0.325 or one third the mass of the Moon. The moons of Uranus, Neptune, Pluto, and Pluto itself—25 objects in all— have a combined mass of one third the Moon's mass. That's not very much!

SUGGESTED READING

Beatty, J. K. "A Place Called Uranus." *Sky and Telescope* (April 1986). Report on the Voyager 2 spacecraft encounter with Uranus.

_ "Getting to Know Neptune." *Sky and Telescope* (February 1990). Additional insight from the Voyager 2 Neptune encounter.

_ "Pluto and Charon: The Dance Goes On." *Sky and Telescope* (September 1987). New discoveries made possible by the decade-long series of mutual eclipses by Pluto and its moon.

Binzel, R. "Pluto." *Scientific American* (June 1990). What was learned about Pluto and its moon Charon during the 1980s series of mutual eclipses.

Burnham, R., "Pluto and Charon: At the Edge of Night." *Astronomy* (January, 1994)

Chiles, J. R. "For Voyager 2: From There to Eternity." *Smithsonian* (September 1988). Popular article on the journey of Voyager 2 through the outer solar system, written just before the Neptune encounter.

Coswell, K. "To The Edge: Missions to Pluto and Neptune." *Astronomy* (May, 1992)

Cunningham, C. J., "The Captive Asteroids." *Astronomy* (June, 1992). Asteroids trapped in the orbits of planets may be the most primitive objects in the solar system.

Cuzzi, J. N., and L. W. Esposito. "The Rings of Uranus." *Scientific American* (July 1987).

Ingersoll, A. P. "Uranus." *Scientific American* (January 1987). Report from the Voyager 2 encounter with Uranus.

Kinoshita, J. "Neptune." *Scientific American* (November 1989). The Voyager 2 encounter with Neptune.

Littmann, M. *Planets Beyond: Discovering the Outer Solar System.* New York: Wiley, 1988. The stories of Uranus, Neptune, and Pluto, the only major planets to have been discovered in recorded history.

Sagan, C., "The First New Planet." *Astronomy* (March, 1995). How the discovery of Uranus changed astronomy forever.

Stern, A. "Where has Pluto's Family Gone?" *Astronomy* (September, 1992). Hundreds of icy planets may have formed along with Pluto.

Chapter 14

SOLAR SYSTEM DEBRIS
Keys to Our Origin

Asteroid Belt

A very common description of asteroids is that they look like potatoes. Bring a couple of potatoes to class and set up a model of the belt environment. The question to be answered is "How far apart must the potatoes be placed to model the asteroid belt environment?" Assume the typical asteroid is 1 km in diameter, that there are 4,000 asteroids in the belt, and the belt extends from 2 AU out to 3 AU and is confined to a plane. I use two large potatoes (for visibility) about 15 cm long, and assuming each represents a 1 km asteroid, the scale becomes 1 km = 15 cm.

The area of the belt is given by $\pi (R^2 - r^2) = \pi (3^2 - 2^2) = 15.7$ AU². Dividing this by 4,000 gives 0.00393 AU² per asteroid. What is the radius of a circle with this area? $\pi r^2 = 0.00393$, so r = 0.0354 AU or 5.3 million km. The distance between asteroids will actually be twice this distance, as illustrated.

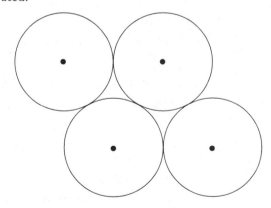

If the dots represent asteroids and the circles are the areas just calculated, then each asteroid is about 2r from the nearest asteroid. The distances between these asteroids will be about 10.6 million km. On the scale of the classroom this will be almost 1,600 km or 1,000 miles.

Keep one potato at the front of the class and give the other to a student who offers to help with your demo. Do the above calculation with the expressed intention of telling the student how far away to stand to properly model the asteroid belt. The result comes as a bit of a surprise to most people when you tell the student to go stand one thousand miles away!

Brightness and Angular Size of Asteroids

Because asteroids are relatively nearby objects it is often believed that they are easily observed. A more realistic view is understood when a typical asteroid's brightness and angular size are calculated.

An easy brightness estimate may be made relative to Mars, which is a rocky planet nearest to the asteroid belt. Assume Mars and a typical asteroid have the same albedo and the asteroid is about twice as far away as Mars. If Mars and the asteroid were the same size this would make the asteroid 4 times fainter. But Mars is 6787 km in diameter and a typical asteroid is only 1 km. Since the brightness depends upon the apparent area of the disc, the asteroid will be fainter by $(1/6787)^2 = 46$ million times. This, combined with the other factor of 4, makes the asteroid a total of about 200 million times fainter than Mars. (Later, when the concept of magnitude is understood, this can be converted to about 21 magnitudes fainter than Mars. Mars is about 0.0 magnitude when at 1 AU from Earth, so a typical asteroid would be 21st magnitude when seen at 2 AU; well within range of larger telescopes but still not easy.)

For the angular size it is helpful to remember that 1 arc second = 1/206265 in radian measure. Thus a 1 km object seen at about 200,000 km appears as 1 arc second. The asteroid 1991BA was slightly larger than 1 arcsec when it passed by the Earth. But this is certainly not typical of the belt asteroids viewed from 2-3 AU. 200,000 km is 0.0013

AU so at 1 AU a 1 km asteroid would appear to be 0.0013 arcsec. At a more typical distance of 2.5 AU the angular size would be 0.0005 arcsec, which is about 100 times smaller than can be resolved by the Hubble Space Telescope!

Asteroid Collisions

This topic has developed increasing interest among the public and is certainly a subject that students find fascinating. Fortunately, the physics is very simple and informative. All that is needed is the concept of kinetic energy = $1/2mv^2$. At the time of the collision, all the energy is in this form. Only a few percent of its velocity is due to "falling" to Earth, i.e. the conversion of gravitational potential energy to kinetic energy, most of the velocity is due to the relative velocities of the Earth and the asteroid. Start with an estimated velocity of 50 km/sec. (For an asteroid with a aphelion distance of 3 AU and a perihelion distance of 1 AU, the velocity at perihelion, which is where the collision is likely to occur, is about 40 km/sec. Since the Earth is moving at 30 km/sec, the range in the relative velocities is 10 to 70 km/sec.) Assume a 1 km diameter spherical asteroid of density 3 gm/cm^3 = 3000 kg/m^3. The volume will be 5.2×10^8 m^3. The mass will be 1.6×10^{12} kg. The kinetic energy will equal 2×10^{21} Joules. One megaton equivalent of energy is equal to 4.20×10^{15} J. This gives 500,000 megatons of energy, close to the one million noted in the text. This is enough energy to boil (from 0° C water to 100° C steam) a cubic volume of ocean water 9 km on a side, just in case it falls into an ocean!)

Remember, the amount of energy goes by the square of the velocity and is proportional to the mass. However, the mass depends upon the cube of the radius of the asteroid. So, for a 10 km asteroid there is 1000 times more volume and mass and 1000 times more energy!

Comets

Comets usually have very eccentric orbits, 0.99 or more. To easily demonstrate this, draw an orbit with a one meter major axis and an eccentricity of 0.99. The minor axis will be 28 cm. Draw the major axis on the chalk board and from the center mark two points vertically 14 cm above and below the center. The ellipse can be easily sketched in. The Sun, at one focus, will be 1 cm from which ever end is chosen. If this were a scale model of a real comet, using a scale of 1 cm = 1 AU, then perihelion occurs at the Earth's orbit and aphelion is over twice the distance to Pluto. Using Kepler's third law, the period would be about 350 years.

Long period comets may have orbits as large as 50,000 AU (aphelion distance). Since, in these cases, perihelion is much less than 1 AU, the semi-major axis is about 25,000 AU. The period would be about 4 million years.

Short period comets have periods less than 200 years. Again, using Kepler's third law, the semi-major axis is cal-

culated to be 34 AU. Assuming a large eccentricity would mean their aphelion distance would take them to about 68 AU; well beyond the orbit of Pluto but much closer than the long period comets.

Sun-grazing comets are interesting because they pass so close to the Sun at perihelion that they are destroyed. Such a comet is likely to be passing the Sun for the first time; any previous passage would, of course, have destroyed it. Sun-grazing comets do not have to actually hit the Sun; if they come to within about one solar radius of the Sun's surface this may be sufficient to destroy them. Let's assume a comet has a perihelion distance of 2 solar radii = 0.01 A.U. If it has arrived from the distant Oort Cloud then a = 25,000 A.U. might be appropriate. The eccentricity is calculated to be 0.9999996!

Halley's Comet

The same type of calculations can be made for this famous comet. With a period of 76 years, the semi-major axis is calculated to be 17.9 AU. Its eccentricity is 0.97, and aphelion distance is equal to a(1 + e) = 35.3 AU; between the orbits of Neptune and Pluto. Perihelion is equal to a(1 - e) = 0.54 AU; about half way between the orbits of Mercury and Venus.

A model of a comet can be easily, although messily, made. Take an empty half gallon milk carton and fill it 80% full of water. Mix in very fine dirt and soot. Ashes from a fireplace are good to use but make sure they are crushed. Put enough soot into the mixture to make it very dark. (You can always add some India ink to help the color.) Add sufficient dirt and soot to fill the carton and freeze over night. While it is freezing you will need to mix it several times so that the dirt does not settle out. Before class, strip away the carton to reveal the frozen, dark mass. Chip off the edges if you want a more realistic appearance. It will be rather messy as it thaws. It's a dirty job I know, but someone has to do it!

An interesting calculation to make for Halley's comet is determining how much of the comet is lost during each orbit (really at each perihelion). Assume it is a sphere 12 km in diameter. It will have a volume of 9×10^{11} m^3. The text gives a typical comet density to be about 0.1 gm/cm^3 or 100 kg/m^3 so the mass is calculated to be 9×10^{13} kg. If Halley's comet is estimated to last only another 5,000 orbits then it must lose an average of 1.8×10^{10} kg each orbit. This is about 20 million tons of material each time it passes by the Sun!

By how much is the radius of the comet reduced by losing this much material? The volume lost will be the area, A, of the sphere times a thickness, t. So the density equals the lost mass divided by At. The area is given by $4\pi r^2$. Solving for t gives 0.4 m or 40 cm.

A good question to ask your more observant students: If Halley's comet shrinks by 0.4 m per passage, and it makes 5,000 passages until its gone, 5000 × 0.4 = 2000 m or 2 km.

But Halley's comet has a radius of about 6 km. So what is wrong with this calculation! (Answer: 0.4 m per passage is the current rate of shrinkage. This will increase in time. The mass lost per passage is what is constant. As Halley's comet shrinks, its area is smaller and therefore a greater thickness of the surface must be lost. For example, when Halley's comet is half its current size, only 3 km in radius, it will have 1/4 the area. Therefore, the thickness of the layer must be 4 times the current value or $4 \times 0.4 = 1.6$ m per passage.)

Meteorites

I feel very strongly about having my students see and feel a meteorite first hand. It will likely be the only time in the their lives when they will actually touch an object that did not originate from Earth. Meteorites are commonly available for sale; I prefer a size that fits easily in the palm of your hand. Pass it around to your students so they can see it and feel its weight.

Virtually all meteorites that are purchased are high density, highly differentiated examples. Do a demonstration to measure the density. Ask your students from what type of object must your meteorite have originated. If the meteorite has a high density then it must have come from the core of a differentiated body. How did it get out of the core? How did it get to Earth?

ANSWERS TO CHAPTER 14 REVIEW QUESTIONS

1. The Trojan asteroids are found in the orbit of Jupiter, at either the L_4 or L_5 Lagrange points. Apollo asteroids have perihelion distances less than 1 A.U., or more simply, they cross the orbit of the Earth. The Amor asteroids are similar to the Apollo asteroids, except they cross only the orbit of Mars, not Earth.

2. The *Galileo* space probe, on its way to Jupiter has photographed two asteroids, Gaspra and Ida. These, to date, are the finest photographs ever taken of asteroids.

3. The Kirkwood gaps are orbits with semi-major axis that are not, or poorly, occupied by asteroids. They represent resonances with Jupiter's orbit. Jupiter essentially pulls asteroids out of these orbits.

4. The C-type asteroids are carbonaceous in composition. They have very low albedos, around 0.05. The S-type asteroids are more reflective, with albedos around 0.15 to 0.25. They have a composition of silicates. S-type asteroids are found in the inner portion of the asteroid belt; C-types are found farther out. 75 percent of asteroids are C-type and 15 percent are S-type.

5. Comets, when they are far from the Sun, are frozen chunks of ices, dust, and rocky particles. They are very cold and dark. When comets approach the Sun, the surface ices start to sublimate, releasing gases and particles of rock and dust. A large cloud of this material surrounds the comet and is called the coma. As the comet approaches the Sun one or more tails are formed, as discussed in the following question.

6. We must be careful answering the question "where are comets found?" because a comet can not be "found" until it becomes visible to telescopes on Earth. This means that only comets entering the inner solar system will be found. A broader view of the solar system tells us that we would find most comets in the Oort cloud, thousands and tens of thousands of A.U. from the Sun. Some are also found in the Kuiper Belt, between 30 and 100 A.U.; observations seem to be confirming the Kuiper Belt comets but the Oort cloud comets will remain invisible for a long time.

7. The nucleus is the solid, rocky-icy body of the comet. Near the Sun it develops a diffuse coma (halo) of dust and sublimated gases. A hydrogen envelope surrounds the coma and has a shape distorted by the solar wind. It can be millions of kilometers across. Finally, there are the two tails to the comet, stretching away from the nucleus; the ion tail and the dust tail.

8. The comet nucleus has a very dark surface with large quantities of dust and gas rising from its surface, as it is heated by the Sun. In some places jets of matter are streaming from the surface. These jets can change the rotation rate of the comet and even make small changes to its orbit.

9. All comets, that we know of, eventually die out. Some impact on planets or moons as they pass through the solar system. Others have a perihelion distance so close to the Sun that the comet either impacts with the Sun, completely disappears from heating, or breaks up into many fragments. Other, more "normal" comets continue to orbit the Sun until they have finally lost all their material.

10. A meteoroid is any particle of material orbiting the Sun which can not be seen from Earth. (If it could be seen, it would be called an asteroid.) Sizes range from kilometers to microscopic dust particles. If a meteoroid passes through the atmosphere of the Earth (or any other atmosphere) it momentarily heats the gases, making them glow, as it passes through. This streak of light is known as a meteor. The meteoroid likely burns up when passing through the atmosphere. If it does not, because of its size, composition, or low velocity, and lands on the surface of a planet or moon, it is known as a meteorite.

11. Meteor showers are caused by the Earth passing through the orbit of a comet. The orbit of a typical comet is filled with many particles of rock and dust left behind as its ices sublimated. When the Earth passes through this swarm of particles, a meteor shower is observed. Many meteors will be seen emanating from one location in the sky.

12. Carbonaceous meteorites are the most primitive meteorites. Their material appears to have not been altered since the formation of the solar system. They are often rich in organic molecules.

13. Meteorites are used to age-date the solar system. Examination of the rocky material tells us much about the body from which the meteorite originated. It can also tell us about the conditions in the early solar system when planets and moons were forming.

14. The Oort cloud of comets, considered the source of most comets, is like a large, spherical halo around the solar system. Comets enter the inner solar system was a large range of orbital inclinations. Asteroids are mostly confined to the ecliptic. Their position indicates they are the product, maybe leftovers, of planet formation. The Comets, from their distribution and composition, may date from an earlier period in the solar system's formation.

15. Earth's surface has been resurfaced many times since it was formed. Erosion and tectonic activity have erased virtually every bit of the original surface. Meteoroids remain in space fairly unaltered by time, except for occasional collisions. When found as meteorites they provide information dating back to when they formed.

16. The consequences of a 10 km meteorite striking the Earth today would be very unpleasant. There would be world-wide effects to the entire environment and likely extinctions of many of the highest-order animals. The Earth would likely be shrouded in clouds of dust, water, and even salt water for years. Huge tidal waves would result from a strike in one of the oceans. Large earthquakes could be triggered. Near the strike, the heat and blast wave would destroy everything for hundreds of kilometers. Debris falling back to Earth from the impact would devastate an even larger region. No part of the Earth would go unaffected. Keep in mind that the possibility of such an impact during your lifetime is very low; unfortunately neither is it zero.

ANSWERS TO PROBLEMS

1. The gravitational acceleration of a body on its surface depends on the mass of that body and inversely on the radius of the body squared. The weight of an object depends directly on this acceleration.

$$\text{Weight } \alpha \frac{0.0002}{0.073^2} \text{ Weight on Earth}$$

$$\text{Weight } \alpha \text{ } 0.0375 \text{ Weight on Earth}$$

A 100 kg astronaut would weight 220 lbs on Earth. On Ceres, the weight would be:

$$\text{Weight} = 0.0375 \times 220$$

$$\text{Weight} = 8.25 \text{ pounds}$$

2. (a) The sum of the perihelion and aphelion distances give the major axis; half of this is the semi-major axis, which will be 25,000 A.U. in this case. Using Kepler's third law, $P^2 = (25,000)^3$. $P = 4 \times 10^6$ yrs, or 4 million years.

(b) Calculating the semi-major axis from its period gives $(125)^2 = a^3$. a = 25 A.U. Its major axis is 50 A.U., so aphelion distance is 50 - 1 = 49 A.U.

3. First find the amount of rocky material in the comet. 0.05×10^{13} kg = 5×10^{11} kg. Since the average mass of a fragment is 0.1 kg, there must be 5×10^{12} fragments. Although this is a lot of fragments, in reality there would be many more; most fragments would be much less than 0.1 kg in mass.

4. From Chapter 2, the velocity of a circular orbit, radius R, around a body of mass M is

$$v = \sqrt{\frac{GM}{R}}$$

The mass is given by the density times the volume; a spherical volume will be assumed. Using the information given, the mass is:

$$M = 3000 kg/m^3 \times 4/3\mu(5000m)^3$$

$$M = 1.57 \times 10^{15} \text{ } kg$$

Calculating the velocity:

$$V = \sqrt{\frac{6.67 \times 10^{-11} \times 1.57 \times 10^{15}}{5000}}$$

$$V = 4.6 \text{ m/s} = 0.0046 \text{ km/s or } 16.6 \text{ km/hr}$$

$$V = 16.6 \times 5/8 = 10 \text{ mph.}$$

Yes, you could throw a rock into orbit!

SUGGESTED READING

Alvarez, W., and F. Asaro. "What Caused the Mass Extinction? An Extraterrestrial Impact." *Scientific American* (October 1990). Debate between those who say it was caused by an extraterrestrial impact and those who claim the cause was a period of extreme Earth vulcanism.

Balsiger, H., H. Fechtig, and J. Geiss. "A Close Look at Halley's Comet." *Scientific American* (September 1988). Data sent by European, Japanese, and Soviet probes to Halley's Comet.

_ "Killer Crater in the Yucatan?" *Sky and Telescope* (July 1991). On the possibility that a crater in the Yucatan is the long-sought site of the impact that triggered the demise of the dinosaurs.

Bond, P., "Close Encounter with a Comet." *Astronomy* (November, 1993). The Giotto probe visits another comet.

Brandt, J. C., and M. B. Niedner, Jr. "The Structure of Comet Tails." *Scientific American* (January 1986). Interrelations of the plasma tail of Halley's Comet with the solar wind.

Cowen, R., "Rocky Relics." *Science News* (February 5, 1994). Sources of near-Earth asteroids.

_ "New comet might be quite a sight in 1997" *Science News* (August 12, 1995) Comet Hale-Bopp may be the next big naked-eye comet.

Delsemme, A. H. "Whence Come Comets?" *Sky and Telescope* (March 1989). The mysterious origin of comets.

Dodd, R. T. *Thunderstones and Shooting Stars.* Cambridge, MA: Harvard University Press, 1986. All about meteorites: types, origins, and the evidence they bring of conditions beyond Earth.

Durda, D., "All in the Family." *Astronomy* (February, 1993). Fragments of asteroid collisions show how the asteroid belt evolved.

_ "Two by Two They Came." *Astronomy* (January, 1995). Evidence grows for numerous double asteroids.

Eicher, D. J., "A New Member of the Family." *Astronomy* (December, 1992). An icy body beyond Pluto is discovered.

Grieve, R. A. F. "Impact Cratering on the Earth." *Scientific American* (April 1990). What happens when a large meteoroid strikes Earth.

Levy, D. H. "How to Discover a Comet." *Astronomy* (December 1987). Advice from a successful comet hunter.

McFadden, L.-A. and Chapman, C., "Interplanetary Fugitives." *Astronomy* (August, 1992). The dangers and opportunity presented by near-Earth asteroids.

Morrison, D., and C. R. Chapman. "Target Earth: It Will Happen." *Sky and Telescope* (March 1990). On the realization that comets and small asteroids still occasionally collide with the Earth.

Spratt, C. E. "On the Trail of a Meteorite." *Astronomy* (August 1989). Excellent article on hunting for meteorites.

Stern, A., "Chiron: Interloper from the Kuiper Disk?" *Astronomy* (August, 1994).

Talcott, R., "Galileo Views Gaspra." *Astronomy* (February, 1992). First detailed photographs of an asteroid using the Galileo probe.

____, "Toutatis seen with Radar." *Astronomy* (April, 1993). This near-Earth asteroid comes in two parts.

Verschuur, G., "Mysterious Sungrazers." *Astronomy* (April, 1992). Comets that plunge into the Sun.

Weissman, P. "Are Periodic Bombardments Real?" *Sky and Telescope* (March 1990). Article discussing the idea that Earth is regularly bombarded by comets, which cause periodic mass extinctions.

Weissman, P. R., "Comets at the Solar System's Edge." *Sky & Telescope* (January, 1993).

Whipple, F. L. "The Black Heart of Comet Halley." *Sky and Telescope* (March 1987). The originator of the "dirty snowball" theory discusses Halley's nucleus.

Chapter 15

THE FORMATION OF THE SOLAR SYSTEM
The Birth of Our World

Students are often confused by the actual sequence of steps in the formation of the solar system. Besides learning the new terminology it is necessary to know the order in the sequence of events. I find that it is often very helpful to present an outline of the various steps prior to lecturing on the details. In this way the students see the process as a series of consecutive events. The following outline may be of help.

Outline of Solar System Formation

1. Interstellar gas and dust cloud: about 1 light-year in diameter, starts to gravitationally collapse.

2. Solar nebula: about 100 AU in diameter in the shape of a rotating disc.

   a. Dust particles in inner nebula are broken down into atoms due to warm temperatures.

   b. Dust particles, from about 10 AU on out, remain.

   c. The inner nebula starts to cool.

3. Condensation and accretion: dust particles form condensation nuclei; through collisions, particles grow rapidly in size.

   a. At about 0.5 AU only metallic grains condense.

b. At about 1 AU rocky, silicate grains condense.

c. At about 3 AU water ice particles condense.

d. Farther out, ammonia and methane condense.

e. Planetesimals, up to a few hundred kilometers across, are formed.

4. Gravitational accretion: planetesimals have sufficient gravity to attract material gravitationally; the largest bodies start to dominate and grow rapidly.

a. The largest bodies form protoplanets; protomoons form around them.

b. The smaller bodies suffer numerous collisions and fragment

c. Some planetesimals, through gravitational interactions with large protoplanets are ejected into the outer solar system forming the Oort Cloud of comets.

5. Gravitational accretion of gas: the largest protoplanets in the coolest parts of the solar nebula accrete gas; the smaller protoplanets in the inner solar nebula are unable to accrete gas due to its higher temperature.

6. Sweep of the debris: over about one billion years the material left over from the solar system formation is cleared.

a. The Sun enters its T-Tauri phase and blows the remaining gas out of the solar system.

b. The jovian planets strongly influence the orbits of the remaining planetesimals (comets), either throwing them out into the Oort Cloud or inward where they collide with the terrestrial planets.

c. Terrestrial planets obtain their atmospheres, and particularly water, from the constant impact of cometary material.

d. In a process that remains uncertain, Jupiter influences the region of the asteroid belt so that some material remains in stable solar orbits but unable to coalesce into a larger body.

Angular Momentum

This is a very new concept to most students and one which often poses problems for them to understand. The common demonstration of conservation of angular momentum is the rotating platform. Stand on the platform and have someone start you turning while keeping your arms fully extended. Then bring your arms in. The increase in angular velocity is quite noticeable. I get awfully dizzy doing this so I always ask for a student volunteer.

A computational approach may also be taken. Angular momentum, L, is rather easy to calculate. For a point mass, m, moving in a circle of radius r and velocity v, L = mvr. For a solid body, moment of inertia of I, that is rotating with angular velocity ω, L = Iω. For a sphere, I = 2/5 mr^2, where r is the radius of the sphere.

Assuming the Sun rotates as a solid body (it doesn't but it is hard to do the problem otherwise) with a rotational period of 25.38 days, $\omega = 2.86 \times 10^{-6}$ sec^{-1}. The moment of inertia is I = 3.86×10^{47} kg m^2. Then L = 1.1×10^{42} kg m^2/sec. Calculate the angular momentum for Jupiter but using mvr, which is easier. Its orbital velocity is 13,100 m/sec and L = 1.9×10^{43} kg m^2/sec. Comparing these two angular momenta we see that Jupiter has about 17 more angular momentum than the Sun. It is actually more than this because we have over estimated the angular velocity of the Sun by using its highest rotation rate.

Could a large amount of angular momentum have been transferred to comets in the Oort Cloud? The same can be tried for a 1 km diameter body at 1,000 AU. L $\approx$ 10^{28} kg m^2/sec. For this you can see that it would take an enormous number of such objects to carry away a significant amount of angular momentum. They would all have to be orbiting in the same direction too, which comets do not do. Even over the life-time of the solar system, there has likely not been this many comets in the Oort Cloud.

ANSWERS TO CHAPTER 15 REVIEW QUESTIONS

1. Properties of the solar system that models must explain:

   isolation and positions of planets,

   nearly circular planetary orbits,

   planetary orbits in nearly the same plane,

   planets' direction of revolution the same and same as Sun's rotation,

   most planets' rotation in same direction as Sun's rotation,

   most moons have revolutions in same direction as planet's rotation,

   highly differentiated planetary system,

   asteroids are very old and unlike planets and moons, and

   comets are primitive, icy fragments that do not orbit in ecliptic plane.

2. An evolutionary theory is one in which the solar system develops as a series of gradual and natural events that conform to physical law. A catastrophic theory invokes an accidental or rare event to explain the formation of the solar system.

3. The nebular theory has the solar system forming out of a large, spinning cloud of gas. As it spins, it flattens into a pancake shape and forms a series of concentric rings. Each of these rings eventually forms a planet; the central condensation forms the Sun.

4. The nebular theory has a large rotating cloud collapse into a disc. The solar system forms out of the disc. The orbits of the major bodies should therefore be approxi-

mately in the same plane and should have the same direction of motion. This is, of course, what is observed.

5. There are two flaws with the nebular theory. The concentric rings of gas would likely not form nor would they eventually condense into planets; the gas would disperse over time. The Sun is also predicted by the theory to have most of the angular momentum of the solar system. Instead, it is observed to have very little.

6. Angular momentum can be defined as the tendency of a body to keep spinning or moving in a circle. Linear momentum is the tendency of an object to keep moving in a straight line in the absence of external forces. Linear momentum is defined as the product of both mass and velocity. Angular momentum also depends on the size or mass distribution of the object.

7. The key ingredient of the modern condensation theory is interstellar dust. The dust helps to both cool off the solar nebula and provides condensation nuclei upon which particles can grow.

8. Accretion begins with dust particles acting as condensation nuclei. These small particles grow through collisions with other particles, when they collide, they stick together. As the cloud collapses, the density of particles grows, so collisions are more frequent and particles continue to grow. When objects as large as a few hundred kilometers are formed, their own gravity is able to attract large quantities of matter, speeding up the rate of growth. The bigger they get, the stronger their gravity is, and the more material is attracted to them.

9. In the solar nebula where the jovian planets are now found, the temperatures were sufficiently low for ices of water, ammonia, and methane to form. This provided much more material for the early accretion that occurred and it proceeded rapidly. The planetesimals that formed could then also attract hydrogen and helium, and the jovian planets grew to a large size. In the region of the inner solar nebula, temperatures were sufficiently high that time had to pass before the first rocky particles could condense and start the accretion process. There was less material to accrete because it was too hot for the icy material to exist. Finally, hydrogen and helium could not be accreted because of the planets' low gravity and high temperatures.

10. Once planetesimals developed sufficient mass, gravity produced collisions of higher speed. Such collisions often fragmented the bodies in to smaller pieces. These small fragments could then be easily swept up by larger planetesimals and protoplanets. In the end, only a few large bodies remained in any location of the solar system. Many of the fragments that did not collide with a forming planet or moon became either asteroids or comets.

11. The Earth's location in the solar system is critical to understanding its composition. It was at 1 A.U. that temperatures were sufficiently high to initially destroy dust grains. When cooling occurred, rocky, silicate grains formed. Earth's formation was to seeded by this material, and for the most part, make up much of the Earth. It was also the Earth's location in the inner solar system that subjected it to the significant bombardment of comet-like material that gave the Earth its atmosphere and water.

12. In the hot inner solar nebula, only metals and then silicates could condense out. This gave rise to the inner planets that are quite rocky. It even accounts for Mercury having a higher density than would be expected for a body of its size; it formed from material with a greater abundance of metals.

It was really more the lack of heat that influenced the formation of the jovian planets. Lower temperatures allowed icy material to initially accrete. The larger planetesimals had sufficiently high gravitational fields to quickly attract hydrogen and helium. But this could not have occurred if the temperature of the gas had not been low enough to retain the gases and prevent their escape.

13. In its initial stage of formation, the Earth was in a relatively hot part of the solar nebula. Only rocky, silicates could condense at this high a temperature. Earth's water appears to have come later, by the collision of numerous comet-like planetesimals ejected into the inner solar system through interactions with the jovian planets. But now this environment was much cooler than before and the planetary surface of the Earth could retain the water and other volatile material that would form its early atmosphere.

14. In its T Tauri stage, the Sun became very bright and developed a strong solar wind. These cleared the solar nebula of any gas that had not been accreted by the planets. In particular, it likely stopped the further development of the jovian planets.

15. After the jovian planets were formed, the many remaining icy planetesimals were gravitationally moved into the inner solar system or flung in to the outer reaches of the solar system. This was done simply through the gravitational interaction of the jovian planets with the orbits of the planetesimals. In this way the Oort Cloud of comets was formed.

16. Some theories predict that the Sun lost most of its angular momentum by the strong solar wind it ejected. The Sun's magnetic field interacted with the particles in the wind, sweeping them about, causing a braking action to slow the Sun's rotation. Other theories prefer an approach in which the early solar system had much more matter in it than we see today. Much of this mat-

ter went unused, and when swept away, took with it much of the angular momentum.

17. Think in terms of angles and resolution. An A.U. seen at a distance of 1 pc appears as one arc second (1"). At 100 pc, 100 A.U. would also appear as 1". 100 A.U. is about the size of the solar system and the solar nebula from which it formed. 100 pc is not very far away; no star formation is found this close. But even if there is a solar nebula at a distance of 100 pc, it would appear as only 1". Even with the HST, little could be observed; planets would be completely impossible to resolve.

18. The condensation theory is an evolutionary theory that would suggest that planetary formation is a naturally occurring process that should be common throughout the Galaxy. Collision theories make the formation of the solar system a rare event that has little chance of occurring again in the entire Galaxy.

19. The comet starts out as part of a planetesimal that fragments during a collision. After moving through the outer solar system for many years it happens to pass close to Jupiter. The gravitational influence of Jupiter alters the comet's orbit and sends it to the outer parts of the solar system, where it remains for a few billion years. A passing star or another comet finally changes this comet's orbit once again, sending plunging towards the Sun in a highly eccentric orbit. Passing around the Sun it may, once again, have its orbit changed by Jupiter or Saturn. Now a short period comet, it remains in the inner parts of the solar system. Each time it passes perihelion it looses more of its material until finally it breaks apart and completely looses all of its icy material. Left behind is a swarm of dusty, rocky particles that produce meteor showers on Earth. Most of these particles eventually impact on the surface of a planet or moon and become a part of them. The gas, from its ices, is slowly swept out of the solar system by the solar wind.

ANSWERS TO PROBLEMS

1. Orbital angular momentum can be expressed as MVR, where M is the mass of the planet, V is its orbital velocity, and R is the radius of its orbit. But in Chapter 2 the orbital velocity was found to depend on the square root of M/R. Putting this all together gives

$$\text{Ang. Mom.} \propto MR\sqrt{\frac{M}{R}}$$

$$\text{Ang. Mom.} \propto M^{3/2}R^{1/2}$$

This now makes it easy to compare the angular momentum of Jupiter and Saturn to that of the Earth. Using Earth units for mass and A.U. for R gives:

$$\text{Jupiter Ang. Mom.} = 318^{3/2}5.2^{1/2}$$
$$= 12,900 \text{ Ang. Mom. of Earth}$$

$$\text{Saturn Ang. Mom.} = 95^{3/2}9.5^{1/2}$$
$$= 2,850 \text{ Ang. Mom. of Earth}$$

2. 2×10^{21} kg / 10^{13} kg water per comet = 2×10^8 comets (200 million comets) 200 million comets / 500 million years = 0.4 comets per year or 1 comet every 2.5 years.

3. F is the force of gravity, M the mass of a planet, and R is its radius. Density, ρ, will be constant.

$$F \propto \frac{M}{R^2}$$

$$\rho \propto \frac{M}{R^3}$$

substituting R^3 for M in the first equation gives

$$F \propto R$$

If the radius doubles, then the surface gravity doubles. Thus, as a protoplanet accretes more material, not only does it grow in size, its gravitational attraction grows in proportion to its radius. It becomes more effective in accreting more matter.

SUGGESTED READING

Barnes-Svarney, P. "The Chronology of Planetary Bombardments." *Astronomy* (July 1988). Collisions in the early solar system.

Black, D. C., and E. H. Levy. "A Profusion of Planets." *The Sciences* (May/June 1989). Excellent article outlining the various theories of solar system formation.

Boss, A. "The Origin of the Moon." *Science* (January 24, 1986). On the theory that the Moon formed following the impact of a Mars-sized object on the protoearth.

Brophy, T., "Motes in the Solar System's Eye." *Astronomy* (May, 1993). Bits of interstellar matter tell how our solar system formed.

Cowen, R. "New Evidence of Budding Solar Systems." *Science News* (March 10, 1990). Good basic article on the ongoing search for newly forming solar systems.

_ "In the Footsteps of Descartes." Science News (April 22, 1995). New views of planetary formation.

"From Ring Particles to Whole Planets." *Science News* (January 19, 1991). How small particles may coagulate and large particles may grow in size.

Kerridge, J. F., and M. S. Matthews, eds. *Meteorites and the Early Solar System.* Tucson: University of Arizona Press, 1988. The broad sweep of meteorite studies. Includes summaries of current astrophysical models of prenebula and solar nebula evolution as well as of models of nebula accretion processes.

Rubin, A. E., "Microscopic Astronomy." *Sky & Telescope* (July, 1995). Application of cosmochemistry to better understand the early and present solar system.

Chapter 16

THE SUN
Our Parent Star

How Average is the Sun

The term "typical" must be used with some caution when referring to the Sun as an average star. As explained at the start of this chapter, the Sun is in the middle of the range of mass, radius, and other properties for stars. Does this necessarily mean it is truly average among stars? The lightest and heaviest adult humans weighed 45 and 1400 pounds. The "average" of this range is 723 pounds. Certainly the average human adult does not weigh this much! In the same way, the average star does not have the mass, radius, and other properties of the Sun. As will be seen later, the average star is an M-type star that is much smaller than the Sun. However, much of what we know about the Sun makes it typical of many stars. If we were able to pick any star to study, as typical of most stars, the Sun would still be a good choice.

Properties of the Sun - Mass

Once the Earth-Sun distance is known, the period of the Earth's orbit gives the mass of the Sun directly from Newton's form of Kepler's third law. However, in previous chapters we have used solar and Earth units in the third law. Now it is important to see the third law as Newton derived it. The advantage is that we will calculate the mass of the Sun in kilograms, not solar masses. The disadvantage is the inconvenience of the units and the need to know G, the universal gravitational constant. In mks units, $G = 6.67 \times 10^{-11}$.

Assuming the mass of the Earth is insignificant relative to the Sun's mass we have

$$MP^2 = \frac{4\pi^2}{G} a^3$$

Using P = 1 year = $365 \times 24 \times 60 \times 60 = 31536000$ sec and a = 1 AU = 1.496×10^{11} m gives M = 1.99×10^{30} kg. The mass of the Sun is an extremely important number in astronomy. Astronomers often measure mass in solar masses; the mass of the Sun gives us the equivalent in a standard mass unit, kilograms.

Solar Constant

It is not difficult to measure the solar constant to within a factor of 2 accuracy. It can be done on any sunny day during a lecture. Take a Styrofoam coffee cup and fill almost to the top with water. Add a little India ink to make the water very black. Weigh the cup before and after this to determine the mass of water in grams (cgs units are much easier to use in this experiment than mks units. The result can always be converted to mks). Measure the temperature of the water (in centigrade or Celsius units) and set it in direct sunlight for about half an hour (time it exactly). Cover the top of the cup with a transparent plastic wrap to reduce evaporative losses. Align the cup in the sunlight so that the cup's sides do not shadow any of the water. Measure the diameter of the circle made by the surface of the water and calculate the area in square centimeters. At the end of the half hour measure the temperature again. Using the specific heat of water as 4.186×10^7 ergs/gm/°C, calculate the amount of energy gained by the water by multiplying by the change in the temperature and the mass of the water. Dividing this energy by the area of the circle and the time will give the solar constant. Again, this will give a result that is about half the true value (which is 1.4×10^6 erg/cm²/s); the other half is lost due to absorption of visible and infrared light by the atmosphere of the Earth. If it is not convenient to do this as a demo, try having the students do it as part of a lab exercise.

The amount of energy received by the Earth via the solar constant is often not appreciated. An area 10 feet on a side receives in one day the equivalent energy of one gallon of gasoline (assuming only half the solar energy reaches the ground). (Since this area is larger than cars, a completely solar car may not be practical.) The typical roof of a house receives tens of thousands of watts of power from the Sun. Little wonder that attics get so hot during the summer! Even at a conversion efficiency of 10%, there is sufficient power to meet most of the power needs of a house. What are some of the limitations and complications in actually using this power? It is a good question to ask students. Typical answers are; no power at night, cloudy weather, roofs facing the wrong direction, variable angle of the Sun during the day, seasonal changes in the position of the Sun, cost of solar power cells, cost of retrofitting houses, apartment buildings with low roof area per capita. It is equally informative to challenge students to suggest solutions to these same problems.

Using the above example of only half the solar constant and a 10% efficiency, every one of the Earth's 5 billion people could be provided with 1000 watts of power by using a square area of land about 160 miles on a side. Although that amount of power is much less than the per capita use in the USA, it is much more than most people in the world have available to them now!

Viewing the Sun

Set up a telescope outside the classroom so that students can view the Sun as they come to class. My favorite setup is a Schmidt-Cassegrain 5 or 8-inch with a Solar Skreen filter (available from Roger W. Tuthill, In., Box 1086ST, Mountainside, NJ 07092). It is a very safe way of showing sunspots, limb darkening, and solar granulation. Since the Sun is close to sunspot minimum during the next few years, it is worth checking out the Sun prior to setting this up. The Sun can be completely void of sunspots during this time!

The Solar Spectrum

In Chapter 3 a demo or student project was described involving the identification of absorption lines in the solar spectrum. If this was not done at that time, now is another opportunity.

Historically, the solar spectrum revealed information on a completely unknown element. In 1868 French astronomer Pierre Janssen (1824 - 1907) discovered a new solar spectral line. He sent his discovery to the English astronomer Sir Joseph Lockyer (1836 - 1920)who was an expert on the solar spectrum. Lockyer confirmed that the line belonged to no known element. He named it helium, after the Greek name for the Sun, helios. The discovery was dismissed by most chemists because it suggested a new element existed that had never been discovered on Earth. In 1895 the Scottish chemist Sir William Ramsay (1852 - 1916), while studying gases from minerals of the Earth and having discovered argon the previous year, found yet another gas that surprisingly had the same spectral lines as discovered by Janssen. Thus helium was discovered on Earth and was confirmed to be a new element. Astronomically it was to be an important discovery; helium is the second most abundant element in the universe!

I particularly like to tell this story to students because it demonstrates how important discoveries are often made by chance, by scientists working together, studying natural phenomena about which they are curious. Janssen was not looking for a new element but was studying the spectrum of the Sun during eclipse. Ramsay was not looking for helium but recognized it because of the previous work by Janssen and Lockyer 27 years before.

Solar Wind

As stated in the text, the Sun loses about a million tons of matter each second. This is 1×10^9 kg/sec. (This sounds like a lot of matter but in fact a billion kg would be equivalent to the mass of a large hill on Earth.) How much of this material does the Earth intercept? Is it a significant amount? Compare the circular area of the Earth, $\pi r^2 = \pi$ (6 $\times 10^6$ m)^2 = 1×10^{14} m^2, to the area of a sphere at 1 AU from the Sun, $4\pi r^2 = 4\pi$ $(1.5 \times 10^{11}$ m)^2 = 2.8×10^{23} m^2. Taking the ratio of these two areas and multiplying by 1 ×

10^9 kg/sec gives about 0.4 kg/sec. This is equivalent to 12 million kilograms per year of mostly hydrogen and some helium! (I am assuming the Earth actually captures this material; the magnetic field of the Earth vastly complicates the situation.) Over the 4.6 billion year lifetime of the Earth this accounts for less than 1% of the hydrogen of the Earth. It sounds like a lot of material but in fact does not amount to much as far as the Earth is concerned!

Energy from the Proton-Proton Chain

The equation $E = mc^2$ is very familiar to most students. But the energy equivalence of mass is rarely appreciated. As the text notes, one kilogram is equivalent to 9×10^{16} J. But how much energy is this? I like to take a one kilogram mass into class. It isn't very big and I equate it with the mass of a quart (a liter, actually) of milk. However, 9×10^{16} J is sufficient energy to lift at once every person on Earth 100,000 feet into the air! (This calculation assumes an average mass of 50 kg per person, which is probably too high, and 5 billion people.)

When lecturing on the proton-proton chain I often have a periodic table of elements located somewhere in the lecture room. To summarize the process, 4 hydrogens go into making 1 helium plus some energy. I note from the table that the mass of hydrogen is given as 1.0080 (atomic mass units, although it is not important for students to understand the units being used). Four hydrogens have a mass of 4.0320. But the mass of helium is given as 4.0026, which is less. The difference, 0.0294, is converted into energy. Comparing this amount to the amount of hydrogen gives 0.7%. So, 0.7% of the mass is converted into energy. This is equivalent of 4 billion kilograms (4 million tons) of hydrogen being converted *into energy* each second; 4 million tons lost from the Sun each second! Does the Sun lose a significant amount of its mass over its lifetime? No! If it converted all of its hydrogen into helium, which it will not, it would only lose 0.7% of its mass. This is like a 150 pound person losing one pound. It is a common misconception that this mass loss somehow forces the Sun or other stars to evolve. It is important to establish the fact that this mass loss is rather insignificant.

ANSWERS TO CHAPTER 16 REVIEW QUESTIONS

1. Refer to Figure 16.1 for help in answering this question.

   The regions are, core, interior, convective zone, photosphere, chromosphere, and corona. You may also want to include the solar wind, although it is really not a part of the Sun because it is material being lost by the Sun. The radius of the core is 200,000 km, the interior is 300,000 km thick, convective zone is 200,000 km thick, photosphere is 300 km thick, chromosphere is 3,000 km thick, and the corona extends about a few million km above the chromosphere.

2. The Sun has 300,000 times the mass of the Earth.

3. The solar surface is 5800 K and the interior is about 15 million K.

4. Knowing basic facts about the Sun, such as its mass and composition, and physical processes allow astronomers to predict the entire structure of the Sun. This is known as a model. The model is correct if it successfully predicts observed properties of the Sun, such as its luminosity, radius, and temperature. Some of the input information to the model is uncertain but the results suggest how correct this input data is. By making slight adjustments in the input parameters, the model is adjusted until its predictions are in agreement with all the observed properties. Once the model "works" astronomers are then able to learn from the model about the properties in the interior of the Sun. Models are used as a test to see whether we fully understand the structure and processes of objects. They are also then used to predict properties that may not be directly observable. Models also make predictions of observables that help us further test the validity of the model.

5. The solar radiation is first produced in the core of the Sun. Because the gas is totally ionized, it is transparent to radiation and so the radiation passes through it freely. But farther out the temperature drops and more and more of the gas is not ionized or only partially ionized. Such a gas is opaque to radiation. At the outer edge of the radiation zone, all of the radiation has been absorbed by the gas. This heats the gas and it physically rises, while cooler gas from the surface falls. This is the region of convection. The energy is transported by convection to the photosphere. Here, the density of the gas is so low that radiation can freely escape into space.

6. Virtually all the visible radiation we receive from the Sun comes from a thin layer called the photosphere. It is only 500 km thick; a small fraction of the Sun's radius. So what we see is a sharply defined region of the Sun, below which radiation can not escape and above which the gas is too thin to emit significant quantities of light.

7. "Coronium" was first discovered in the 1920s when spectra of the corona during a solar eclipse showed emission lines never before seen. These lines were at first thought to indicate the presence of a new element, "coronium." Further investigation showed that these lines were actually due to highly ionized elements. The high ionization was due to the corona's very high temperature, about one million K.

8. Because the corona of the Sun is hot, some of the gas can escape into space; it escapes the gravity of the Sun. The gas is mostly composed of ionized hydrogen, that is, protons and electrons. The rush of particles away from the Sun is known as the solar wind.

9. All of these objects are caused by magnetic fields of the Sun. Sunspots are caused by kinks or loops of magnetic field extending through the lower atmosphere. Flares are not well understood but are the result of magnetic instabilities. They produce large quantities of energy in just a matter of minutes. Prominences are caused by very large loops of magnetic field that carry luminous gas far above the solar surface.

10. The Sun's energy output is fueled by the fusion of hydrogen into helium. In this process that takes place in the core of the Sun, 4 hydrogen atoms (really just protons) come together and fuse to form a heavier element, helium. In this process, a small amount of matter is lost; it has been converted into energy.

11. Only hydrogen goes into the proton-proton chain. What comes out is helium, two neutrinos, and energy in the form of gamma rays. The mass of helium produced is 0.7% less than the mass of the hydrogen that was fused to make it. This small amount of mass was converted into energy. The amount of energy is easily calculated from $E = mc^2$.

12. The detection of solar neutrinos is very important to the complete understanding of the Sun's interior. Neutrinos are produced in the proton-proton chain, which occurs in the core of the Sun. The neutrinos pass unimpeded through the Sun. So neutrinos, in a sense, allow astronomers to directly observe the core of the Sun and the processes that occur there. At this time, the number of neutrinos observed is about half that predicted by the standard model.

13. If the Sun's internal energy source suddenly shut down, nothing immediately would be observed from Earth other than a stop in the emission of neutrinos. The Sun would continue to shine for possibly millions of years before it would noticeably dim.

ANSWERS TO PROBLEMS

1. From Chapter 3, Wien's law is the following.

$$\lambda_{max} = \frac{0.29}{T}$$

T is the temperature in Kelvins and λ is the wavelength measured in centimeters.

a. For a core temperature of 10^7 K the $\lambda_{max} = 2.9 \times 10^{-8}$ cm = 2.9 Å. X-rays

b. For the 10^5 K temperature of the convection zone $\lambda_{max} = 2.9 \times 10^{-6}$ = 290 Å. Extreme UV

c. For the 10^4 K of the lower photosphere $\lambda_{max} = 2.9 \times 10^{-5}$ = 2900 Å. UV

2. The granule material will move 1000 km in 1000 s, which is 16.7 minutes. The granule should be disrupted faster than this because 1000 km is its diameter;

the material does not have to flow completely across it for the granule to disappear. So the 10 minute lifetime observed sounds about right.

3. Use the ratio form of Stefan's Law to find the fractional amount of light emitted by a sunspot.

$$\text{Flux} = \frac{4500^4}{6000^4}$$

$$\text{Flux} = 0.32$$

So, a sunspot emits about one third as much light as the photosphere.

4. The Sun's luminosity is 4×10^{26} J/sec. How much matter must be processed in order to produce this energy for one second? The proton-proton chain produces 4.3×10^{-12} J when 6.7×10^{-27} kg of matter (4 protons) are fused. By dividing the Sun's luminosity by the energy of one proton-proton chain we will get the number of these reactions needed to produce the Sun's luminosity for one second. 4×10^{26} J / 4.3×10^{-12} J = 9.3×10^{37}. How much hydrogen is fused in order to produce this many reactions? Multiply this number times the mass of 4 protons. $9.3 \times 10^{37} \times 6.7 \times 10^{-27}$ kg = 6.2×10^{11} kg/sec. (Note this is equivalent to about 600 million tons per second as stated in the text.)

Finally, we need to compare the mass of hydrogen fused each second to the mass of the Earth and find how many seconds that amount of fuel would last the Sun. The mass of the Earth is 5.98×10^{24} kg. 5.98×10^{24} kg / 6.2×10^{11} kg/sec = 9.6×10^{12} sec. Since a year is about 30 million seconds, 9.6×10^{12} sec / 3×10^7 sec/yr = 320,000 years.

SUGGESTED READING

Akasofu, S.-I., "The Shape of the Solar Corona." *Sky & Telescope* (November, 1994).

Bahcall, J. N. "The Solar-Neutrino Problem." *Scientific American* (May 1990). Solar neutrinos and how they complicate our ideas about the Sun.

Bennett, G. L. "Rendezvous with a Star." *Sky and Telescope* (November 1990). Article about *Ulysses*, the mission to study the Sun's polar regions.

Foukal, P. V. "The Variable Sun." *Scientific American* (February 1990). How the Sun does not shine as steadily as was once believed.

Giampapa, M. S. "The Solar-Stellar Connection." *Sky and Telescope* (August 1987). What studies of other stars may reveal about the Sun.

Giovanelli, R. *Secrets of the Sun.* Cambridge: Cambridge University Press, 1984. Excellent, very clear book explaining many aspects of solar science.

Golub, L., "Heating the Sun's Million Degree Corona." *Astronomy* (May, 1993).

"Great Balls of Fire." *Sky and Telescope* (May 1989). A spectacular sunspot, flares, and auroras seen in March 1989.

Hathaway, D. H., "Journey to the Heart of the Sun." *Astronomy* (January, 1994).

Harvey, J. W., J. R. Kennedy, and J. W. Leibacher. "GONG: To See Inside Our Sun." *Sky and Telescope* (November 1987). A telescope network for solar studies.

Maran, S. P. "Do Solar Fireworks Bring Stormy Weather?" *Smithsonian* (March 1990). Written near the peak of a solar cycle, this article focuses on how the Sun's activity may affect the Earth.

McIntosh, P. S., and H. Leinbach. "Watching the Premier Star." *Sky and Telescope* (November 1988). How observations by amateurs can help scientists understand how the Sun works.

Robinson, L. J. "The Sunspot Cycle: Tip of the Iceberg." *Sky and Telescope* (June 1987). New discoveries suggesting that the 11-year sunspot cycle is only part of the story of the Sun's cycle.

Sampson, R., "Fire in the Sky." *Astronomy* (March, 1992). Explosions on the Sun create fantastic displays of northern lights on Earth.

Smith, D. H. "The Solar-Neutrino Mystery Deepens." *Sky and Telescope* (October 1990). The solar neutrino saga.

Williams, G. E. "The Solar Cycle in Precambrian Time." *Scientific American* (August 1986). Thin layers in an Australian rock formation reveal the Sun's activity 680 million years ago.

Chapter 17

MEASURING THE STARS
Giants, Dwarfs, and the Main Sequence

This is a particularly long chapter in terms of content; there is a lot of material to cover and many important concepts. This chapter also uses material presented in earlier chapters and so it provides an opportunity to apply and integrate much of that material in the study of stars. You may want to allow additional time in your course for this chapter.

Parallax

Review the demonstrations used in Chapter 1 on parallax. That was 16 chapters ago and students will get a little rusty; parallax is a very important concept in the study of stars.

Another way of looking at how the parsec and the parallax equation for distance is derived, consider for a moment the "skinny" triangle made the apparent motion of the star, the distance to the star, and the Earth at the apex of the smallest angle.

Earth —————————————————————— Star
                        d

The two angles at the star end are one arc second or less than being 90°. The angle at the Earth end, p, will be one arc second or less. In reality, though, the star has not moved; the Earth has. The Earth has moved 1 AU. (It actually moves 2 AU but the equation uses a baseline of 1 AU by convention.) Simple trigonometry tells us that the small side will equal the distance times the angle,

$$1 \text{ AU} = dp$$

if the angle is measured in radians. One radian is equal to about 57.3° or 206,265 seconds of arc. We must divide p by 206,265 if we wish to use seconds of arc instead of radians. Solving for d we get,

$$d = \frac{1 AU}{p(rad)/206265}$$

This gives the distance to the star in AU. By defining the parsec as being equal to 206265 AU, we have,

$$d(pc) = \frac{1}{p(\text{arc sec})}$$

Uncertainties in Parallax

The smallest parallax measured is about 0.03″. This gives a distance of 30 pc. However, what if the uncertainties in that angle are ± 0.01″? The parallax might be as low as 0.02″ or as high as 0.04″. So the uncertainty actually gives the distance in the *range* of 25 to 50 pc! Although astronomers can measure parallaxes more accurately than in this example, there remain very large uncertainties for measured distances at 30 pc and beyond. Knowing uncertainties is a very important part of any measurement. Without knowledge of the uncertainty we have no knowledge of the accuracy of the measurement. We may deceive ourselves into thinking we know a distance is, say, 30 pc when in fact our measurements have only succeeded in determining the distance to within some range of values. The true value may not be 30 pc at all.

Stellar Motion

Stars appear to move very slowly, yet we find they have high relative velocities of tens of kilometers per second. How is that possible? Of course we say this is caused by their great distance. I like to use the following example to explain this further. We often see a high-flying jet moving slowly across the sky. The jet appears to move slowly although it is actually moving at around 600 mph. Imagine the same jet flying a few hundred feet over head. It would sweep by in a matter of a second or two. The only difference between these two circumstances is the distance to the jet. We are not observing its true velocity but rather its angular velocity in the sky. High it the sky the jet appears to move at 1 or 2° per second. Close over head it will appear to move at 50 or 100° per second!

Proper Motion

A rather mixed set of units are used in the proper motion equation

$$V_t = 4.7\mu d$$

The distance d is in parsecs, μ is in arc seconds per year, and V_t is in kilometers per second! The justification for this equation comes from the above-shown triangle except now, the star is actually moving a distance, given in kilometers. Because of the division by time, the distance is seen as a velocity and the angle is now an angular velocity given in the form of the proper motion.

$$V_t = \frac{\text{Distance (km)}}{\text{time (sec)}} = \mu \frac{\text{arc sec}}{\text{year}} \frac{\text{rad}}{206265} \frac{1 \text{ year}}{3.156 \times 10^7 \text{ sec}} d(pc) \frac{3.09 \times 10^{13} \text{km}}{pc}$$

Doing the arithmetic gives the constant 4.7.

Space Motion

The space motion is a velocity *relative to the motion of the Sun.* Determining the space motion of a star is similar to finding the relative speed of a car next to you while driving down the freeway; it won't be the car's actual speed, just how much faster or slower it is moving than you.

The proper motion gives the transverse velocity (also known as the tangential velocity). This motion is perpendicular to the radial velocity. For any particular star, the radial velocity will be directed towards or away from the Earth. The space motion is given by solving the following triangle using the Pythagorean Theorem.

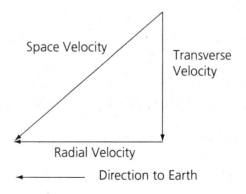

Returning to the example of cars on a freeway, if you find the car next to you is traveling 5 mph faster than you, and you are going 65 mph, then the other car's true speed is 65 + 5 = 70 mph. The true velocity of a star can be determined by adding (or subtracting) its space velocity to the Sun's velocity in space (about 220 km/s). Whereas the space velocities calculated above are typically a few tens of kilometers per second, the true velocities are typically a couple of hundred kilometers per second.

Stellar Sizes

The difficulty of resolving the image sizes of the nearest stars is realized by asking what the angular size of the Sun would be at one parsec. The diameter of the Sun is 1.34×10^{11} cm. One parsec is 3.09×10^{18} cm. Taking the ratio of these two numbers and multiplying by 206265 to convert the answer to arc seconds gives 0.0093 arc seconds or about 0.01''. The atmosphere of the Earth blurs stellar images to 0.5'' or more.

A star like the Sun 100 times farther away will appear 100 times smaller than this, or .0001''. A star 100 times larger than the Sun, at one parsec, will appear 100 times larger or 1''. Of course no star is as close as one parsec and large stars are rare and generally much farther away. Betelgeuse, shown in Figure 17.5, is a good example. At a distance of 150 parsecs, Betelgeuse would appear as 0.000067'' if it were the same size as the Sun. However, it is 300 times the size of the Sun and therefore appears to have a diameter of 0.02''. Speckle interferometry is able to resolve detail a little smaller than this, so Betelgeuse and some of its detail can be seen. But relatively nearby stars that are this large are certainly the exception and most stars can not be resolve this way.

A useful and convenient comparison is that of the radius of the Sun to the astronomical unit. This ratio is 1/215. A star about 200 times the size of the Sun has a size the same as the orbit of the Earth. At 300 times the size of the Sun, like Betelgeuse, the size is that of the orbit of Mars (1.5 AU). So the equivalence of 1 AU $\approx$ 200 R$_\odot$ is helpful to remember.

Radius-Luminosity-Temperature Relationship

This relationship, given as a proportionality in the text, is a fundamental radiation law used extensively in astronomy. It comes simply from Stefan's Law (see Chapter 3; also known as the Stefan-Boltzmann Law) applied to a spherical body such as a star. Stefan's Law gives the energy emitted per square meter per second. If this is multiplied by $4\pi R^2$, the surface area of a sphere of radius R, then the total luminosity of the star is determined.

$$L = 4\pi P^2 \sigma T^4$$

$$\sigma = 5.670 \times 10^{-8} \text{ J/m}^2 \cdot \text{K}^4 \cdot \text{sec}$$

This relationship can also be put in solar units, where L, R, and T are compared to the Sun's values. This is commonly done for convenience and they are regularly used units in astronomy. This simplifies the relationship to

$$L = R^2 T^4 \quad \text{(all in solar units)}$$

In the earlier example of Betelgeuse, with a radius of 300 times the Sun's radius and 0.59 of its temperature, the luminosity is calculated to be

$$L = (300)^2 (0.59)^4$$

$$L = 11{,}000 \text{ solar luminosity.}$$

Betelgeuse is obviously an intrinsically bright star and at a distance of 120 pc it is not surprising that it is one of the brightest stars in the sky.

Although this radiation law is very useful, it does have some limitations. The luminosity depends strongly on the temperature; any significant error in the temperature will be raised to the fourth power and give a poor result. The radius depends only on the square of the temperature, so the situation is not as bad, but still the temperature needs to be known as accurately as possible. Lastly, astronomers must be very careful not to use this equation when the object is not spherical.

Temperature of the Sun

Using the measurement of the solar constant from Chapter 16, the temperature of the Sun can easily be determined with the radiation law and a little additional information. It makes for an excellent lab exercise or demo. Start by using the radiation law.

$$L = 4\pi P^2 \sigma T^4$$

The solar constant, S, is just L divided by the area of the sphere at the Earth's distance.

$$S = \frac{L}{4\pi R_{Earth}^2}$$

Substituting for L in both equations results in

$$\sigma T^4 = \left(\frac{R_{Earth}}{R}\right)^2 S$$

$$\sigma T^4 = \frac{S}{\theta^2}$$

Remember to convert S over to mks units; it was measured in cgs units. θ is the angular *radius* (in radians) of the Sun. This angular *radius* is about one quarter degree but can easily be measured in a telescope by timing how long it takes the Sun's *diameter* to drift across a selected point. This is best done around an equinox, when the Sun is at or near the celestial equator. Objects on the equator move at one degree in 4 minutes of time.

Putting in the correct values should give a temperature of 5800 K (which is the Sun's true temperature). Even if the observed value of the solar constant is as low as half of what it should be, the temperature still comes out to be 4900 K (16% in error). Amazingly enough, the temperature of the Sun can be determined from just the solar constant and its angular radius, both relatively easy to measure. The resulting temperature only depends on the fourth root of the solar constant, so this does not have to be extremely well known.

Inverse-Square Law

This law can be easily demonstrated using a standard frosted light bulb, turned on edge, and any simple photo-tube and meter. Many student optics experiments in physics have these components available. Do the demo in a darkened room and show how the meter readings decrease inversely with the square of the distance.

Replace the bulb with a low power laser and repeat the demonstration. This time, however, the law is not followed. Explain that this law is only correct for spherical luminous bodies. Beamed radiation will get fainter with distance, but not as quickly, and will not necessarily follow this law.

Apparent and Absolute Magnitudes

The magnitude scale, which is still very much in use today in astronomy, is a logarithmic scale. Although a discussion of log scales is avoided in the text, you may still wish to present the material of Interlude 17-1 by using this approach. It is sometimes thought that students can not understand logarithms, however, they need to know little about them in order to understand magnitudes.

A logarithm is simply a power of ten. The log of 100 is 2; log of 1000 is 3; log of 537 is 2.73, that is, between 2 and 3, since 537 is between 100 and 1000. Even cheap calculators have a log key available.

A magnitude is a logarithmic comparison of two luminosities. The defining relationship for magnitudes is simply

$$m_1 - m_2 = 2.5 \, \mathrm{Log} \frac{L_2}{L_1}$$

If object 2 has a luminosity 100 times that of object 1, then the difference in magnitudes is exactly 5. That is the purpose of the constant 2.5; each factor of 100 in luminosity results in exactly a change of 5 magnitudes. This is fundamental to the definition of magnitudes and is the connection to the original system devised by Hipparchus in 130 B.C.

Notice that magnitudes are determined in comparison to another object; the magnitude of object 2 depends not just on its luminosity but on the luminosity and magnitude of object 1. The zero-point of the system is arbitrary and has been based on certain types of stars, typically A0 stars.

How much brighter is an object if it is one magnitude brighter than another? From the above equation $L_2/L_1 = 2.51188643..... = 2.512$. This number is the fifth root of 100. Two magnitudes is a factor of $2.512 \times 2.512 = 6.310$.

If a star has a magnitude of 1.000 and a second star is 100 times *fainter*, what will be the second star's magnitude? Solving the above equation, $m_2 = 6.000$. Notice that the fainter the star is, the larger is the number representing its magnitude. Again, this reflects on Hipparchus' original system of first class stars being the brightest and sixth class stars the faintest to the unaided eye.

These magnitudes are referred to as apparent magnitudes because they measure how bright stars appear in the sky. Apparent magnitudes do not tell us how intrinsically bright stars are because stars are all at different distances and that affects their apparent brightness. The absolute magnitude represents the magnitudes of stars at a common distance of 10 pc. Since stars are not going to be at exactly this distance, we much calculate how bright they would be at 10 pc compared to their apparent brightness at their known distance. We use the magnitude equation to do this. Let the absolute magnitude of a star be referred to as M, its apparent magnitude is m at distance d, its luminosity (actually flux) is L(d) at its distance and L(10) at 10 pc.

$$m - M = 2.5 \, \mathrm{Log} \frac{L(10)}{L(d)}$$

But we know from the inverse square law that L is inversely proportional to the square of the distance; $L \propto 1/d^2$.

$$m - M = 2.5 \, \mathrm{Log} \frac{d^2}{10^2}$$

Using several of the properties of logs, this reduces to

$$m - M = 5 \, \mathrm{Log} \, d - 5$$

The absolute magnitude can be calculated directly from a stars apparent magnitude and its distance. Betelgeuse, whose apparent magnitude is 0.41 and distance is 150 pc, is calculated to have an absolute magnitude of M = -5.47. Increasingly negative values for magnitudes indicates increasing brightness. Betelgeuse is an intrinsically bright star. The absolute magnitude of the Sun has been calculated to be about 4.7. How much brighter is Betelgeuse than the Sun? Using the original magnitude equation and letting Betelgeuse be object 2 gives $L_2/L_1 = 11,700$. This is in good agreement with the 11,000 we calculated using the radiation law.

Temperature and Colors From Magnitudes

There is one additional specification needed when referring to any type of magnitude; where in the spectrum is the magnitude being observed? The region of the spectrum is specifically defined by use of filters that pass a band of wavelengths a few hundred Å wide. Instead of referring to apparent magnitudes as m, astronomers use the symbol for the filter, e.g. U, B, or V. In the case of absolute magnitudes, the capital M is used but is subscripted with the appropriate symbol, e.g. M_v.

Figure 17.8 shows how sampling the spectrum through just two filters, B and V, allow the temperature to be determined. This is a very efficient process, since the measurement at the telescope may take only a few seconds to a few minutes. Recording the entire spectrum can take much longer.

Astronomers always express the color index of stars as the difference B - V. In the example given in the text, for a 10,000 K star, the B and V intensities are the same. The magnitude equation gives B - V = 0. This relates back to the zero-point of the magnitude system which is set at zero for all filters for an A0 star (which has a temperature of 10,000 K). For the 3,000 K star the B to V ratio is 1/5. The resulting B - V is 1.75. The B - V scale runs from about -0.5 for the hottest stars to about 2.5 for the coolest stars. Besides the speed in observation, another advantage of the color index over the spectral types for determining temperature is that the color index is a continuous numerical scale whereas there are only 70 discreet spectral types and there can be significant temperature differences between some of the types.

Spectral Types

The mnemonic for O-B-A-F-G-K-M, Oh, Be A fine Girl, Kiss Me! is best updated to be a bit less sexist. Make it Girl or Guy. Better yet, have students try to come up with their own mnemonic; they may not succeed but will remember the spectral types in their attempt.

The 10 subdivisions of each spectral type is sometimes a bit confusing to the uninitiated. Be certain to show some of the entire sequence, such as .... A8, A9, F0, F1, F2, F3, F4,... F9, G0,.... This continues towards lower temperatures.

I believe it is important to show college students the contributions made by women in astronomy. Here is an ideal chance to do so. Annie Jump Cannon (1863 - 1941), Harvard, determined all the spectral types of stars in the Henry Draper Catalog. There were over 250,000 stars! Harvard astronomy students were known to select a star previously classified by Annie years before and ask her to classify it. They wanted to see how consistent she was in her work. It is said that she was always able to classify a star exactly the way she had done so in the past.

HR Diagram

Non-science students often are quite inexperienced with two dimensional classification, as is done in the HR diagram. They often confuse brightness and temperature as being one and the same. Project a large HR diagram during lecture and review the general properties of stars in the 4 quadrants of the diagram; bright and hot, bright and cool, faint and hot, faint and cool.

Help students remember how the properties of stars change along the main sequence. Everything increases as one goes up the main sequence; to higher luminosity, temperature, size, mass, and (faster) rates of evolution. (In truth, the main sequence lifetimes decrease as one goes up the main sequence but I reverse this and talk about the rate.)

Introducing the lines of equal radius on the H-R diagram can be very confusing to students, mainly because the diagram becomes a three dimensional classification; the two dimensional diagram may have been difficult enough for them to get use to. Show how the radiation law relates luminosity to radius and temperature and that this must be reflected in the diagram. Give an example in the diagram for a constant radius how the luminosity increases with temperature. Likewise, for a constant temperature, the luminosity increases with increasing radius. An often -asked question is "What if a star has a high temperature but a small radius; what will be its luminosity?" The answer, of course, is not obvious. The answer is, you have to calculate the luminosity. But using solar units for temperature, radius, and luminosity really simplifies the computation. Choose a set of properties that are diverse but realistic and make the calculation. Better yet, have the students choose the properties and show where the star would be in the diagram. For some sets of properties, stars do not exist in the diagram.

Along the main sequence it is often confusing to students to use the terms "giants" and "dwarfs" when referring to the high and low mass ends. Although the lines of constant radius show us why giants also occur elsewhere, the terminology can be confusing. I try to avoid this by referring to stars as a B-type main sequence stars or an M-type main sequence star. This reinforces both the region of the main sequence and the spectral types. Likewise, an M super giant is immediately recognizable.

Binary Stars

We see here again the power of Newton's form of Kepler's third law. Virtually all of our information of stellar masses come from its application to binary stars. Remember that the mass in the third law is the sum of the two masses. In the solar system, often there was one large central mass, like Jupiter, and one rather insignificant mass, like Io. So we would assume the sum of the masses to be just the larger of the two. But stars have comparable masses so we can't make that simplification.

Apply the third law to a few examples in order to better see how the period, semi-major axis, and masses interplay. For example, let two 1 solar mass orbit each other and let a = 1 A.U. What is the period?

$$P^2 = \frac{1^3}{1+1}$$

$$P = 0.71 \text{ yrs}$$

The size of this orbit is the same as the Earth's but with a solar mass in orbit around another, the period is reduced. Another example; some short period binaries have periods around 1 day. What is the semi-major axis of the orbit? P = 1/365 = 0.00274 yrs.

$$0.00274^2 = \frac{a^3}{1+1}$$

$$a = 0.0247 \text{ A.U.}$$

Remembering that one A.U. = 200 solar radii, a = 0.0247 A.U. × 200 solar radii/A.U. = 5 solar radii. That's rather close together!

ANSWERS TO CHAPTER 17 REVIEW QUESTIONS

1. Parallax is the apparent motion of a nearby object due to the change in the viewing position of the observer. Astronomers view a nearby star from opposite sides of the Earth's orbit. The position of this star appears to change, relative to background distant stars. The amount of this motion is inversely proportional to the distance. The inverse of this motion measured in arc seconds is equal to the distance measured in parsecs.

2. If an object had a parallactic angle of one arc second, its distance would be exactly one parsec. Conversely, one Astronomical Unit will subtend an angle of one arc second at a distance of one parsec. The parsec is equal to 206,265 A.U.

3. A star's real space motion is observed as two components; the radial velocity and the proper motion. The radial velocity is just the star's motion towards or away from us. The proper motion is an angular motion measured in seconds of arc per year. If the distance to the star is known it can be converted into the true transverse velocity. the transverse velocity and radial velocity can be combined to obtain the true space motion.

4. Giants can be tens of time, up to about 100 times, larger than the Sun. Main Sequence dwarfs are about 10 times smaller than the Sun. White dwarfs are 100 times smaller than the Sun. Giants are brighter than the Sun. Main Sequence dwarf stars are fainter and less massive than the Sun. White dwarfs may have a mass about the same as the Sun or a little more or less, but they are much fainter than the Sun.

5. The apparent brightness of a star depends on its intrinsic brightness and its distance; it is what the astronomer always measures. The absolute brightness is a measure of the star's intrinsic brightness. Using the magnitude system, the absolute magnitude is the magnitude of the star if it were at a distance of 10 parsecs. For the absolute magnitude to be calculate, the apparent magnitude and distance to the star must be known.

6. The temperatures of stars are measured photometrically by using the B and V filters. The brightnesses are compared and matched to a blackbody curve of a specific temperature. Temperatures of stars are also determined from their spectral types. See the answer to the next question for more details.

7. The absorption spectra of stars depends strongly on temperature. The temperature determines which elements produce absorption lines in the visible spectrum. Spectra are classified as either 0, B, A, F, G, K, or M. The O type is the hottest and the M type is the coolest. Within each of these types is a numerical sub-classification ranging from 0 to 9, e.g. F0, F1, F2, ... F8, F9, G0, G1, ... For a specific spectral type, the number 0 is the hottest and 9 is the coolest. To classify a star's spectrum, the absorption lines have to be identified. They are then matched to the corresponding spectral type. A spectrum with strong ionized helium lines is type O; one with strong hydrogen lines is type A, and so forth.

8. The Hertzsprung-Russell (H-R) diagram is a plot of stars' absolute magnitude against spectral type. Each star to be plotted must have its spectral type determined. The apparent magnitude must be observed and the distance determined by some method such as parallax so that the absolute magnitude can be calculated. Absolute magnitude is on the vertical scale, with the brightest end of the scale at the top. Spectral types are on the horizontal scale, with O-type on the left and M-type on the right. Note, that the corresponding temperature scale goes from hottest to coolest from left to right. See Figures 17.11, .12, or .13 for examples.

9. About 90% of all stars plotted in the H-R diagram are found along a narrow S-shaped band running diagonally from upper left to lower right. This is the main sequence. Stars along the main sequence all have a common source of energy, the fusion of hydrogen into helium. The main sequence exists because stars have different masses. The most massive are in the upper left end; the lowest mass stars are in the lower right end. The Sun is in about the middle of the main sequence. See Figures 17.12 and 17.13 for examples.

10. If an observation of a star can place it in the H-R diagram *without* the distance being known, then the star's absolute magnitude can be compared to its apparent magnitude and its distance calculated. The spectrum of a star will determine the spectral type, e.g. K5. But is this a main sequence star, giant, or supergiant?

Closer examination of the absorption lines allows astronomers to distinguish between the luminosity classes. With this, the absolute magnitude is known and the distance is then calculated.

11. The most commonly occurring stars in the H-R diagram are M-type main sequence stars. About three-quarters of all stars are of this type. However, these are not the stars that we commonly see with our eyes or even with telescopes. The most commonly seen stars are those with high intrinsic brightness, which can be seen over large distances. M-type main sequence stars are intrinsically faint and are difficult to detect.

12. The mass of stars in binary systems can be determined using Kepler's third law. If the period of the orbit and the semi-major axis can be observed, then the sum of the two stellar masses can be directly calculated. If the center of mass of the system can also be determined, then the individual masses can be calculated. Generally, the complete solution can be done with visual and eclipsing binaries. Spectroscopic binaries provide only partial information on the masses.

13. The lifetime of a star does not only depend on the amount of fuel available to it; it also depends on how fast it uses that fuel, given by its luminosity. One star may have 10 times as much mass (fuel) as another star, but it also uses that fuel 1000 times faster. The net result is the more massive star having a lifetime 100 times shorter than the low mass star. It pays to be an underweight, among stars!

14. The difference between open and globular clusters was, at first, one of appearance. Open clusters have stars that are widely separated; globular clusters have stars that appear densely packed together. Upon closer examination there are other equally important differences. Open clusters tend to have few stars, a few hundred to a few thousand, whereas globular clusters have about 100,000 stars. Globular clusters are much older, in the range of 10 to 15 billion years old. Open clusters are normally under 1 billion years old. Finally, open cluster are only found in the disc of the galaxy. Globular clusters are found in the spherical halo of the galaxy, concentrated towards the center of the galaxy.

15. The bright, hot, massive stars of the main sequence have short lifetimes; there is no such thing as an old O- or B-type star. But fainter, cooler, less massive stars have long lifetimes, in many cases much longer than the age of the universe. In this case there is a mixture of ages in the main sequence (assuming the main sequence is not that of a star cluster, where all the stars formed at the same time and have the same age). A K- or M-type main sequence star may recently formed or may be billions of years old; they all look pretty much the same in the H-R diagram. For A-, F-, and G-type stars the ages will not be extremely old but could be rather young. Again, there can be a mixture of ages but not as extreme as for the K- and M-type stars.

16. When a cluster of stars form, the H-R diagram shows only a main sequence. With time, the brightest stars evolve away from the main sequence. The more time that passes, the more of the bright end of the main sequence is missing. The top of the remaining main sequence is called the *turn-off point* and is used by astronomers to measure the age of the cluster.

ANSWERS TO PROBLEMS

1. The distance in parsecs is 1/parallax. For Spica its distance is 1/0.013 = 77 pc.

2. In *solar units*, the radius-luminosity-temperature relationship is $L = R^2 T^4$. Using the values provided, $64 = R^2 2^4$. R = 2 solar radii.

3. The first question to ask is How much brighter is star B than star A? This is easy, it is 4.5/0.5 = 9 times brighter. This is how they would appear if at the same distance from us. But both stars appear to be the same brightness. Obviously star B, being intrinsically brighter than star A, must be farther away than star A. But how much farther away must it be? It must be dimmed by a factor of 9. Using the inverse square law, making a star 3 times farther away makes it 9 times fainter, so star B must be 3 times farther away than star A.

4. The magnitude range of the human eye is 6 - (-27) = 33. A difference of one magnitude is 2.51188643... or the fifth root of 100. Raising this to the 33 power will give the result. $(2.51188643)^{33} = 1.6 \times 10^{13}$. This is a factor of 16 trillion, between the brightest and faintest objects visible to the human eye. There is no instrument that can be built that has this dynamic a range!

5. (a) The 0.2 solar mass means that this star has 5 times less mass or fuel than the Sun; it should last 5 times less than the Sun considering this factor alone. But it also has a luminosity of 0.01 solar luminosities which means it is putting out 100 times less energy. That also means it is using its fuel 100 times slower than the Sun, so considering this factor alone, it should last 100 times as long as the Sun. The result, 100 times longer × 1/5 as long = 20 times longer than the Sun or 200 billion years.

   (b) Using the same type of argument as in part (a), 3 solar masses means 3 times as long. 30 solar luminosity means using its fuel 30 times faster and lasting 1/30 as long as the Sun. The result is 3 × 1/30 = 1/10 as long as the Sun or 1 billion years.

   (c) Similarly to part (b), 10 × 1/1000 = 1/100 as long as the Sun. The result is 100 million years.

SUGGESTED READING

Fortier, E. "Touring the Stellar Cycle." *Astronomy* (March 1987). Using a small telescope to observe different objects in various stages of stellar evolution.

Griffin, R. "Radial-Velocity Revolution." *Sky and Telescope* (September 1989). A new era in the study of stars' motions toward and away from Earth.

Kaler, J. B. "The B Stars: Beacons of the Skies." *Sky and Telescope* (August 1987). Hot, young objects that shine brightly and mark regions of recent star formation.

_ "Cousins of Our Sun: The G Stars." *Sky and Telescope* (November 1986). Stars of the same spectral class as our Sun.

_ "Extraordinary Spectral Types." *Sky and Telescope* (February 1988). Stars that can't be pigeonholed into any of the usual spectral classes.

_ "Journeys on the H-R Diagram." *Sky and Telescope* (May 1988). How stars change as they age.

_ "The K Stars: Orange Giants and Dwarfs." *Sky and Telescope* (August 1986). Some are among the most familiar sights in the heavens, while others are the least luminous stars visible with the unaided eye.

_ "M Stars: Supergiants to Dwarfs." *Sky and Telescope* (May 1986). The biggest and the coolest of stars, some famous variables, and feeble red dwarfs.

_ "Origins of the Spectral Sequence." *Sky and Telescope* (February 1986). How astronomers classify spectra and interpret them to unlock the secrets of all kinds of stars.

_ "The Spectacular O Stars." *Sky and Telescope* (November 1987). Hottest, bluest, brightest, rarest, and most massive, the O stars form the blazing tip of the main sequence.

_ "The Temperate F Stars." *Sky and Telescope* (February 1987). F stars mark the transition from hot to cool stars and include the pulsating Cepheid variables.

_ "White Sirian Stars: Class A." *Sky and Telescope* (May 1987). The spectral class of two of the most famous stars in the sky: brilliant Sirius and its faint white-dwarf companion.

Sneden, C. "Reading the Colors of the Stars." *Astronomy* (April 1989). Using stellar spectra to understand stars.

Trimble, V. "White Dwarfs: The Once and Future Suns." *Sky and Telescope* (October 1986). The whys and hows of white dwarf stars.

White, R. E. "Globular Clusters: Fads and Fallacies." *Sky and Telescope* (January 1991). How much of the conventional wisdom concerning these clusters may not be so certain after all.

Chapter 18

THE INTERSTELLAR MEDIUM
Gas and Dust Between the Stars

Density of Interstellar Gas

It is difficult to appreciate the amount of matter that lies between the stars, particularly when the densities are so low. But that is because we also have difficulty appreciating the enormity of the distances (and volumes of space) involved. A density of only 10 hydrogen atoms per cm³ is not unusual, although regions can be found with densities 100 times higher or lower than this. This density is better expressed as 1.7×10^{-20} kg/m³. A volume of space one parsec in radius (a typical distance between stars) contains 1.3×10^{50} m³. Since density is mass divided by volume, it is simple to calculate the total amount of mass in this typical volume of space due to interstellar gas. The result is 2×10^{30} kg, which is exactly one solar mass.

The Galaxy, which is about 15,000 pc in radius and about 300 pc thick contains 2×10^{11} pc³. Even at only 1 atom per cm³ the total mass of interstellar gas is 20 billion solar masses. There is potential for star formation far into the Galaxy's future.

Interstellar Dust

Small particulates and molecules in the Earth's atmosphere have much the same effect on light as does interstellar dust on distant star light. Because the particles selectively pass longer wavelength waves but reflect (scatter) shorter wavelength waves, the Sun appears reddish at sunrise and sunset. Seen through less atmosphere when higher in the sky, the effect lessens as the Sun rises towards noon.

Students often do not realize that the Earth's atmosphere affects all objects seen through it in the same way. This is fairly obvious for the Moon but is also important when viewing stars. Stars, the Moon, and the Sun all appear redder *and fainter* when viewed low in the atmosphere. Since the shorter wavelengths are scattered out of the line of sight (causing the sky to appear blue) we do not see all of the light from the object and it consequently appears fainter. The exact same process occurs for stars viewed through interstellar dust.

The effects of the dimming of starlight by dust can not be overstated. On the average dust dims starlight by about 1 magnitude every 1,000 pc. A star that would appear at magnitude 10 at this distance would appear as magnitude 11. This does not seem all that significant at first. But the same star at the distance of the center of the Galaxy should appear at magnitude 15 without dust. With dust it would appear at magnitude 25; this is near the faint limit of our largest telescopes! In deed, dust limits our view of the Galaxy to such an extent that we see little of it in visible light. It was not until the 1930s, when interstellar dust was proven to exist, that astronomers realized the Galaxy was not just a few thousand parsecs in radius but much larger; about 30,000 pc.

Dust Clouds, Dark and Bright

Is a dust cloud dark or is it bright? We normally think of dust clouds as dark, as seen in Figure 18.1 and 18.5 of the Milky Way or in Figure 18.12 of Rho Ophiuchi or 18.13 of the Horsehead nebula. So, what happens to the blue light that the dust particles scatter? Generally, it is still there but it may be hard to see. At other times it is easy to see. Examine Figure 18.8 of M 20; the blue light around the star at the top is starlight reflecting off of the dust cloud that surrounds it. Another example is in the previous chapter and is the photograph of the Pleiades star cluster, Figure 17.19. Again, the blue light is originating with the stars but is reflected or scattered off of the dust that remains in the cluster. Under these circumstances, dust clouds are sometimes referred to as "reflection nebulae."

Dust clouds also emit light of their own, a fact often overlooked and possibly confusing to students. They emit light in the infrared because the dust is warm, about 100 K. Each dust particle is like a little black body which absorbs starlight, is warmed up, and re-radiates this energy back into space. Using Wien's law, the peak of radiation coming from dust is about 0.0029 cm or 29 μm.

So, are dust clouds dark or bright? They appear dark when blocking the light of background stars, they appear deep blue when a star near to them provides sufficient light to reflect, and they appear bright in the infrared, especially when warmed by star light.

Polarization

A very simple demonstration can be used to show polarization. Use a light source that produces a beam of light and several sheets of Polaroid. With light passing through one sheet, nothing much is observed. Place another sheet in front of the first and rotate it. It is very obvious that as the second sheet is rotated the amount of light passed varies from what was passed by the first sheet alone to virtually zero.

The first Polaroid passes light of only one electric field orientation. When the second sheet is aligned perpendicular to the first no light can pass through. Students can usually understand the geometry of this simple explanation. It is not quite this simple. While the two sheets are perpendicular and no light is passing through insert a third sheet between the first two and at about 45° to the other sheets. Some light now passes out of the third sheet! Although this effect is difficult for students to understand (because it involves the vector nature of the electric field) it shows them that there is additional complexity beyond the scope of this course.

Emission Nebulae

The term nebula comes from the same word in Latin which means "cloud." Early astronomers with small and poor quality telescopes saw many objects that appeared as clouds which now can be well-resolved. The word nebula is still used in describing those objects that are indeed "cloudy."

Emission nebulae are among the largest luminous objects in the sky. Several are easily visible to the naked eye under dark sky conditions. M 42, Orion Nebula, is 460 pc distant and 5 pc in diameter. It appears about 0.5° in diameter, the angular size of the Moon. M 8, Lagoon Nebula, is 1200 pc distant and 14 pc in diameter and appears about the same size. The density of gas in these nebulae is typically about 10 hydrogen atoms per cm^3. Using the fact that a sphere of 1 pc radius and this density contains one solar mass of gas, a nebula with a radius of 10 pc should contain 10^3 times as much mass or 1000 solar masses. This is in fact the approximate mass of M 8.

Because emission nebulae produce an emission spectrum, demonstrating emission spectra with gas discharge tubes is once again useful if not done previously. In particular, point out the red emission line of hydrogen. In color photographs of emission nebulae, this red shows up very distinctly. This red emission line is produced from electrons making downward transitions from the third to the second energy levels. It is helpful to relate this process back to the discussion in Chapter 3 about emission and absorption processes.

I like to show lots of color photographs of emission regions; they are among the most beautiful objects in astronomy. Many of the available photographs (slides, laser disc, or CD-ROM images) show not only the red emission of hydrogen, but dark dust clouds, blue reflection nebulae, young stars usually in a cluster, and the ever-present, multicolored background stars. Describe what is happening in each image and try to give the third dimension perspective, a depth perception. There is a wealth of information going on in each one. I like to project these pictures as large as possible and have the room completely dark. Students may not be able to take notes, but that's good. Let the visual images and drama of the scenes sink in a bit.

In the tubes, fast moving electrons excite the gas atoms through collisions. The electrons in the atoms then make transitions downward and produce the characteristic emission lines. In the nebula the gas atoms are excited by absorbing ultraviolet light from a hot luminous star nearby. In both cases the gas being excited must have a relatively low density although admittedly the gas in the tube is at a much higher density than that found in the nebulae.

Ask students the following question. Would you feel hot if placed inside an emission nebula? We know the temperature is about 8,000 - 10,000 K; this is much hotter than the surface of the Sun. A typical answer to this question is "yes" because of the high temperature. In fact the answer is "no" unless you stayed a very long time inside the nebula. Ask another follow-up question. Which feels hotter, the air on a hot day at 105 °F or a hot bath (or hot tub) whose temperature is usually no more than 105 °F? Here the answer is obviously the hot water. What is the difference between these two situations? It is the density of the material in which you are in contact. More atoms or molecules in the water are in contact with you than with air. Likewise, the nebula with 10^{22} times lower density will not feel hot because so few atoms collide with you and transfer their energy to you. You would feel very cold inside this very hot object!

ANSWERS TO CHAPTER 18 REVIEW QUESTIONS

1. The interstellar medium is made up of gas and dust. Gas is much more abundant yet has a density of only about 1 atom per cubic centimeter. The density of dust is even lower, about 100 times less by mass. The composition is about 90% hydrogen, 9% helium, and 1 % heavier elements. Most of the heavier elements are found in the dust particles. Temperatures average around 100 K although it can be much higher in emission nebulae and lower inside molecular clouds.

2. Interstellar gas is composed of 90% hydrogen, in atomic and molecular forms, 9% helium, and 1% heavier elements. Some of the heavy elements are underabundant compared to stars and our solar system. Presumably these elements have gone into making up interstellar dust. The dust is believed to be composed of silicates, graphite (a form of carbon), and iron.

3. The density of interstellar matter is about 1atom/cm^3, however local values can far exceed this by 1000s and some places have a density 100 times lower. Dust is even rarer, 1000 particles/ km^3.

4. A near-perfect vacuum is not completely free of matter. Dust particles average about 1000 for every cubic kilometer. Although that is quite low, space is very, very large. Those cubic kilometers add up quickly when considering distances of parsecs to the nearest stars. A parsec is 31 trillion kilometers and so the effects of dust add up over these enormous distances.

5. Interstellar matter is not spread uniformly through space. By just examining Figure 18.5 it is obvious that the clouds of interstellar dust vary greatly over the galaxy. Our view of the stars, in some directions is severely limited, in other directions there is virtually no dust. Gas is also unevenly distributed. On average there may be only 1 atom per cubic centimeter but in large molecular clouds the density can be 100s and 1000s of times greater.

6. Astronomers can study dust clouds by examining how it both dims and reddens starlight that passes through them. Spectra of the starlight can indicate the composition and temperature of the gas that is mixed in with the dust. Starlight also can reflect off of dust particles and this light tells astronomers about the size and possible composition of the particles. Lastly, dust particles emit infrared light, from their own warmth. The infrared spectrum gives added information about the composition of the dust.

7. An emission nebula is a region of hot glowing interstellar gas. Such a region surrounds a newly formed star or stars. It absorbs ultraviolet light emitted by the bright young stars and in return, emits a variety of emission lines characteristic of the gases of which it is composed.

8. Hydrogen gas is in emission. One of its brightest emission lines is H-alpha, which has a red color. It is so strong that it often overwhelms all other emissions and colors that might be seen.

9. Dark dust clouds are typically parsecs across in size and about 100 K in temperature. Their densities are thousands or millions of times higher than other interstellar regions and they very effectively block starlight. They appear as dark silhouettes against the field of stars of the galaxy.

10. Dust selectively reflects short wavelength light and allows longer wavelength light to pass through. The short wavelengths, such as blue light, is actually reflected off of the dust particles. Under the right circumstances, the dust can be seen shining blue. Light that is viewed passing through a dust cloud appears reddened and dimmer because it is missing much of its blue light.

11. 21-cm radio radiation is emitted by cold hydrogen gas. This gas is found throughout the entire galaxy. This wavelength of radiation passes through dust clouds without being scattered; the entire galaxy is visible in 21-cm radiation. The temperature and density of the gas can be determined along with its motion. 21-cm radiation has been used to map out the entire galaxy.

12. In molecular clouds, the hydrogen is virtually all in molecular form. 21-centimeter radiation is emitted only from atomic hydrogen not molecular hydrogen.

13. Molecular clouds occur in the densest and darkest interstellar clouds. Here molecules of hydrogen and other complex substances form. The dense dust cloud protects the molecules from destruction by starlight and may also provide a surface on which the molecules can form.

14. Our Sun would not produce much of an emission nebula because it emits very little ultraviolet light. What little it emits would be quickly absorbed by the gas in its immediate vicinity; an emission nebula would not be seen because of the glare of sunlight.

15. The reasons for the reddening of stars by interstellar dust and the reddening of the setting (or rising) Sun are the same. Particles of dust selectively reflect short wavelength light and pass long wavelength light.

16. Polarization is an alignment of the electric fields of which light is made. This can happen when light passes through interstellar dust where the dust particles have all been aligned by a magnetic field. Studies of the polarization yield information on the interstellar magnetic fields and the size and shape of dust particles.

ANSWERS TO PROBLEMS

1. Each cubic meter will contain 10^7 atoms/m^3 x 1.7×10^{-27} kg/atom = 1.7×10^{-20} kg/m^3. The Earth is a sphere with a radius of 6.378×10^6 m and which has a volume of

$$\text{Vol.} = \frac{4}{3}\pi r^3$$

$$\text{Vol.} = 1.1 \times 10^{21} \text{ m}^3.$$

Mass is equal to density times the volume, so 1.7×10^{-20} kg/m^3 × 1.1×10^{21} m^3 = 1.9 kg.

2. Wien's Law states λ_{max} = 0.29/T, where λ_{max} is measured in centimeters. 9.12×10^{-6} cm = 0.29/T, T = 31,800 K.

3. f = c/λ. Substituting values and solving for the frequency gives f = 3×10^{10} cm/s / 21 cm. f = 1.4×10^9 Hz or 1.4 GHz.

4. Every 3 pc it gets fainter by a factor of 2.5. For example, in 6 pc it gets $2.5 \times 2.5 = 6.25$ times fainter. It gets reduced by 2.5 a total of 60/3 = 20 times as it passes through the cloud. This is $2.5 \times 2.5 \times 2.5 \times .....$, or more easily $2.5^{20} = 9.1 \times 10^7$. The light is seen 91 million times fainter than it was before it entered the cloud. (On the magnitude scale, the light is reduced in intensity by about 20 magnitudes.)

5. A cloud density of 10^{12} hydrogen atoms per cubic meter multiplied by the mass of a hydrogen atom will then give the mass density of the molecular cloud. The mass of a hydrogen atom is given in the Appendix (mass of proton), so 10^{12} atoms/m^3 x 1.7×10^{-27} kg/atom = 1.7×10^{-15} kg/m^3. The mass of the Sun is 2×10^{30} kg, and because density is mass divided by volume, the volume is equal to the mass divided by the density. Vol. = 2×10^{30} kg / 1.7×10^{-15} kg/m^3 = 1.2×10^{45} m^3.

This volume is that of a sphere, $4/3\pi R^3$. Solving for the radius, gives 6.5×10^{14} m. Since 1 A.U. = 1.5×10^{11}m, this radius = 4,400 A.U.

SUGGESTED READING

Bowyer, S. et al., "Observing a Partly Cloudy Universe." *Sky & Telescope* (December, 1994).

Gillett, F. C., I. Gatley, and D. Hollenbach. "Infrared Astronomy Takes Center Stage." *Sky and Telescope* (August 1991). The 1990s should see major new infrared telescopes for use on the ground, in the air, and in space.

Kanipe, J. "Inside Orion's Stellar Nursery." *Astronomy* (August 1989). How an infrared image revealed hundreds of stars forming inside the Orion Nebula.

Malin, D. "In the Shadow of the Horsehead." *Sky and Telescope* (September 1987). Photographic feature about a famous dark nebula.

Malin, D., and D. Allen. "Echoes of the Supernova." *Sky and Telescope* (January 1990). The detailed, three-dimensional structure of interstellar dust sheets in the Large Magellanic Cloud, as revealed by studies of Supernova 1987A.

O'Dell, C. R. "Exploring the Orion Nebula." *Sky & Telescope* (December, 1994).

Paresce, F. and S. Bowyer. "The Sun and the Interstellar Medium." *Scientific American* (September 1986). The Sun in the larger context of the Galaxy.

Schorn, R. "The Strange Case of NGC 6164-6165." *Sky and Telescope* (September 1986). A bizarre S-shaped nebula, possibly the work of an evolved O star.

Van Buren, D., "Bubbles in the Sky." *Astronomy* (January, 1993). Interstellar bubbles blown by the hottest stars.

Verschuur, G. L., "Star Dust." *Astronomy* (March, 1992). Infrared images of interstellar dust.

Chapter 19

STAR FORMATION
A Traumatic Birth

The Interstellar Cloud and Escape Velocity

The cloud that will eventually collapse to form stars must have the correct balance of density and size, as noted in the text. A large number of atoms are required to provide sufficient gravitational pull to attract a single atom. This concept may be described in terms used previously: temperature of a gas and the velocity of the atoms and escape velocity.

Imagine an atom at the edge of an interstellar cloud. The temperature of the gas determines the average velocity of the atom. This is given by

$$\frac{1}{2}mv^2 = \frac{3}{2}kT$$

where m is the mass of a hydrogen atom and k is the Boltzmann constant. This reduces simply to $v = 160 \sqrt{T}$ m/s. . In order for the cloud to collapse, the velocity of the atom must be less than the escape velocity. From previous discussions we know this to be

$$v_{esc} = \sqrt{\frac{2GM}{r}}$$

where M and r will be the mass and radius of the cloud. For a large cloud of 1000 solar masses and 10 pc radius (a density of 10 atoms per cm^3), as might be typically found, the escape velocity is 900 m/sec. Using this velocity to find the temperature gives T = 30 K. The temperature must be no more than 30 K for this atom to not escape. This and lower temperatures are found commonly in molecular clouds.

This same condition must be met at each stage of star formation. For the cloud fragment in stage 2, from Table 19-1, the total mass is about 3.5 solar masses and the size if about 0.03 pc (6700 AU) but the escape velocity is still about 900 m/sec and the surface temperature is still well below 30 K. Throughout the rest of the table this condition continues to be met and by a wider and wider margin, i.e. the escape velocity becomes much larger than the velocity of the atoms. By stage 7 the diameter has decreased by a million from stage 2, so the escape velocity has increased by 1000. The temperature has increased by a factor of 60, but the gas velocity has increased by only about 8.

Table 19-1

This table is the basis for much of the chapter. One difficulty is the visualization of the time scale of cloud collapse and star formation. Since the time it takes to reach stage 7 is a little over 40 million years, set up a time line on a chalk board and show the times between each stage.

Example: Use a scale of 10^5 years per cm. The distances on the board between each stage are the following. (This requires at least a 15 foot chalk board.)

1 - 2	20 cm
2 - 3	0.3 cm
3 - 4	1 cm
4 - 5	10 cm
5 - 6	100 cm
6 - 7	300 cm

With this visualization the students can see the relative rapidity of some of the stages. For comparison, tell them the subsequent main sequence time would be 1 km on this scale! Indeed star formation takes place relatively rapidly.

On another scale of time, the birth (43 million years) and life (10 billion years) of a star may be compared to the human gestation period (9 months) and life time (75 years = 900 months). One the human scale, stars have a gestation period half that of humans. (This comparison and all others given here based on Table 19-1 are true only for a one solar mass star.)

Free-fall Time Scale

In a very simple-minded approach to cloud collapse, the time it takes a single atom to fall to the center of the cloud (as the cloud collapses and neglecting all other effects) is known as the free-fall time and gives a rough idea of the length of time the process should take. Although there are various ways of calculating this time, here is a very simple approach. Let the cloud have a mass M and radius R. The acceleration due to gravity at its surface is

$$g = \frac{GM}{R^2}$$

This will not be constant but will vary strongly during the collapse as R changes. An average g can be used at 1/2 R, so

$$g = \frac{4GM}{R^2}$$

The distance an object travels under a constant acceleration a in time t is

$$x = \frac{1}{2}at^2$$

In our case the distance will be R and a will be g, so

$$R = \frac{1}{2}gt^2$$

Putting in the expression for g and then solving for t gives

$$t = \sqrt{\frac{R^3}{2GM}}$$

For the initial cloud of 1000 solar masses and 10 pc radius, $t = 10^7$ years. This is approximately the right time scale of star formation. But it is easy to also see how this quickly breaks down as the star forms. If the calculation is repeated at stage 2, t = 34,000 years which is much too small. Obviously the gas is not in free-fall after stage 2 and effects such as gas pressure become very important to the process of star formation.

Luminosity

From the discussion of black body radiation we know that the luminosity goes as the square of the radius and fourth power of the temperature. Using the surface temperatures and sizes given in Table 19-1 and converting to solar units we can calculate the luminosities at each stage in solar luminosities. Of course where in the spectrum this radiation will peak depends on the temperature alone (Wien's Law). The following may be useful.

Stage	Luminosity	Peak Wavelength
1	34,000	0.3 mm
2	3	0.3 mm
3	3	0.03 mm
4	300	10,000 Å
5	9	7500 Å
6	0.6	6700 Å
7	1.0	5000 Å

These numbers are approximate but do reflect what occurs in Figures 19.6. and 19.8. It is immediately obvious from this table why infrared astronomy is so critical to the study of star formation. In stages 1 to 4, the forming star shines brightly in the infrared. Being imbedded in a dusty molecular cloud would normally obscure it. But infrared can also pass through the dust of the cloud. The result is a view as shown in Figures 19.14 and 19.21.

ANSWERS TO CHAPTER 19 REVIEW QUESTIONS

1. Star formation starts with a interstellar cloud of low density and temperature, tens of parsecs in diameter. It becomes unstable to gravitational collapse and starts to fragment. Tens, hundreds, even thousands of fragments are produced, each collapsing further, eventually to form a star. In a fragment the collapse raises the central temperature to 10,000 K but the exterior remains cool and is able to radiate it energy. As the collapse continues, the central density and temperature increase and the object is known as a protostar. The protostar has a size hundreds of times larger than the Sun and a luminosity thousands of times larger, although its surface temperature is still relatively cool. The collapse slows and the luminosity of the protostar decreases, while the central temperature gradually increases. While still several times larger and brighter than the Sun, the central temperature reaches 10 million K and hydrogen fusion begins. At this point it is finally a star. Continued slow contraction raises the central temperature to about 15 million K and the star finally becomes a main sequence star.

2. The temperature of the gas must be initially low enough so that the gas can gravitationally collapse. As it does so it radiates away its gravitational energy and does not heat up much. Then, as the cloud gets denser, radiation can not escape so easily and the interior of the cloud starts to heat up. Slowly at first, and then ever increasingly, heat pushes against gravity and slows the collapse of the protostar. Gravity continues to compress the gas and heat it until finally the core temperature reaches 10 million K which is sufficient to initiate hydrogen fusion. The object is now a star.

3. As an interstellar cloud collapses, it must spin faster as it conserves angular momentum. The cloud forms a flattened, rotating disk. The formation of the disk, in effect, concentrates the matter in the cloud, allowing it to eventually form a solar system.

4. As the interstellar cloud collapses, its gas is heated and becomes ionized, particularly toward the center of the cloud. The weak interstellar magnetic field gets concentrated during the collapse and can influence the ionized gases during the collapse. The magnetic field can be a stronger influence than gravity and can resist the force of gravity during the collapse, producing distortions in the cloud.

5. In the 100 K environment of space, the number of atoms needed to gravitationally pull themselves together, to form a star, is roughly 10^{57} atoms. This is one solar mass. Depending on the temperature, rotation, and amount of magnetism present, this number can change by a factor of ten either way.

6. An evolutionary track is the "path" taken in the H-R diagram of the changes in a star. In this chapter the evolution is traced from birth to main sequence star. The track is simply a plot of the luminosity against the surface temperature and how it changes with time. Tracks are predicted by computer models and stars are observed at various stages along the track.

7. The large interstellar clouds in which star formation stars are very massive. They fragment into small clouds

each which eventually forms a star. Therefore a cluster of stars is formed rather than just single stars.

8. A protostar becomes a star when its core temperature reaches about 10 million K and hydrogen starts to fuse into helium.

9. A protostar becomes a full-fledged star when it first begins to fuse hydrogen into helium.

10. Brown dwarfs occur when a cloud fragment has insufficient mass to form a star. As the gas collapses and the core temperature increases, there is not enough gas to compress and heat the core to 10 million K. Hydrogen fusion never occurs and the object just radiates off its excess energy from formation. This is a brown dwarf.

11. T Tauri stars occur at stage 4 in the formation of stars. It is a time when the protostar becomes less luminous as it shrinks and develops strong protostellar winds. The outer part of the protostar is shed in this wind.

12. Star formation takes place too slowly for astronomers to watch and follow over time. But astronomers have two other methods. First they make computer models which can be changed rapidly with time. Second, there are very many stars in the sky and astronomers can try to locate stars at the various stages of formation and evolution. The observations are then used to further refine the computer models.

13. Radio and infrared observations are used in the study of star formation because the entire process occurs deep inside a molecular cloud, which, itself, is deep inside a dark, dense dust cloud. Visible light can not escape from this environment but long wavelength radio and infrared can.

14. A shell of gas, moving rapidly through space, builds up a thin sheet ahead of it of dense gas known as a shock wave. Shock waves can be formed by supernovae, spiral-arm waves, and HII regions from newly formed O and B stars.

15. Shock waves are thought to be a trigger for star formation by helping collapse a normal interstellar cloud.

16. The H-R plots the changes in luminosity and surface temperature that occur during the various stages of star formation. This can then be compared to observations. Stages 1-3 can not be plotted easily because the cloud is generally too cool to fall within the normal boundaries of the diagram.

17. The times are given in Table 19-1 and will not be repeated here. Evolutionary times are fast when the material is able to collapse under the influence of gravity. This collapse is slowed when the material becomes opaque to the flow of its radiation and the protostar forms an photosphere, after state 3. Upon further collapse, the interior gas is so hot that it pushes strongly outward, resisting the collapse by gravity, further slowing the collapse.

18. If a star cluster forms any O or B stars, they will completely evolve and die out before many of the lowest mass stars even evolve onto the main sequence. The HII region or supernova blasts from these massive stars can significantly affect further star formation, disrupting it in some places and initiating it in others.

ANSWERS TO PROBLEMS

1. Mass $= 10^{60} \times 0.9 \times 2 \times 10^{-27} + 10^{60}$
   $\times 0.1 \times 4 \times 2 \times 10^{-27}$

   Mass $= 2.6 \times 10^{33}$ kg. Dividing this by one solar mass gives 1300 solar masses.

2.
$$L = \left(\frac{1 \times 10^6}{2 \times 10^8}\right)^2 \left(\frac{4500}{3000}\right)^4$$

   L = 0.00013, so there is a large drop in luminosity going from stage 4 to 6, due to the shrinking in size of the protostar.

3. $L = (0.1)^2 (0.1)^4$

   $L = 1 \times 10^{-6}$ solar luminosity

4.
$$v_{esc} = \sqrt{\frac{2 \times 6.67 \times 10^{-11} \times 1000 \times 2 \times 10^{30}}{10 \times 3.1 \times 10^{16}}}$$

$$v_{esc} = 930 \text{ m/s}$$
$$v = 160\sqrt{10}$$
$$v = 500 \text{ m/s} < 930 \text{ m/s}$$

With the escape velocity higher than the velocity of the atoms, the condition is met for the cloud to contract.

SUGGESTED READING

Byrd, D. "Do Brown Dwarfs Really Exist?" *Astronomy* (April 1989). The search for brown dwarfs, and why some astronomers think they will not be found.

___ "Bad News for Brown Dwarfs." *Sky and Telescope* (October 1990). More on the struggle to discover brown dwarfs.

Caillault, J-P., "The New Stars of M42." *Astronomy* (November, 1994). Star formation in the Orion nebula.

Elitzur, M. "Masers in the Sky." *Scientific American* (February, 1995). Coherent beams of microwaves from the birth and death of stars.

Fienberg, R. T. "Brown Dwarfs Coming and Going." *Sky and Telescope* (November 1989). More on why brown dwarfs should exist, despite the fact that no one has yet discovered one.

Fortier, E. "Touring the Stellar Cycle." *Astronomy* (March 1987). Stellar evolution explained.

Hartley, K. "How a Star Is Born." *Astronomy* (December 1989). The birth of stars.

Lada, C. J. "Star in the Making." *Sky and Telescope* (October 1986). How astronomers observed an interstellar cloud of gas and dust collapsing to form a protostar.

Norris, R. "Cosmic Masers." *Sky and Telescope* (March 1986). Cosmic radio amplifiers and what they tell us about comets, dying stars, and active galactic nuclei.

Schild, R. E. "A Star Is Born." *Sky and Telescope* (December 1990). Why the birth of a star is one of the least understood events in astronomy.

Stahler, S. W. "The Early Life of Stars." *Scientific American* (July 1991). The complex life cycle of stars, beginning when clouds of interstellar gas coalesce into protostars detectable only in the infrared and becoming optically visible stars.

Stahler, S., and N. Comins. "The Difficult Birth of Sunlike Stars." *Astronomy* (September 1988). How stars like the Sun come to exist.

Stephens, S., "Needles in the Cosmic Haystack." *Astronomy* (September, 1995). Where are all the brown dwarfs?

Chapter 20

STAR EVOLUTION
From Middle Age to Death

Main Sequence Equilibrium

This equilibrium is also called hydrostatic equilibrium and is simply the balance between gravity, inward, and pressures, outward. The pressure is due to both gas pressure and radiation pressure. Depending on the star's mass and the location inside the star, one or the other of these pressures may dominate. Refer your students to Figure 20.1 when considering this equilibrium.

This equilibrium is important for all stars, not just main sequence stars. I like my students to understand what happens to the star when this equilibrium is disturbed. What happens if the energy source at the center of the star starts to increase? The outer part of the star will expand and equilibrium will be re-established at some new, larger size. What happens if the energy source starts to decrease? Just the opposite of the previous case.

Burning vs. Fusing

A note on terminology. Regularly remind students that although astronomers use the terms "burn" and "fire" when referring to hydrogen or helium fusion, the hydrogen or helium are not really burning; they are fusing. These are different processes and can be very confusing to students learning the jargon.

Helium Core Contraction

What happens to the helium core when it contracts? Obviously it heats up; gases do that when compressed. But the core also radiates off some of the gravitational energy from its contraction. When an object is dropped in a gravitational field it converts gravitational potential energy to kinetic energy. But particles in the helium core are not simply free-falling, they interact with each other. The result of this type of contraction is well-known. Exactly half of the energy of collapse goes into heating the gas (the kinetic energy of the particles) but the other half is radiated away. Thus the helium core, while contracting, radiates a substantial amount of energy. This, along with the higher temperature of the hydrogen burning shell, increases the overall energy output of the star.

Now is the perfect time to apply hydrostatic equilibrium. Why does the core collapse? The core lacks the energy source to keep pushing outward. What must be the response by the outer part of the star to an increased energy output from the center? Expansion.

Helium Fusion—The Potential Barrier

It was established earlier that for hydrogen to fuse into helium the temperature must be very high in order for the protons (hydrogen) to overcome the repulsion of their positive charges. This is known as a potential barrier. For helium to fuse, two protons (helium) must get equally close to two other protons (helium). Obviously the potential barrier is higher than for hydrogen fusion and so the temperature required must be higher. How much higher? This can be rather easily predicted using a little simple physics.

The average kinetic energy of atoms in a gas and the temperature of the gas are related by

$$\frac{1}{2}mv^2 = \frac{3}{2}kT$$

But the kinetic energy must be equal to the work, force

times distance, needed to move the particles together to a distance x.

$$\frac{1}{2}mv^2 = Fx$$

So, for a fixed distance x, the kinetic energy is proportional to the force and, from above, proportional to the temperature. So we find that

$$T \alpha F$$

The force, F, is the electric force, which depends on the product of the charges. Again, remember we are keeping the distance of separation constant, for simplicity, we finally have

$$T \propto Q_1 Q_2$$

The force necessary to get two helium nuclei, which have 2 protons each, together is 4 times that necessary to get 2 hydrogen nuclei together. Therefore a temperature 4 times that of hydrogen fusion is needed. If hydrogen fusion occurs at about 12 million K then helium fusion should occur at about 48 million K.

The fusion of helium with another helium does not produce carbon, it produces beryllium, which has 4 protons. The second step of the process involves the fusion of a beryllium nucleus (4 protons) with a helium nucleus (2 protons). This is even harder to do and requires a higher temperature. The force needed is really 8 times that of hydrogen fusion or 96 million K. Thus the well-known result that a temperature of about 100 million K is needed for helium fusion in to carbon.

The above situation can be demonstrated using some small magnets. I like to use small, disk magnets. Orient two magnets so they repel. Then take two in each hand and show how they repel harder. The magnets behave like protons in this analogy. The more magnets, the harder you have to push to get them close to each other.

Luminosity During Evolution

Just as the luminosity changed dramatically during pre-main sequence evolution, so it changes similarly during post-main sequence evolution. Besides examining the changes in luminosity, changes in the size of the star (as compared to the Sun's size) are equally interesting. Since the surface temperatures are in a "normal" range for stars, the wavelength of peak radiation is of less interest. Using the data from Table 20-1 the following may be easily calculated.

Stage	Luminosity	Radius
7	1.0	1
8	35	13
9	900	70
10	90	13
11	88,000	670
12	—	—
13	0.2	0.01

Although the luminosities are in comparison to the Sun an additional comparison may be useful. To convert luminosities to magnitudes use m = -2.5 Log (Lum.). To convert to absolute magnitude, add this magnitude to the Sun's absolute magnitude of 4.7. For example, at Stage 9 the star would have a magnitude 7.4 brighter than the Sun or an absolute magnitude of -2.7.

Look at the "Time to Next Stage" column in Table 20.1 and compare to Figure 20.9. Where the times are the longest, you should find the most stars. Likewise, for short times you should see few stars. Stage 7, the main sequence stage is the longest and certainly there are large numbers of stars seen along the main sequence in Figure 20.9. Stage 8 is next longest, with evolution away from the main sequence and up to the giant branch. Again, many stars are seen. But the helium flash occurs quickly and so no stars are actually seen going from the tip of the red giant branch over to the *left* side of the horizontal branch. The horizontal branch is the third longest stage and a number of stars are seen there, but not as many as in stages 7 and 8. Astronomers can judge the validity of their model's time scale for evolution by making a comparison to the number of stars at each location in a star cluster.

Densities

(cgs units are used here because it is hard to demonstrate a cubic meter!) Find a marble with a diameter of 1.2 cm. It has a volume of just 1 cm^3. Its density should be around 2.5 gm/cm3 and therefore has a mass of 2.5 gm. (A ball bearing of the same size is also good to use but it will have a mass of about 8 gm.) Now the question is, what will be the mass of this marble if it is composed of the gases in the core of the Sun at various stages of evolution.? If you think some of these are high, wait until we make the same calculation for an iron core and a neutron star in the following chapters!

Masses of One Marble (1 cm^3) At Core Densities

Stage	Composition Object	Mass	Equivalent Object
7	Hydrogen/Helium Main sequence star	100 gm	1/4 Pounder meat patty
8	Helium subgiant	10 kg	Adult wiener dog
9	Helium red giant	100 kg	College football player
12	Carbon asymptotic red giant	1,000 kg	A small car
13	Carbon white dwarf	10,000 kg	100,000 meat patties or 1,000 wiener dogs or 100 football players or 10 small cars!

Planetary Nebulae

Expanding at a rate of 20 km/sec it takes 50,000 years to move one parsec. Most planetary nebulae are smaller than 1 pc in radius. But it can be easily seen, then, that most planetary nebulae are at most a few tens of thousands of years old and by 100,000 years are completely dissipated. They typically contain about 0.2 solar masses so by the time they have expanded out to about 1 pc they have densities indistinguishable from the interstellar matter (remembering from Chapter 18 we found that a 1 pc radius of space with a density of 10 atoms/cm^3 has a total mass of one solar mass. So in the same volume of space, 0.2 solar masses will give a density of 2 atoms/cm^3.)

White Dwarfs

The luminosity and radius for a white dwarf was calculated at Stage 13. Actually, this is just the beginning of the white dwarf stage; typical white dwarfs are significantly fainter than this but about the same size. Note that 0.01 solar radii is about the size of the Earth. So if white dwarfs have a size of 0.01 that of the Sun, they will have a volume $(0.01)^3 = 1$ million times smaller than the Sun. With a mass about equal to the Sun's mass, the *average* density should be about 1 million times that of the Sun; just over 1 million gm/cm^3. These numbers are easy to come by and are good examples how a little understanding of concepts like density and volume can lead to immediate insight into the properties of a new object.

Evolution Up the Main Sequence and Other Misconceptions

Over many years of teaching I have found that some students are confused about the main sequence. Although they appear to understand that the main sequence is the result of stars having different masses, when it comes to evolution they seem to feel that evolution must proceed up the main sequence. Thus, low mass stars evolve into high mass stars! Now this never made any sense to me until I realized one day that the model from which these students are working is the one of living organisms; they start out small and grow up to adult size. Once at adult size, they then evolve further into old age. It is an obvious model, it works quite well, and it can be applied to other circumstance; snowballs grow as they roll down a hill. The problem is, this model just happens to be incorrect when applied to stars.

Another very common misconception is that as stars evolve, they literally move. We do say that stars "move" from the main sequence to the red giant branch and so on. This is taken literally and is combined with an earlier misconception that the H-R diagram is actually a map of star positions in the sky. (Again, we do talk about the "position" of a star in the diagram.) Students who are making these errors are typically having difficulty understanding a graph and two dimensional classification.

Laboratory exercises in which students plot their own H-R diagrams help a lot in understanding this and other diagrams. Questions about red giants, supergiants, and white dwarfs help them understand why these stars are exceptional. Refer to Figure 20.16 for an excellent demonstration of the gradual evolution of stars to and from the main sequence. An advantage of this figure is that it shows stars plotted as dots; each one represents a single star. Relate the changes in star positions with the evolutionary tracks seen in earlier figures. Instead of talking about a star moving from this location to another in the diagram I prefer saying "The star now appears cooler but brighter and is plotted in this new location."

With knowledge of these typical misconceptions, take steps to address this confusion early in your discussions. Show real star charts and compare them to the H-R diagram. Ask what is being plotted in each case. We have said that the stars actually move (proper motion), how does that affect their positions on the charts? Address the question of why stars don't gain mass with time (grow with age). Can't they pull more matter in with their strong gravity? Don't they sweep up more matter as they move through the galaxy? Don't stars collide and grow that way? All these questions have a logic to them, one based on models that work for these students. We have to help our students understand why such models do not work and to understand a new model for stellar evolution. Who knows how helpful this model may be to them under different circumstances!

Binary Stars

About half of all visible stars are actually multiple star systems; binaries are the most common. If their orbit around each other is small enough, then sometime during the evolution of one or both stars, they will interact. How far apart do the stars have to be in order *not* to interact? The largest supergiants are about 600 solar radii. Remembering that 200 solar radii equals 1 A.U., 600 solar radii equals 3 A.U. So we would expect stars separated by twice this amount, 6 A.U. will not interact; for stars with smaller masses and sizes this will reduce to about 2 A.U. The orbital periods, calculated from Kepler's third law, are in the range of 2 to 4 years. Any binary star with a period of a few years or less will probably experience interactions at some time; those with longer periods will probably not experience any interactions. The stars in the latter case evolve just like single stars. Visual binary systems are known to have long periods, decades to hundreds of years to thousands of years, so non-interacting binaries are not rare. When interactions do occur for the short period binaries, the effects are often not subtle!

Figure 20.21 is very helpful in showing the different types of binary and their Roche lobes. Then Figure 20.22 can be shown (both of these figures are available as transparencies) to trace the evolution of Algol-type binaries.

Use a blank transparency overlay on Figure 20.22 and show the original masses of the two stars and the amount mass transfer, about 2 solar masses, that has taken place.

To further develop why the mass transfer takes place, bring up the concept of hydrostatic equilibrium mentioned at the beginning of this chapter. The red giant is expanding and filling its lobe. It looses mass and therefore its gravitational force is reduced. But remember, it is expanding because its core is overwhelming gravity with additional pressure. If gravity is reduced by mass loss, the star becomes even more out of equilibrium and the expansion will be increased. To make matters worse, the Roche lobe also shrinks because of the reduction in gravity. All of this produces further mass loss. Two solar masses of material is transferred to the other star; this is a lot of material and has essentially reversed the roles of the two stars.

About the same amount of mass will be transferred back to the first star when star 2 starts to evolve. Can your students guess what may occur when a hot white dwarf is suddenly loaded with lots of hydrogen gas? They will find out in the next chapter but it is interesting from them to speculate what the consequences will be!

ANSWERS TO CHAPTER 20 REVIEW QUESTIONS

1. The lowest mass main sequence stars last the longest because they have the least amount of fuel. Although this sounds contradictory, their low mass makes them fuse hydrogen very slowly. They have about 10 times less mass than the Sun but use it 10,000 times more slowly. Their hydrogen fuel lasts them a very long time.

2. Main-sequence equilibrium is a balance between the force of gravity inward and the pressure of the hot gases pushing outward. A balance or equilibrium must be attained in order for a star to have a stable size. Main sequence stars have reached such a balance.

3. Stars don't live forever because they run out of fuel. A star is a star because it generates energy from the fusion of light elements into heavier elements. Eventually the star runs out of fuel sources for fusion to occur and the star dies out.

4. As a main sequence star, stars like the Sun fuse hydrogen into helium for about 10 billion years. As the hydrogen is depleted in the core, hydrogen fusion continues in a shell around the core for about another billion years.

5. Without the fusion of hydrogen into helium occurring in the core, the core no longer has an energy source. Gravity is then able to collapse the core, forcing major changes in the entire structure of the star.

6. When a star runs out of hydrogen in its core, the core collapses. As a result, the core's temperature increases and additional energy is radiated away. With a higher temperature, the fusion in the hydrogen shell around the core becomes more efficient. So the core puts out even more energy than it did as a main sequence star. the increased gas pressure pushes on the outer part of the star, expanding it into a red giant.

7. A star like the Sun will evolve into a red giant with a size about 100 times its current size. This is equivalent to about half an A.U.

8. It takes a star like the Sun about 100 millions years to evolve from the main sequence to the top of the red giant branch.

9. By the time the helium core has formed, the core has a high density of electrons that produce a pressure unlike that of normal gas. This electron pressure is not influenced by temperature. When the core temperature finally reaches about 100 million K, helium begins to fuse into carbon. Normally the increase in temperature would expand the core and help cool it off. Because of the electron pressure, this does not happen. The fusion of helium raises the core temperature, producing more and more helium fusion, so that over a few hours a large quantity of helium fuses into carbon. This rapid fusion of helium is known as the helium flash.

10. Helium fusion occurs in the core and hydrogen fusion occurs in a shell around the core.

11. Red giants put out a strong stellar wind of gas. Apparently this gas cools sufficiently to form dust particles around the star. As a result, these stars contribute a significant amount of gas and dust to the interstellar medium. They are returning that which they once received.

12. Low mass stars eventually form a carbon core which collapses but is unable to attain a high enough temperature to allow the fusion of carbon. The outer part of the star continues to expand and as the final shells of hydrogen and helium fusion die out, this outer part of the star is ejected into space. This cloud of gas is known as a planetary nebula. The core of the star remains, continues to cool, and is known as a white dwarf.

High mass stars also form a carbon core which collapses and fuses into still heavier elements. This happens again and again, very quickly. With the formation of the last core, the star suddenly explodes.

13. A planetary nebula is the ejected shell of a giant star. It is in the shape of a spherical shell and is composed of relatively cool, thin gas. It was once the outer part of the star. This shell often appears as a ring; the thickest parts are seen in cross-section and look like a ring, the parts toward the core are thin and emit little light.

14. The remnant of a star at the center of its planetary nebula is the carbon core. As it cools and shrinks in size it becomes a white dwarf. Its size is about that of

the Earth, its density about one million times that of the Sun, its luminosity about one thousand times less than the Sun. Although initially rather hot, the white dwarf will cool and fade until it becomes a black dwarf.

15. A black dwarf is a white dwarf that has cooled so much that it produces very little light. A black dwarf will continue to cool off for ever. It's size will be maintained by the electron pressure it initially had. Black dwarfs will ultimately be just cold, dark embers of very dense matter. Such objects will always produce some light (infrared is more likely) because they will never have a temperature of 0 K. This takes a very long time, so long, that the universe may not be old enough to have produced any black holes as yet..

16. The primary factor as to whether stars in a binary will affect one another's evolution is the separation of the two stars. If separated by a few A.U., most stars will never expand to a sufficiently large size to ever affect each other. Closer than this and interaction is inevitable. For a given separation, the masses of the stars also play a role. More massive stars have larger Roche lobes than do less massive stars. A larger lobe enhances the possibility that the two stars will interact.

17. In a binary star system, the region around each star in which its gravity dominates is known as its Roche lobe. The region is teardrop-shaped; seen around both stars it appears like a three-dimensional figure-8.

18. If two stars in a binary are sufficiently close to each other, during stellar evolution, mass-transfer may occur. Since the more massive star would be the first to evolve, it would transfer mass over to the lower mass star. The mass-transfer can be so extensive that the lower mass star becomes the more massive of the two.

ANSWERS TO PROBLEMS

1. (a)

$$10,000 = R^2 \left(\frac{3,000}{6,000} \right)^4$$

R = 400 solar radii

This stars radius is about 2 A.U. and would engulf the four inner planets of our solar system; Mercury, Venus, Earth, and Mars.

(b)

$$0.0004 = R^2 \left(\frac{12,000}{6,000} \right)^4$$

R = 0.005 solar radii

= 3480 km

This size is just slightly larger than the planet Mars.

2. In solar units $L = M^3$. We also know the main sequence lifetime of a star (T) is M/L times the lifetime of the Sun. That is

$$T = 10^{10} \frac{M}{L}$$

Substituting for L gives

$$T = 10^{10} \frac{M}{M^3}$$

$$T = \frac{10^{10}}{M^2}$$

For a value of T = 400 million years gives

$$4 \times 10^8 = \frac{10^{10}}{M^2}$$

M = 5 solar masses

3. 100 L / 10^5 yr = 0.001 L/yr. This 0.1% / yr. In the magnitude system, in which observations would be made, this change can be calculated as follows. Let the initial luminosity be 1.000 and in the following year it is 1.001. What is the change in the magnitude?

$$4 \times 10^8 = \frac{10^{10}}{M^2}$$

Δm = 0.001 magnitude

This change in magnitude would just barely be detectable.

4. The core radius is 1.5×10^7 m, resulting in a volume of $4/3 \pi (1.5 \times 10^7)^3 = 1.41 \times 10^{22}$ m^3. The mass of the core is $0.25 \times 1.99 \times 10^{30}$ kg = 4.98×10^{29} kg. The density is mass divided by volume; 4.98×10^{29} kg / 1.41×10^{22} m^3 = 3.5×10^7 kg/m^3. By the same approach, the density of the envelope is 0.0024 kg/m^3. The core density of the Sun is given on p. 423 as 150,000 kg/m^3. The giant's core density is 230 times higher than the Sun's core density; the envelope is 1.6×10^{-8} the core density of the Sun.

5. The total time spent between stages 8 through 12 is 1.5021×10^8 years. The odds of finding a star at each stage is simply the time for evolution at that stage divided by the total time. For calculating the odds including the main sequence stage, the division is done using the main sequence lifetime. The following table gives the results of both of these calculations.

Stage	Odds Post MS Only	Odds MS
7	—	98.5%
8	67%	1.0%
9	0.07%	0.001%
10	33%	0.5%
11	0.007%	0.0001%
12	0.07%	0.001%

SUGGESTED READING

Balick, B. "The Shaping of Planetary Nebulae." *Sky and Telescope* (February 1987). New images help explain the varied and intricate forms of planetary nebulae.

Cannizo, J. K. et al., "Accretion Disks in Interacting Binary Stars." *Scientific American* (April, 1992).

Croswell, K., "Compelling Capella." *Astronomy* (February, 1995). Four stars in one.

Eicher, D. J., "Ashes to Ashes and Dust to Dust." *Astronomy* (May, 1994). How stars evolve into planetary nebulae.

Jayawardhana, R., "The Age Paradox." *Astronomy* (June, 1993). Stellar ages appear to be billions of years older than cosmological ages.

Kaler, J. B. "Journeys on the H–R Diagram." *Sky and Telescope* (May 1988). How stars may change dramatically as they age, taking on an amazing variety of characters.

_____, "Hypergiants." *Astronomy* (March, 1994). How big can stars get?

Kawaler, S. D., and D. E. Winget. "White Dwarfs: Fossil Stars." *Sky and Telescope* (August 1987). Why many stars will end their lives as crystals.

MacRobert, A. "Epsilon Aurigae." *Sky and Telescope* (January 1988). New light on a long-mysterious star.

Schorn, R. A. "Goodbye to Supermassive Stars." *Sky and Telescope* (January 1986). A star thousands of times heavier than the Sun was suspected to lie in the heart of the Tarantula Nebula. But it's not there.

Soker, N. "Planetary Nebulae." *Scientific American* (May, 1992).

Tomkin, J., and D. L. Lambert. "The Strange Case of Beta Lyrae." *Sky and Telescope* (October 1987). This familiar eclipsing binary star offers a rare glimpse of an exposed stellar core.

Trimble, V. "White Dwarfs: The Once and Future Suns." *Sky and Telescope* (October 1986). White dwarf stars.

Chapter 21

STELLAR EXPLOSIONS
Novae, Supernovae, and the Formation of the Heavy Elements

Core Densities

In the last chapter white dwarf matter was compared to ordinary matter using a "marble" to represent 1 cubic centimeter of matter. That white dwarf marble had a mass of 10,000 kg, which is, as you know, rather high. The same question can now be asked for the iron core of a massive star. The text gives a density of 10^{12} kg/m^3, that is 10^9 gm/cm^3. So our marble will have a mass of 1,000,000 (one million) kg. This is one hundred times greater than the white dwarf core. Comparisons become difficult but this mass is about equal to the mass of all the books in a large university library. That's a lot for a marble!

Core Collapse

When an iron core final forms in a massive star it immediately collapses. For reasons explained in the text, little can stop this collapse. It is one of the most catastrophic and energetic events known to exist in the universe. It is genuinely hard to believe the amount of energy that is capable of being released and the short amount of time during which the collapse occurs. I don't mind using just a little physics to demonstrate this in a very simple way. Even better, the results agree with the results of more complex calculations.

Let's look at the iron core of a massive star. There is about one solar mass of matter that will collapse over a distance of its radius (its about the size of the Earth). So the mass is 2×10^{30} kg and the radius is approximately 5×10^6 m.

How much energy is released by a falling object? Quite a bit, actually. Drop a bowling ball from 1 meter and it develops a lot of energy on the way down! Actually, it had that energy while you held it, it was gravitational potential energy. This energy is easily calculated from the formula mgh; m is the mass, h is the distance it will fall, and g is the acceleration of gravity on Earth.

If we imagine the collapse of the iron core being simply modeled as a solar mass falling a distance of 5 million meters, we should get a rough idea of the energy that will be released. Of course we will need the acceleration of gravity in the core to do this simple calculation. Newton's law of gravity tells us this is just Gm/r^2 at the surface and will keep increasing while the collapse occurs. Let's be a bit conservative and use twice the initial surface gravity $\approx 10^7$

m/sec^2 (about a million times what it is on Earth). Now we calculate mgh.

$$mgh = 2 \times 10^{30} \times 10^7 \times 5 \times 10^6$$

$$mgh = 10^{44} \text{ J}$$

This is just about right for a supernova. The light emitted totals about 10^{43} J but the neutrinos carry away about 10^{45} J. As the text notes, the light emitted is about what the Sun emits during its entire main sequence lifetime. That is also easily calculated by multiplying the Sun's luminosity by the number of seconds in a year and multiplying this by 10 billion years.

$$(4 \times 10^{26)} \times (3 \times 10^7) \times 10^{10} = 10^{44} \text{J}$$

Now for how fast the collapse occurs. For falling bodies, simple physics tells us the following:

$$h = \frac{1}{2}gt^2$$

Before we start doing a lot of arithmetic, notice that our h (5×10^6) has a numerical value equal to one half of our estimate of g (10^7). So $t^2 = 1$ and $t = 1$ sec!

We have discovered, with very little effort, that dropping the Sun a distance equal to the radius of the Earth equals the total energy output of the Sun ..... and it does all of this in one second. I do not know which is more amazing, the energy released in this event or the fact that we can approximately calculate it with such simple concepts and arithmetic. No matter how non-mathematical my courses are, I can not help but do a few demonstrations of this sort. Students need to understand that many things make sense to us if we can use a little math and physics.

Supernovae

Both type-I and type-II supernovae become exceptionally bright. If a type-II becomes about one billion times brighter than the Sun then this is 22.5 magnitudes brighter ($-2.5\text{Log} (10^9) = -22.5$) than the Sun's absolute magnitude. Since the Sun's absolute magnitude is 4.7 then this supernova has an absolute magnitude of about -18. Type-I supernovae are brighter and can easily reach -19 or -20. If a bright supernova occurred 300 pc distant (1,000 light years) it would appear as bright as the full moon!

Supernovae are very important for determining distances to the most distant galaxies in the universe. Modern telescopes can detect a star as faint as magnitude 25. Knowing the absolute magnitude of a bright supernova allows us to calculate the distance to a supernova that is just barely detectable. Distance, d, in parsecs, apparent magnitude, m, and absolute magnitude, M, are related as follows:

$$m - M = 5 \text{ Log } d - 5$$

Using m = 25, M = -20, the distance is calculated to be d =

10^{10} pc. This covers the entire universe! In principle, then, supernovae allow astronomers to see and measure the distances to all parts of the universe. Unfortunately it is not this simple in practice. First, faint supernovae are extremely difficult to discover. A large telescope would have to continually observe a section of the sky and wait for a supernovae to occur. The galaxy in which the supernova occurs may not even be visible to the telescope. M = -20 is the maximum magnitude of the supernova. But it is important for astronomers to watch the supernova decline in brightness in order to determine which type it is. Finally, supernova 1987A reminded us that the peak brightness depends on the type of star going supernova. 1987A was not as bright as a "typical" supernova.

Why aren't more supernovae seen in our own galaxy? Supernovae occur, on average, about once every 50 years. If one occurred at a distance of 10,000 pc, and using M = -18, the apparent magnitude would be -3. But this neglects the effects of interstellar dust. Minimally, dust dims starlight by one magnitude for every 1,000 pc; it can be much more than this. So this supernova would appear at least at +7 and probably much fainter. Although searches are carried out, primarily by amateur astronomers, on a nightly basis, the infrequency of supernovae and their probable faintness results in a low rate of discovery. We could easily miss a supernova in our own galaxy!

Helium and Neutron Capture

Figure 21.12 has a tremendous amount of information in it about how the lighter elements have formed. Starting with carbon, there is a saw-tooth pattern to the abundance of the elements. It is hard for carbon to fuse with itself because of the 6 protons that the carbon contains. There is a strong repulsion between these nuclei; very high temperatures are required to bring them close enough for fusion to occur. But helium can fuse with carbon much easier and at a lower temperature. Since helium has 2 protons, the next element to form has 6 + 2 = 8 protons; this is oxygen.

Oxygen will fuse with helium to form an element with 8 + 2 = 10 protons; neon. This continues on for every other element. Notice the rise in abundances peaking at iron. This is an indication of the stability of the iron nucleus.

The elements that are skipped are formed by another process, neutron capture. When neutrons are captured inside a nucleus they sometimes decay into a proton and an electron is emitted from the nucleus in order to conserve charge. There is no repulsive force between a neutron and the nucleus, so neutron capture is relatively easy; the neutrons don't even have to be moving very fast. In terms of the magnet demonstration used in Chapter 20, neutron capture is analogous to bringing a piece of non-magnetic material close to one of the magnets. Use a piece of aluminum shaped similarly to the magnets and show how it takes no force to move the two together.

SN1987A

This supernova, although occurring in a nearby galaxy, is ideally placed for study. Since we know the distance to the Large Magellanic Cloud (LMC), we know the distance to the supernova. There is little dust in the direction of the LMC. Astronomers could then easily calculate the absolute magnitude, but were in for a surprise when they did. The LMC has a distance of about 50,000 pc and SN1987A reached a peak apparent magnitude of 3. This gives an absolute magnitude of -15.5 which is 2.5 magnitudes (10 times) fainter than was predicted. The text explains why this occurred.

Comment

There is a profoundness to the material presented in chapters 20 and 21. The life cycle of the stars is more than a curiosity. Our understanding of this entire process answers questions about the origin of our very substance. Throughout human civilization there have been creation myths and philosophies that attempted to provide answers to our curiosity about the matter of our environment. We finally have found a rational explanation, one based on naturally occurring processes, one that irreversibly links us to the rest of the universe. This is a good time to reflect back on the formation of the solar system and how the Earth was formed. Humans have an origin, not only linked to the Earth, but to the very stars. Our carbon, oxygen, nitrogen came to us through the stellar evolution of countless numbers of stars, billions of years ago, that died out, and whose many elements mixed together to finally rest here. It is a marvel, in deed, but it is all the more so because it is now understandable.

ANSWERS TO CHAPTER 21 REVIEW QUESTIONS

1. A nova is a star in a binary star system that suddenly brightens and then slowly fades back to normal. They are caused by an evolving star in a binary that is expanding and loosing gas to a companion white dwarf. After a while the gas builds up on the white dwarf and reaches a high enough temperature to fuse. In doing so, it explodes off the surface of the white dwarf.

2. A light curve is a diagram that plots the changes in the brightness of an object such as a star, as a function of time. Time is plotted on the horizontal scale; brightness on the vertical scale. The light curves of novae and supernovae appear rather different. In particular, if the amount of brightening is observed, supernovae are known to brighten about one million times more than novae. How the light dims after the explosion is noticeably different for novae and supernovae.

3. A massive star will eventually build up a core of iron. But iron can not fuse and release energy. As the core collapses under gravity it can not produce additional energy to stop the collapse. As the collapse proceeds high energy photons break up the iron nuclei, further absorbing energy and neutrinos are released when neutrons are formed from protons and electrons. This further destablizes the core producing a catastrophic collapse.

4. A supernova is a very large explosion of a star that virtually destroys it. There are two different types of supernovae, Type-I and Type-II. Type-I are observed to have hydrogen-poor spectra and are fainter than the Type-II. There is also a difference in shape of the light curve as can be seen in Figure 21.7.

5. Type-I supernovae occur in binary stars. The process is similar to a nova but with one big difference. The white dwarf initially has a mass near the upper critical limit for white dwarfs, 1.4 solar masses. As gas is accreted from the companion star, the white dwarf's mass exceeds this limit and collapses. Suddenly the carbon of the white dwarf detonates the blows the star up. Type-II supernova result from the collapse of the iron core of a massive star.

   In a type-II supernova, the core is surrounded by a hydrogen and helium rich layer. The spectrum of such a supernova has lots of lines of these two elements. A type-I supernova contains virtually no hydrogen or helium, so the spectrum is very weak in these elements. The light curve of a type-I supernova is almost totally due to the radioactive decay of elements. Type-II supernovae have light curves appropriate for an expanding cloud of gas, blown into space by a shock wave.

6. Models of stellar evolution suggest that supernovae should occur about once a century. This is sufficiently long that it has not been possible to test this observationally.

7. When the supernova explosion occurs, it rapidly ejects a vast cloud of gas. This is called a supernova remnant. Supernova remnants can last for thousands of years and provide evidence of an earlier supernova.

8. Depending on the type of supernova, the explosion produces a peak in brightness. The two types seem to be consistent in the peak brightness reached. Knowing this brightness allows the distance to an observed supernova to be calculated. Type-I supernovae are consistent in their properties and are the most reliable. Type-II supernovae have light curves that depend on the makeup of the outer part of the star. This can vary from star to star, making type-II supernovae not as reliable as a distance indicator.

9. There are two lines of proof that heavy elements are formed in stars. First, the abundance of the elements varies greatly with atomic number. The variation in the abundances of the elements can be reproduced by the theories of nucleosynthesis. Second, observations

of events like supernovae allow us to see elements virtually in the process of formation. The light curve, spectra, and neutrinos are all evidence of the explosion that allow our models to be tested.

10. The fusion of like nuclei, such as carbon with carbon, requires a higher temperature than the fusion of carbon with helium. The reason for this is that carbon has 6 protons and helium has only two. Because like charges repel, it is 3 times more difficult to bring two carbon nuclei close enough to fuse compared to bringing a carbon and a helium nuclei together. It depends on the product of their charges, 6x6=36 compared to 6x2=12, respectively.

11. The process of helium capture eventually leads to producing iron. This occurs only for the most massive stars. However, helium capture by iron does not produce energy and so the process stops with iron.

12. Nuclei heavier than iron are formed by neutron capture. The nucleus of an element captures one or more neutrons, which can then decay into a proton, forming a new and heavier element. This process can proceed slowly inside of massive stars or very rapidly during the supernova explosion.

13. The r-process stands for "rapid" neutron capture. It can occur only during a type-II supernova explosion. Various isotopes of elements normally unstable are able to capture additional neutrons, resulting in the formation of elements that could not be formed by the s-process.

14. Supernova 1987A will continue for a long time to be a very important supernova because astronomers have been able to follow it, from its progenitor stage completely through its development as a type-II supernova.

ANSWERS TO PROBLEMS

1. Speed is distance divided by time. The distance is 1 pc or 3.1×10^{16} m. The time is 940 years (using 1994 and 1054). Since one year is 3.2×10^7 sec, the time is equal to 3×10^{10} sec. The speed is then just 1×10^6 m/sec or 1,000 km/sec.

   This answer assumes a constant expansion velocity which is certainly not too good. The expansion must take place very rapidly at first but then will slow down as the gas runs into the interstellar medium. Gravity probably plays almost no role in slowing it down.

2. Use the inverse-square law of light, in a ratio.

$$\frac{1}{10,000^2} = \frac{10^5}{R^2}$$

$$R = 3 \times 10^6 \text{ pc}$$

For the supernova a similar expression is used.

$$\frac{1}{10,000^2} = \frac{10^{10}}{R^2}$$

$$R = 1 \times 10^9 \text{ pc}$$

3. The Sun is just 1 A.U. from us. In parsecs this distance is 1/206,000 pc. Use a ratio as in problem 2.

$$\frac{1}{\frac{1}{206,000}^2} = \frac{10^{10}}{R^2}$$

$$R = 0.5 \text{ pc}$$

There are no stars this close to the Sun so it is not likely that a supernova would ever be as bright as the Sun in our sky. That's probably just as well!

4. The total energy output of the Sun over its lifetime is given by it current luminosity times the number of seconds in a year times its ten billion year lifetime.

$$4 \times 10^{26} \times 3 \times 10^7 \times 10^{10} = 10^{44} \text{J}$$

A supernova emits about 10^{43} J in visible light and 10^{45} J in the form of neutrinos.

SUGGESTED READING

Filippenko, A. V., "A Supernova with an Identity Crisis." *Sky & Telescope* (December, 1993). Interpreting the 1993 supernova in the M81 galaxy.

Hayes, J. C. and Burrows, A., "A New Dimension to Supernovae." *Sky & Telescope* (August, 1995). New computer models for supernovae produce realistic results.

Lattimer, J. M., and A. S. Burrows. "Neutrinos from Supernova 1987A." *Sky and Telescope* (October 1988). Scientists' first ringside seat at the formation of a neutron star.

Malin, D., and D. Allen. "Echoes of the Supernova." *Sky and Telescope* (January 1990). How light from Supernova 1987A revealed the detailed, three-dimensional structure of interstellar dust sheets in the Large Magellanic Cloud.

Maran, S. P. "In Our Backyard, a Star Explodes." *Smithsonian* (April 1988). Popular articles about the first supernova visible to the naked eye since 1604.

_ "A Supernova in Our Backyard." *Sky and Telescope* (April 1987). An early report on the discovery of a naked-eye supernova.

_ "Supernova Shines On." *Sky and Telescope* (May 1987). More on SN 1987A.

_ "Supernova 1987A's Changing Face." *Sky and Telescope* (July 1988). The supernova, a year and a half later.

Seward, F. "Neutron Stars in Supernova Remnants." *Sky and Telescope* (January 1986). The discovery of many more pulsars and neutron stars in supernova remnants.

Starrfield, S. and Shore, S. N. "The Birth and Death of Nova V 1974 Cygni." *Scientific American* (January, 1995). New insights on novae from an unusual nova.

Talcott, R., "Inside the Crab Nebula." *Astronomy* (December, 1994).

Thorpe, A., "Giving Birth to Supernovae." *Astronomy* (December, 1992). Ten nearby stars are future supernovae candidates.

van den Heuvel, E. P. J. and van Paradijs, J. "X-ray Binaries." *Scientific American* (November, 1993).

Woosley, S., and T. Weaver. "The Great Supernova of 1987." *Scientific American* (August 1989). Comprehensive article on Supernova 1987A.

Chapter 22

NEUTRON STARS AND BLACK HOLES
Strange States of Matter

Neutron Stars

In Chapters 20 and 21 a marble of 1 cm^3 was used to make comparisons about density and mass. Such a marble of neutron star matter will have a mass of 5×10^{14} gm or 500 billion kg. As the text suggests, this is the mass of a mountain. Another way of looking at this marble, it would have an acceleration due to gravity on its surface of about 100,000 times that on the Earth. Not only would you gravitationally "stick" to this marble, you would weigh 100,000 times more on this marble than you do on Earth! (However, at a distance of only 5 m, you would experience your normal weight, just don't get too close to neutron star matter, it is dangerous stuff!)

Since the acceleration due to gravity is proportional to the mass of the marble, you may want to go back and see what you would weigh on marbles of other material. You will find that your weight is insignificant until you get to these high densities as found in an iron core or in a neutron star.

Pulsars

How does the neutron star get rotating so fast? As the text notes, it is the conservation of angular momentum. The period of rotation depends on the radius squared. A typical rotation period for a star is a few days, let's say 5 days. There are 430,000 seconds in 5 days. The iron core is about the size of the Earth and shrinks to about 10 km. This is a reduction in size by a factor of 640. Squaring this to see how the period is reduced gives 410,000. The original period in seconds is about the same as this number, and so the new period will be about 1 second. This is a little slow for a new pulsar but not far off either. If the core is

much bigger than the Earth this will produce a significantly shorter period.

Very few pulsars emit sufficient visible light to make them detectable. The Crab Nebula pulsar is the only one bright enough to be visible to the eye using a telescope. However, it flashes at a rate of about 30 times/sec and so is too fast for the eye to see. It is seen as a constant light source like any star.

A simple demonstration of the flashing of a pulsar is made by using a strobe light with a variable flash rate. (Some people are quite bothered by strobe lights, so you should warn your students about what you are about to demonstrate.) Set the rate at about 1 flash/sec. Increase the rate until your students agree they can not make out the individual flashes. Typically, most people can not see beyond about 10 flashes/sec. Set the rate at 30 flashes/sec to show the Crab Nebula pulsar; there is no way to detect the flashing with the naked eye.

An instrument can be built to look at an object at a specific rate. Working at a frequency of about 30 Hz, the Crab pulsar will either appear "on" or "off", depending on the synchronization of the instrument with the pulsar. Such an instrument was used in 1969 on the Steward Observatory 36-inch telescope on Kitt Peak to examine some of the stars in the middle of the Crab Nebula and to see if any were flashing. On the very first star examined, the flashing was discovered and the optical pulsar confirmed.

Why can't pulsars be explained using rapidly rotating white dwarfs? The answer to this uses simple, classical physics. Due to its rotation, gravity provides the centripetal force necessary to hold it together. If the object rotates too fast, it flies apart. The gravitational acceleration is GM/R^2 and the centripetal acceleration is v^2/R, where M and R are the mass and radius of the rotating object. The equatorial velocity, v, may be written as $2\pi R/P$, where P is the period of rotation. How do the gravitational and centripetal accelerations compare for a rapidly rotating white dwarf?

$$M = 1 \text{ solar mass} = 2 \times 10^{30} \text{ kg}$$

$$R = 5000 \text{ km} = 5 \times 10^6 \text{ m}$$

$$P = 0.1 \text{ sec (typical for a pulsar)}$$

$$GM/R^2 = 5 \times 10^6 \text{ m/sec}^2 \quad \text{and} \quad v^2/R = 2 \times 10^{10} \text{ m/sec}^2$$

The white dwarf would fly apart rotating this fast! The problem could be turned around and the question asked "What size object is just stable under these conditions?" The radius must be about 300 km, so anything smaller will be stable against rotation. The same calculation done for a typical neutron star shows how stable they are.

$$M = 2 \text{ solar mass} = 4 \times 10^{30} \text{ kg}$$

$$R = 10 \text{ km} = 1 \times 10^4 \text{ m}$$

$$P = 0.1 \text{ sec}$$

$$GM/R^2 = 3 \times 10^{12} \text{ m/sec}^2 \quad \text{and} \quad v^2/R = 4 \times 10^7 \text{ m/sec}^2$$

For the millisecond pulsars, this situation is not quite so stable. The first such pulsar, PSR 1937+214, whose period is 0.001558 sec (642 rotations and flashes per second!), gives $v^2/R = 2 \times 10^{11} \text{ m/sec}^2$; it is stable but not by much.

The Crab Nebula gives off a lot of energy at all wavelengths. After over 900 years of expansion a question arose as to how it still manages to have a luminosity of 10^5 times that of the Sun. The Crab pulsar is known to be slowing down at a rate of 10^{-5} sec/year. The loss in rotational energy is about 5×10^5 times the solar luminosity. Thus the rotational energy is transferred to the nebula and allows it to continue to shine.

Black Holes

This is a good time to review the concept of escape velocity. I find that using escape velocity to explain black holes is conceptually the easiest for most students (their knowledge of general relativity being usually somewhat limited!). It is important to emphasize the dependence of escape velocity on both the mass and the radius.

Surprisingly, the size of a black hole can be calculated from classical physics even though general relativity is required to describe its details. Very simply, when the escape velocity of an object equals the speed of light, the object is a black hole. From previous chapters we know that the escape velocity is given by v_{esc} $\sqrt{2GM/r}$. If v_{esc} is set equal to the speed of light, c, then the equation can be solved for the radius. The result gives the Schwarzschild radius = $2GM/c^2$. This gives a radius of 3 km for a one solar mass object; thus the well-known result of 3 km for each solar mass of a black hole.

Black holes are really tiny when compared to ordinary stars. This is not always appreciated. The Sun would have a radius of 3 km but it currently has a radius of about 7×10^5 km. Taking the ratio of these two numbers, and multiplying by the angular size of the Sun, will give its apparent size if turned into a black hole (which I remind you is impossible for the Sun). The Sun is about half a degree or 1800 arc seconds in diameter. The answer is the Sun would appear 0.008 arc seconds in diameter. This is 100 times smaller than the atmospheric turbulence in the Earth's atmosphere will allow us to see. Not only would it not give off light, its size would make it much too small to see (if there were anything to see). And this is at the distance of the Sun.

If the Sun magically turned into a black hole, what would be the effect on the Earth's orbit? I ask this question of my students and am often told that the Earth would be "sucked into it." Point out that the gravitational force on the Earth is still the same as before, since the mass of the Sun (now black hole) and our distance from it have not changed. And even if the Earth somehow encountered the Sun, the Earth is much larger (but not more massive). In fact, the Earth would be about 4,000 times larger than the black hole Sun. This is comparable to a person standing next to the period at the end of the sentence.

The rubber sheet model of a black hole really works well as a demonstration. Stretch the sheet on an open frame just enough so there are no wrinkles and little sag. Put a mass at the center to warp it. Roll small marbles, ball bearings, or coins tangentially to the center. They will "orbit" around the center, moving faster as the center is approached, and finally spiraling into the center because of friction. Try different speeds and angles to change the trajectories. Small coins often work the best because of the reduced friction. Students will want to play with this demo after class. There are also some commercially available plastic models. Small ones are very popular for collecting coins for charities. (It would be best not to compare the charity with a black hole, however!)

ANSWERS TO CHAPTER 22 REVIEW QUESTIONS

1. Some of the basic properties of a neutron star include its high density, rotation, and magnetic field. How these come about to be this way is a direct result of the core collapse that forms the neutron star. The collapse and shock wave that propagates into the core give the high density. Although the star is rotating initially at a normal rate, the collapse must conserve angular momentum and this results in the core "spinning up" as it gets smaller. The magnetic field is confined by the gas in the core and is therefore concentrated as the core shrinks.

2. The gravity at the surface of a body depends on the mass of that body and inversely on the square of the distance to the center, i.e. its radius. A neutron star has

both a high mass, 1-2 solar masses, and a small size, 10 km radius. Both of these properties result in a very high pull of gravity on its surface. An average human would weight about 1 million tons on its surface. A person would be flattened out by this huge force.

3. All neutron stars are not seen as pulsars because their orientation does not allow their beam of radiation to pass in the direction of the Earth. The beam can be only a few degrees across, so the alignment must close to pointing towards the Earth in order for us to see it. A neutron star that is not observed as a pulsar by us could be viewed by others in a different direction as being a pulsar.

4. X-ray bursters are found in mass-transfer binary stars where one of the stars is a neutron star and the other is a normal star. The mass transfer forms a disc around the neutron star and slowly accumulates on its surface. Finally, the gas undergoes fusion and there is a burst of X-rays released as a result. This can occur again and again as the mass continues to be transferred to the neutron star.

5. In a mass-transfer binary, something other than just mass is transferred to the neutron star; angular momentum can be transferred too. This results in making the neutron star spin faster and faster. The angular momentum is taken from the orbital motions of the two stars.

6. A supernova explosion should completely destroy any planetary system. However, if the star that goes supernova is in a binary system, the effects of the explosion may destroy most, but not all, of the companion. What is left behind could form a disc of material that eventually accretes to form planetary-sized objects in orbit around the pulsar. This theory is still unproved, though.

7. If an object moves towards me at 10 mph and I move towards it at 5 mph, then the object's speed, relative to me, is 15 mph. If, instead, I am moving 5 mph away from this same object, its speed relative to me is only 5 mph.

   Now, if the object is actually a beam of light moving at the speed of light, the previous example of the addition or subtraction of speeds no longer applies. I will always measure the speed of light to be a constant, independent of my own speed. This was discovered by Michelson and Morley, much to their own amazement, because they believed the speeds would add together. It was a discovery that lead Einstein to the special theory of relativity.

8. The escape velocity from the surface of a body depends on the mass the radius of that object. It is quite possible for an object to have sufficient mass and small size to have an escape velocity equal to the speed of light. This occurs for a solar mass at a radius of 3 km, or any multiple thereof. What this means is that light itself can not escape from this object. By definition, this is what is meant by a black hole.

9. General relativistic effects, although always present, at not obvious unless a gravitational field is very strong. Most of the gravitational fields we encounter in the solar system, for instance, are fairly weak. But the theory can still be tested under these conditions; it just requires very careful and sensitive measurements to be made.

10. Before entering the black hole, tidal forces would pull them apart. Gravity is so strong near the black hole that the difference in the force on the two sides of the person is sufficient to him or her apart. This would be true of any type of matter that would venture close to the black hole.

11. Cygnus X-1 is a good black hole candidate because it is in a binary system; its mass has been determined to be in the range of 5 to 10 solar masses. Mass transfer is occurring and produces X-rays from the black hole candidate. The X-rays vary at a rate suggesting the candidate is small, less than 300 km.

ANSWERS TO PROBLEMS

1. Since angular momentum is conserved, the "before" and "after" values must be equal. Thus we have,

$$\frac{1 \text{ rev}}{1 \text{ day}} \times 10,000^2 = \frac{1 \text{ rev}}{X} \times 10^2$$

$$X = 10^{-6} \text{ day}$$

$$X = 0.086 \text{ sec or}$$

$$11.6 \text{ rev/sec}$$

2. The Schwarzschild radius is the mass of an object, given in solar masses, times 3 km.

   For the 1 million solar mass black hole:

   $$10^6 \times 3 \text{ km} = 3 \times 10^6 \text{ km},$$

   dividing by the radius of the Sun gives

   $$3 \times 10^6 \text{ km} / 6.96 \times 10^5 \text{ km} = 4.3 \text{ solar radii}.$$

   For the 1 billion solar mass black hole:

   $$10^9 \times 3 \text{ km} = 3 \times 10^9 \text{ km},$$

   dividing by the radius of the solar system (= 40 A.U.) gives

   $$3 \times 10^9 \text{ km} / (40 \times 1.5 \times 10^8 \text{ km}) = 0.5 \text{ solar system radii}$$
   $$\text{or } 20 \text{ A.U.}$$

3. A point on the equator travels 1000 circumferences each second.

   $$1000 \times 2\pi \times 10 = 63,000 \text{ km/sec}.$$

But the speed of light is 300,000 km/sec, so the speed is

63,000 / 300,000 = 0.21 or 21% speed of light.

4. Determine the luminosity for the first example, at T = 10^5 K. Remember, T must be put into solar units, as will be R and L.

$$L = \left(\frac{10}{7 \times 10^5}\right)^2 \times \left(\frac{10^5}{6000}\right)^4$$

L = 1.6×10^{-5}	for 10^5 K
L = 0.16	for 10^6 K
L = 1600	for 10^7 K

In the first case, the luminosity is so low, it could not be plotted on the H-R diagram. In the second and third cases, the temperatures are so high, again, neither could be plotted on the H-R diagram. The luminosities in the last two cases suggest that these neutron stars might be visible; the temperatures, though, would place the peak radiation in the X-ray region of the spectrum.

SUGGESTED READING

Abramowicz, M. A., "Black Holes and the Centrifugal Force Paradox." *Scientific American* (March, 1992).

Backer, D., and S. Kulkarni. "A New Class of Pulsars." *Physics Today* (March 1990). How binary pulsars, pulsars with millisecond periods, and pulsars in globular clusters are providing tools for fundamental tests of physics.

Chaisson, E. *Relatively Speaking: Relativity, Black Holes, and the Fate of the Universe.* New York: W. W. Norton, 1988.

Croswell, K., "The Best Black Hole in the Galaxy." *Astronomy* (March, 1992).

Dolan, J. F. "Placing Faith in the Masses?" *Nature* (February 13, 1992). Detecting black holes in space.

Flam, F. "How to Find a Black Hole." *Science* (February 14, 1992). Uses a new black hole candidate, V404 Cygni, as an example while discussing the black hole search strategy of looking for an X-ray signature, then trying to measure masses.

Graham-Smith, F. "Pulsars Today." *Sky and Telescope* (September 1990). Current research on pulsars.

Greenstein, G. *Frozen Star.* New York: Freundlich Books, 1983. A historical perspective on neutron stars and black holes, along with many fine explanations.

Hawley, K. "What Are Gamma Ray Bursters?" *Sky and Telescope* (August 1990). Discusses these high-energy phenomena.

Kaler, J., "Stellar Oddballs." *Astronomy* (September, 1994). Epsilon Aurigae, SS 433, and the Black Widow pulsar.

Kaspi, V. M., "Millisecond Pulsars: Timekeepers of the Cosmos." *Sky & Telescope* (April, 1995).

Parker, B., "Where Have All the Black Holes Gone?" *Astronomy* (October, 1994).

Piran, T. "Binary Neutron Stars." *Scientific American* (May, 1995). Tests of general relativity using gamma rays emitted from pairs of neutron stars.

Shapiro, S. L. "Black Holes, Naked Singularities and Cosmic Censorship." *American Scientist* (July–August 1991). Comprehensive article concerning some of the amazing concepts surrounding the subject of black holes.

Shipman, H. L. *Black Holes, Quasars and the Universe.* Boston: Houghton Mifflin, 1976. Excellent basic explanations of black holes and other energetic phenomena.

Chapter 23

THE MILKY WAY GALAXY
A Grand Design

Naked Eye View of the Milky Way

To truly understand and appreciate the magnificence of the Milky Way, it must be viewed on a dark, clear, moonless night. In the northern hemisphere summer is best, but the winter Milky Way, with the great constellation of Orion and its nebulae, is still very impressive.

Take your students out to a suitable location so they can see for themselves. Make sure everyone has sufficient time to become dark adapted (15-30 minutes). Don't worry about setting up telescopes because they will not allow you to see the large scale structure. Binoculars are good to use just so the Milky Way can be resolved into the multitudes of stars that first so impressed Galileo when he looked at the Milky Way through his telescope.

If a suitable location is not immediately available to you and your students, encourage them all to seek one out at a later time. The Milky Way and the night sky is part of their environment, their heritage, and they should not be denied it by lights, pollution, and man-made obstructions.

Model of the Milky Way

Many slides and diagrams of the Milky Way distort the actual dimension, often exaggerating the thickness of the disk and nuclear bulge. Show Figure 23.11 as a transparency. Refer to the COBE image of the Milky Way in this figure, it is an actual cross-sectional view of our Milky Way.

Now let's try for a model that will fit into your classroom. I don't know the size of your classroom but let's assume a 15 m × 15 m room; the numbers work out nicely this way. For a diameter of 30,000 pc, the scale will be 1 m = 2,000 pc. The center of the Milky Way will be in the center of the room; the nuclear bulge will be 2 m high, top to bottom, and 3 m in diameter, in the plane of the disk. The disk is only 15 cm thick at the location of the Sun, which is about half way (4 m) out from the center, but thickens towards the center.

On this scale, the solar system is so small (2×10^{-7} m or 0.2 microns) you would need a high powered microscope just to see its diameter of about 100 A.U.! When you look up at the stars at night, the stars you see with your naked eye will extend away from the Sun about 25 cm on this scale. Vega, the bright summer star, is only 4 mm from the Sun. In winter, the great Orion nebula is 21 cm from the Sun and located in a direction about opposite the direction to the center of the Milky Way. One of the largest globular clusters, Omega Centauri, lies to the right of the center, 1 m above the disk, and 2.5 m distant. It's the size of a quarter (coin).

Stand at the position of the Sun, in your model. With your arm extended in the plane of the disk, sweep your arm and hand around 360°. The section of the disk that you just swept contains about 4 billion stars, i.e. the observable stars available to all but the largest telescopes. Dust is so thick beyond this distance, you would have trouble seeing your fingers (assuming they were luminous like stars!). And yet, you have only swept a few percent of the total number of stars in the Milky Way.

Andromeda Nebula—What Could It Be?

It was historically a real problem. On a very clear, dark night you can actually see this fuzzy, elongated patch in the constellation of Andromeda. Of course there are other fuzzy patches of sky, but most are located in the Milky Way; this object is definitely not in that swath of light known as the Milky Way. On photographs, its elliptical shape extends for 3°, that's 6 times the diameter of the Moon! Now 3° is 0.05 radians and the angle in radians times the distance equals the size of an object. Here is where the problem was at. Assuming any distance, the corresponding size did not fit the possible objects. Here are some examples.

Distance	Size
10 pc	0.5 pc
100 pc	5 pc
1,000 pc	50 pc
10,000 pc	500 pc
100,000 pc	5,000 pc

At 10 pc its size was much too large to be a solar system or even one in formation. At 100 and 1,000 pc the size was about right for an emission nebula but spectroscopy indicated a spectrum more like a star. At 10,000 pc it would be outside the Milky Way, larger than any known object, and comparable to a sizable portion of the (then known) Milky Way. At the (then) ridiculous distance of 100,000 pc it would be as large as the known size of the Milky Way, which was supposedly the entire universe. At any greater distance the size would grow unimaginably large and so no distance seemed right for this object. Worse yet, there were other examples of these spiral nebulae that appeared smaller but were equally inexplicable.

If astronomers in the early part of this century were told the correct answer, they simply would not have believed it; at its true distance of 700,000 pc, its size is 35,000 pc! Both the distance and the size would have been considered unacceptably large. I like to use this example with students because it is simple and illustrates how, when data does not fit anything in the status quo, the unimaginable just might be the solution. The gamma ray bursters are a good modern-day version of this same problem; theories range from them being very local objects to extremely extragalactic. At least we know the distance to the bursters *must* be in this range!

Cepheids and RR Lyrae Variables

Students often confuse these pulsating stars with pulsars; the cause of the confusion is obvious. These stars are "radially pulsating" which means they are simply growing larger and smaller, larger and smaller, etc. with time. Use a balloon demonstration, but vary the size by only about 10%. The luminosity-radius-temperature relation, $L = R^2 T^4$ (all in solar units), reminds us that it takes only a small change in the temperature to produce a large change in the luminosity. A typical Cepheid might change from 6000 K to 7500 K. This is sufficient to produce a one magnitude change in brightness (about 2.5 in luminosity).

In the magnitude nomenclature of Chapter 17, the absolute magnitude of a Cepheid is directly related to its period of pulsation. A 10 day period Cepheid would have an absolute magnitude of about -5. The period-luminosity relation has been determined by observing Cepheids in nearby clusters of stars whose distances have been determined using main sequence fitting. Knowing the distance to a Cepheid allows us to calculate its absolute magnitude. Once the relationship is established, it can be used in reverse, i.e. to determine the distance to the Cepheid from its period and apparent magnitude.

How far away can Cepheids be used for determining distances? For the above example of a Cepheid, and knowing that modern telescopes can observe down to at least magnitude 25, we can calculate the distance.

$$25 - (-5) = 5 \log(d) - 5$$

$$d = 10^7 \text{ pc}$$

Certainly 10 million parsecs is very far away and sufficient to determine distances to a number of the nearest galaxies. Cepheids are among the brightest stars to be seen in a galaxy, they change their brightness by a lot and so can be easily discovered, and they provide reliable distances. They are one of the best methods for determining distances to nearby galaxies.

RR Lyrae variables have an absolute magnitude of about 0. They could be used out to about one million parsecs, a little farther than the Andromeda galaxy. However, they are most useful for determining distances to globular clusters in our own galaxy. It is the distribution of these clusters that help determine the distance to the center of the galaxy.

Kapteyn Universe

The universe (galaxy) was only 5,000 pc in radius. Absorption of starlight by interstellar dust was not understood. To make a simple example of what was being imagined at this time, take two types of stars with apparent magnitudes of 10 and 15. Now if you live in a very large, or infinite, universe filled with stars, then there should be many more magnitude 15 stars than magnitude 10 because the volume of space is much bigger farther away than it is nearby. But at 5,000 pc there is about 5 magnitudes of absorption, so the magnitude 15 stars are now magnitude 20 and invisible. The magnitude 10 stars are seen as magnitude 15 and there are not as many of these as you would expect at this distance. So, they thought they were seeing the edge of the galaxy and universe. They were, of course, wrong.

Looking at stars this way is analogous to looking at your surroundings when there is a thick fog present. You see the nearby objects easily and they do not appear to be affected by the fog. Your nose, your hand, your feet all look all right. But objects 10 feet away look a little hazy and by 20 feet they get hard to see. 30 feet and beyond you are not so sure you can see anything; maybe there is nothing at all. But it is night time and you do see a faint set of lights ahead. Is it nearby or far away ? You can't tell because of the fog. Normally, lights that faint are far away but you know the fog deceives you and the oncoming car might be much closer. Up to the 1920s, astronomers were deceived by the dust. They thought they were seeing distant stars when, in fact, they were seeing nearby stars through dust.

Most areas have fog, dust storms, haze, smoke, or pollution so most students can identify with this analogy. Give this analogy in a darkened room so the students can use their imaginations. Then show a picture of a typical star field in the Milky Way. Point to lots of faint stars and ask; "Are these distant stars or nearby stars dimmed by dust?" It's neither obvious nor easy to tell, so we shouldn't fault early 20th century astronomers for not knowing either.

The Color Of The Disk

Are the stars that make up the disk that much different than the stars in the rest of the Galaxy? The primary difference is that star formation produces a few hot, bright main sequence stars. If such a star has an absolute magnitude of -5 and a typical star is a faint, low mass main sequence star of absolute magnitude 10, then the bright star is one million times brighter than the typical faint star. It will actually take one million of those typical faint stars to equal the brightness of one bright main sequence star. The ratio of their numbers is not far from a million-to-one, but the combined light will still appear bluer than the disk stars without any bright main sequence stars present.

The point is, the disk stars are rather similar to the halo stars and the stars of the nuclear bulge, but a few bright main sequence stars changes the overall appearance. It should be noted too that the dust clouds in the disk preferentially reflect blue light. This can enhance the blueness of the disk.

Galactic Rotation

A typical galactic rotation curve (velocity versus distance) for a spiral galaxy or the Milky Way can be described as follows: from the center the velocity increases rapidly, starts to drop off slowly, then rises slowly or becomes constant. Some may show a final slow drop. The reason for these shapes and changes are actually very simple.

Let's assume that the stars and gas clouds are all moving in circular orbits around the center of the galaxy. This is a good assumption. Then we already know that gravity from inside the orbit must balance the centripetal force. From Chapter 2, the velocity of the orbit is given by

$$v = \sqrt{\frac{GM}{R}}$$

But the mass, M, increases with radius R unless there is negligible mass outside of R. M can be thought of as varying three different ways with respect to R. For a spherical distribution of mass $M \propto R^3$; for a disk $M \propto R^2$; with little or no mass outside of R, M is a constant.

In these three cases, the velocity v will vary with R as either $\propto R$, $\propto R^{1/2}$, or $\propto R^{-1/2}$. Coming out from the center, the nuclear bulge is like a spherical distribution of mass and so the velocity varies linearly with R. As R increases and the disk is entered into, the velocity varies as $R^{-1/2}$ because it "sees" the bulge as one large mass and does not yet see much mass in the disk. As more disk is encountered, the velocity varies as $R^{1/2}$ and therefore increases slowly with distance. Sooner or later, at some large value of R, the velocity should return to a $R^{-1/2}$ dependence and slowly drop off. This is not always seen and often the velocity remains constant. This implies $M \propto R$ which is somewhere between a disk and a central distribution of mass, the additional mass coming presumably from the outer halo or corona. There is more mass there than meets the eye (or detector).

Use the following figure to interpret the velocity curve of the Milky Way shown in Figure 23.19. The shape of the curve tells us something about the mass distribution "felt" by the stars and gas at these locations.

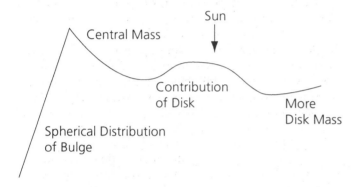

The Galactic Halo and Corona:

As noted in the text, there is little doubt that the Milky Way has a halo and corona that contain substantial amounts of matter. The form the matter is in remains a question. However, the halo contains substantially more volume than the disk, so the matter filling it may be very sparsely distributed. For the disk with a radius of 15 kpc and a average thickness of 500 pc, the volume is 3.5×10^{11} pc^3; for the spherical halo of the same radius the volume is 1.4×10^{13} pc^3 or 40 times the volume of the disk. For a corona with a radius of 50 kpc the volume is 1500 times the volume of the disk! That is a very large volume in which matter might hide.

ANSWERS TO CHAPTER 23 REVIEW QUESTIONS

1. Spiral nebulae were observed by astronomers of the last century as cloudy patches of light that had a spiral shape, in some cases. With the advent of photography this description was only better defined but not understood. At one time early this century they were thought to be swirling regions of star formation. When finally resolved into stars, these nebulae were discovered to be galaxies like our own.

2. Cepheids have the unique property of a relationship between their period of pulsation and their luminosity. By observing the Cepheid and determining its period of variation, its true luminosity is known. Comparing the true luminosity with the apparent luminosity allows the distance to be determined.

3. Because of their intrinsically high luminosity, Cepheids can be seen, and therefore used, out to a few million parsecs. They are used to determine distances to the nearest galaxies.

4. RR Lyrae variables are very useful for determining distances to globular clusters. By knowing how the globular clusters are distributed in the Galaxy, the halo is mapped out. But most importantly, the distribution of globular clusters gives the distance to the center of the Galaxy from the Sun. This also helped tell astronomers how large the Milky Way actually is.

5. The central regions of the Galaxy are obscured by thick clouds of interstellar dust. Visible light can not penetrate these clouds. However, infrared and especially radio waves can easily penetrate these clouds and so we can see the center of the Galaxy at these wavelengths.

6. In the radio part of the spectrum, atomic hydrogen gas emits 21-cm radiation. Because its long wavelength allows it to travel throughout the Galaxy, astronomers can use it to map the structure of gas clouds in the Galaxy. Molecular hydrogen is very difficult to observe but other molecules, such as carbon monoxide, are used to map molecular clouds.

7. The stars in the Galactic disk move in roughly circular orbits around the center of the Galaxy. The orbits all lie in the plane of the disk. The halo stars have approximately the same velocities as the disk stars but are moving in various directions, relative to the disk, forming a spherical halo around the Galaxy. These stars pass in and out of the disk, towards the center of the Galaxy and back out again into the halo. When seen locally, they appear to have high velocities relative to the Sun and other disk stars and the direction of their motion is at an angle to the plane of the disk.

8. The spiral arms of a galaxy are bright and contain very luminous stars, open star clusters, and emission nebulae. All of these objects are found in star formation regions and are all considered young objects.

9. The gas and dust enter the spiral arm from behind and becomes compressed as it encounters the density wave. Star formation starts from the compressed gas and dust. The stars and unused gas and dust move on through the spiral arm and continue with their normal orbital motion around the Galaxy.

10. Imagine a group of newly formed massive stars somewhere in the galactic disk. When these stars form, the H

II regions, or emission nebulae, that appear around them send shock waves through the surrounding gas. These waves can trigger new star formation. Similarly, when the stars explode in supernovae, more shock waves are formed. The formation of one group of stars provides the mechanism for the formation of more stars.

11. The stars in the halo have orbits that form a spherical halo around the Galaxy. This tells us the original shape of the cloud of gas that was the galaxy before stars formed. The entire halo appears to rotate which further tells us that this cloud was rotating. The formation of a disk is the result of the cloud having some initial rotation.

12. Different parts of the Galaxy rotate at different rates. The rotation is actually the motions of the stars and gas around the Galaxy. Because the Galaxy is not a solid body, like the Earth, different parts of it move at different rates. The orbital motions are determined strictly by the amount of mass interior to the orbit. The velocity of the orbits at differing distances gives us the rotation curve of the Galaxy. By looking at the outer-most orbits, the total mass of the Galaxy can be determined.

13. The rotation curve for the Galaxy provides strong evidence for dark matter. By studying the motion of stars around the Galaxy, the mass interior to their orbits can be determined. However, more mass is found, by about a factor of 2, than can be accounted for by ordinary matter. Further more, the Galaxy seems to be larger than previously known. The rotation curve of the outer part of the Galaxy continues to show greater and greater amounts of matter, extending out to what is know as the galactic corona.

14. Possible explanations for dark matter makes for a long list. Some are: brown dwarfs, black dwarfs, black holes, WIMPS, MACHOS, ...

15. From a disk of hot gas spanning 10 pc across the center of the Galaxy, infrared spectral lines are broadened indicating the motion of the gas. For this motion to be possible, there must be a massive central mass. Yet it must be of small size and very faint or non-luminous. This is best explained by there being a one million solar mass black hole at the center of the Galaxy.

ANSWERS TO PROBLEMS

1. Using the inverse square law, if a Cepheid is 100 times brighter than an RR Lyrae variable, it should be visible at 10 times the distance. In other words, placing the Cepheid 10 times farther away will make it 10^2 times fainter, or 100 times fainter. Therefore it would equal the RR Lyrae star's brightness.

2. Again, using the inverse square law, if a Cepheid is 10,000 times brighter than the Sun, they should be vis-
ible at a distance 100 times greater than the Sun would be. If HST could see the Sun at 100,000 pc then it should be able to see a Cepheid at $100 \times 100,000 = 10^7$ pc or 10 million parsecs.

3. At 20 kpc, the circumference of the orbit is $2\pi \times 20,000$ pc = 126,000 pc. A parsec = 3.1×10^{13} km, so the circumference is 3.9×10^{18} km. At a rate of 240 km/sec it will take 1.6×10^{16} sec to orbit once. A year has 3.2×10^7 sec in it, so the period of the orbit is 509 million years.

Using Kepler's third law, we have the period in years but we need the size of the orbit in A.U. There are 206,000 A.U. in 1 pc, so 20 kpc = 4.12×10^9 A.U. Finally we can apply Kepler's third law; the result will be in solar masses.

$$(5.09 \times 10^8)^2 = \frac{(4.12 \times 10^9)^3}{M}$$

M = 270 billion solar masses

4. Let's try an easy approach to this question. The Sun is moving at 220 km/sec around the Galaxy but is approaching spiral arms at a speed of 220 - 120 = 100 km/sec. This is about half its speed. We also know from the text that it takes the Sun 225 million years to go around the Galaxy once. Think about the Sun moving half as slow now. But the distance to be covered between spiral arms is also half its normal orbit because there are two spiral arms. So the Sun must cover half the distance with half the speed; it will take about as long as a normal orbit does, 225 million years. In 4.5 billion years the Sun has gone around 20 times, so it should have passed through a spiral arm about twenty times.

If you want a more precise measure of this, just realize the previous calculation is correct for a speed of 110 km/sec, not 100 km/sec. The Sun is really moving 100/110 = 0.91 times *slower* than what we had assumed, meaning it will take *longer* to move between spiral arms and complete 0.91 *fewer* passes than we had calculated. This gives $0.91 \times 20 = 18$ passes instead of 20.

SUGGESTED READING

Binney, J., "Evolution of Our Galaxy." *Sky & Telescope* (March, 1995).

Bok, B. J. *The Milky Way.* 5th ed. Cambridge, MA: Harvard University Press, 1981. Timeless exposition of the Milky Way, as it was known to one of the first experts on the subject.

Croswell, K., "What Lies at the Milky Way's Center?" *Astronomy* (May, 1995).

Harrington, P. "Journey to the Center of the Galaxy." *Astronomy* (July 1991). What it might be like to go there.

Jayawardhana, R., "Destination: Galactic Center." *Sky & Telescope* (June, 1995).

Kaufmann, W. J. "Our Galaxy, Part I." *Mercury* (May–June 1989). First part of a popular article on the Milky Way.

_ "Our Galaxy, Part 2." *Mercury* (July–August 1989). Second part of a popular article on the Milky Way.

Rees, M. J. "Black Holes in Galactic Centers." *Scientific American* (November 1990). On the possibility of black holes at the hearts of many galaxies.

Trimble, V. and Parker, S., "Meet the Milky Way." *Sky & Telescope* (January, 1995).

Tucker, W. "A Massive Halo, Part 1," *Mercury* (January–February 1989). First part of a comprehensive article on dark matter in our Galaxy.

_ "A Massive Halo, Part 2." *Mercury* (March–April 1989). Second part of a comprehensive article on dark matter in our Galaxy.

van den Bergh, S. and Gesser, J. E. "How the Milky Way Formed." *Scientific American* (January, 1993).

Verschuur, G. L., "In the Beginning." *Astronomy* (October, 1993). Globular clusters yield clues to the Galaxy's birth.

Waldrop, M. M. "Heart of Darkness." *Science* (February 19, 1988). Evidence that the Andromeda Galaxy harbors an ultramassive black hole at its center, with implications for our Galaxy and others.

Chapter 24

NORMAL GALAXIES
The Large Scale Structure of the Universe

Galaxy Classification—Spirals

This is a great opportunity to show video images (from a laser disc) or slides of some magnificent galaxies. When showing spiral galaxies, take to class a paper plate (or two taped together to form a disc) and indicate the tilt of the galaxy by tilting the plate. The near-side of the galaxy is usually obvious because of the dust clouds that are silhouetted against the rest of the galaxy. Point out large emission nebulae that will later play an important role in determining distances. For most spirals, individual stars can not be seen. But usually a lot of stars are present. Remind the students that these stars belong to the Milky Way and, as we look through it to see other galaxies, we see some of its stars in the foreground.

Most photographs of spirals do not show the disc very well. This is because the photographs are exposed to show the spiral structure. If exposed longer to show the disc, the image looks over-exposed. There are many dark areas in spirals but don't make the mistake made by astronomers early in this century. These are not areas missing stars but regions of large dust clouds obscuring the stars. Most photographs of spirals do not show evidence of a halo although the best photographs of M104, the Sombrero Galaxy, will show a large cloud of star-like objects in its halo. These are its globular clusters.

Ellipticals

Far less attractive, but no less important, are the ellipticals. Show a variety that indicate the range in ellipticity. In this case, use a football or rugby ball as a possible (prolate) model. Show how, when viewed from different positions, the ball may look like anything from an E0 to an E7 galaxy. Use the double paper plate (oblate) model in the same way. Face on it gives the appearance of an E0; tilted, it can have almost any ellipticity up to E7. It is very easy to confuse the terms prolate and oblate. Make sure your students understand the differences in the shapes. Not long ago I had a student tell me after class that I should simply refer to M&Ms regular for oblate and M&M peanuts for prolate; the shapes are perfect for this!

Why isn't there a class more elliptical than E7? The most oblate elliptical may still have a rather thick disc so even viewed edge-on it will look rather elliptical. Also, a highly flattened elliptical may be what we refer to as an S0 galaxy which is just a disc-like elliptical. The prolate model is usually favored among astronomers because the oblate model requires a significant amount of rotation to be present which should be easily seen, but isn't, in very elliptical galaxies.

Be certain to show images of dwarf ellipticals and giant ellipticals. The dwarf ellipticals contain so few stars, they appear transparent. Their absolute magnitude is about -10, about as bright as one massive supergiant star or one million stars like the Sun! Obviously, they do not contain very many stars. For giant ellipticals, M87 is a must to show. Most photographs of M87 will show large numbers (several thousand are known) of globular clusters surrounding it. Note other galaxies in the field that may be similar to the size of the Milky Way. Giant ellipticals in the centers of other clusters of galaxies are truly enormous when compared to the other galaxies in their clusters.

It is said that ellipticals have no detectable gas and dust but astronomers are virtually certain that some must exist. This is because of stellar evolution. Main sequence stars can produce stellar winds and occasional flares will eject gas from stars. Single stars eject planetary nebulae and close binaries can go nova. There still must be large numbers of red giants that may produce dust clouds, although the heavy element abundance is likely to be rather low.

Irregulars

The best examples of this class of galaxy are the Large and Small Magellanic Clouds (LMC and SMC) and NGC 6822, all in the Local Group. As a group they might be characterized as being like small spirals without having ever developed their organized structure. There is some observational evidence suggesting irregular galaxies may be younger than most galaxies and that they go through epochs of star formation. They are rich in emission nebulae and also help provide the calibration for their use in the distance scale. The LMC contains one of the largest nebulae known.

The LMC and SMC provide a rich source of young, massive stars by which astronomers study stellar evolution in a way not possible in the Milky Way. All the stars either in the LMC or SMC can be assumed to be at the same distance from us, a distance which we know fairly well. Therefore all objects in the LMC and SMC have known absolute magnitudes or luminosities. The Cepheids of the LMC and SMC provide the details of the period-luminosity relationship that then allows Cepheids to be used for determining distance to other galaxies. There are literally thousands of Cepheids and RR Lyrae variables in the two Magellanic Clouds.

Peculiar Galaxies

These galaxies are often thought of as a fourth type of galaxy although most astronomers agree that each of these galaxies was previously one of the other types. For the most part, they are the result of galaxy-galaxy collisions and close encounters. Colliding galaxies and close encounters are covered later in the chapter but this is a good time to mention several basic facts about this type of galaxy.

It is helpful to remember that a velocity of 1 km/sec = 1 pc / 1 million years. Velocities between galaxies are typically a few hundred km/sec (possibly higher inside of galaxy clusters). Large galaxies around the Milky Way are separated by roughly 1 Mpc. At a velocity of 500 km/sec a distance of 1 Mpc will be traveled in 2 billion years. Although this is a long time, it is much shorter than the age of the universe. Galaxies, who are separated by 1 Mpc or less will likely have encountered other galaxies rather often over the past 15 billion years. (Note: there are many smaller galaxies at much closer distances than 1 Mpc. Collisions and encounters with these may occur very frequently.)

As mentioned in Interlude 24-2, when galaxies collide their stars "slide past one another" because stars are very small compared to the distances between them. Not so for the interstellar clouds of gas and dust that occur in spiral and irregular galaxies. These clouds are very large and easily collide with one another. The result of these collisions are the starburst galaxies mentioned at the very end of this chapter. Bursts of star formation may also be induced by tidal interaction between galaxies in a close encounter. Even a collision of a spiral with an elliptical may produce significant and sudden star formation through tidal effects on the gas and collisions with very low density gas remaining in the elliptical.

The Local Group of Galaxies

Throughout this manual I suggest visualizations to help students with the concepts of size and distance. The same is true here, but fortunately, it will not be necessary to model the entire local group. The Milky Way and the Andromeda galaxy (M31 in Figure 24.12) are the major players here.

I suggested a model of the Milky Way in the previous chapter that would fit into a room 15 m × 15 m. Let's do the same here. Use a scale of 1 m = 50,000 pc. The Milky Way and Andromeda galaxy are separated by 14 m. Notice that this scale is 25 times the scale used for the Milky Way. Just as we tried to see the solar system when viewing the Milky Way, can we view the Milky Way or Andromeda galaxy at the current scale?

These two galaxies are about the same size, 30,000 pc in diameter. At the current scale they would each be 60 cm in diameter. There is no trouble seeing them at all! The Milky Way and the Andromeda galaxy are separated by 23 of their diameters. Although stars are very small compared to the distances between them, galaxies are not small compared to the distances separating them. This is why galaxy collisions are much more common than star collisions. You can also see from Figure 24.12 that there are many more galaxies near to each of the two large galaxies, so collisions are even more likely.

Distances to Galaxies

Several methods for determining distances to galaxies are discussed throughout the chapter. The primary purpose behind these significant efforts is to provide a reliable Hubble Law. Since it saw first light in 1948, the 200-inch Hale telescope at Mt. Palomar has had much of it use dedicated to various aspects of this one problem. The Hubble Space telescope is also spending part of its time working on this problem too. With a reliable Hubble Law, distances to galaxies and quasars in the universe become almost trivial to determine. But a reliable Hubble Law can only be had through careful measurements of distance to most nearby and some distant galaxies. The distances to nearby galaxies are most often used to calibrate other methods of distance determination to more remote galaxies. I would like to note several additional methods of importance to this process.

Spectroscopic parallax can be used to nearby galaxies. The brightest stars have absolute magnitudes between -5 and -10 and can be used out to 10 to 100 Mpc. Although elliptical galaxies may lack such bright stars (because they are massive stars and have already evolved), they are readily available in spirals, irregulars, and peculiars.

Novae have peak absolute magnitudes in about the same range as the brightest stars. Although difficult to discover because they occur unpredictably, when a galaxy is caught with a nova it may provide useful information on the distance.

Supernovae may provide one of the best methods for determining the Hubble Law. Since supernovae brighten to almost the luminosity of the entire galaxy they are in, they allow us to determine distances to virtually any galaxy we can see. There are two problems in using them, however. First, a supernova has to be "caught" prior to its maximum because it is the maximum light that provides the best calibration for distance. Second, supernovae occur very infrequently in any one galaxy. To address both of these problems, astronomers have established automated surveys that examine hundreds of galaxies per night. An image of a galaxy is taken using a CCD and compared with a standard image of that galaxy. If anything has changed, like the sudden brightening of a supernovae, astronomers are notified immediately in order to conduct further observations. If these surveys are allowed to run for enough years they have the potential for providing excellent information on extragalactic supernovae.

Regarding the method which uses the sizes of a galaxy's largest H II regions to determine its distance, we do not use the H II regions in the Milky Way since we can not see the entire galaxy and are uncertain the H II regions we see here are the largest in the Milky Way. We must observe H II regions in other nearby galaxies to whom distances are known and establish the calibration using them.

Masses of Galaxies

Astronomers observe the rotation curve of a galaxy to obtain the galaxy's mass. But what if the galaxy does not rotate? Only spiral galaxies have significant rotation and their tilt or inclinations can be determined because we know they are disc-shaped. Elliptical galaxies do not have significant rotation and, even if they did, we would not know their inclinations. For nearby ellipticals and distant galaxies of all types, the method of velocity dispersion is used. Stars in an elliptical galaxy are moving about with a variety of velocities. The more mass, the higher the velocities. The absorption lines from all these stars will be broadened in proportion to the velocities. If the galaxy is rotating then the velocity dispersion is a measure of the rotational velocities. This method provides good information on the masses of nearby elliptical galaxies (where the velocity dispersion can be seen as a function of distance from the galaxy's center) and approximate masses for more distant galaxies.

The Virial Theorem

Objects in a cluster, such as stars or galaxies, moving under the influence of their mutual gravity will encounter each other over a period of time in such a way as to distribute their energies equally among all members of the cluster. If sufficient time passes so that the energy is equally shared among all members it is said that the cluster is in a state of statistical equilibrium.

At this point the Virial Theorem may be applied to the cluster. It states that the gravitational potential of the entire cluster is equal to twice the total kinetic energy of all of its members. Although a proof of the Virial Theorem is not appropriate for this level of text, in the next chapter I have actually shown it for two bodies in orbit.

$$PE = -2KE$$

The negative sign in front of the kinetic energy reminds us that the potential energy is a negative quantity. The potential energy term contains the mass of the entire cluster. The velocities and separations of each member must be observed in order for the mass of the cluster to be calculated. The masses for clusters of stars have been calculated and found to agree well with the known masses of stars in the cluster, thus the virial theorem is true for these clusters. We say that these clusters are *virially stable* because the stars are in a state of statistical equilibrium.

When applied to clusters of galaxies, the virial theorem does not hold. The kinetic energy is typically 10 to 100 times larger than the potential energy. Either the cluster is not in statistical equilibrium or there is something wrong with either the velocities, separations, or masses used in the calculation.

Using the velocities of the galaxies in a cluster we can calculate how long it takes a galaxy to move across the cluster—the crossing time. If the crossing time is short compared to the age of the universe, then the cluster should be in statistical equilibrium. Earlier I showed that a galaxy moving at 500 km/sec will travel 1 Mpc in 2 billion years. This is rather typical for a crossing time and, although the galaxies may not have crossed a large number of time, the clusters should be in statistical equilibrium. Therefore there must be something "wrong" with either the velocities, separations, or masses of the galaxies. The Hubble Constant is used in determining the separations so there may be an uncertainty of a factor of 2 at most; certainly not a factor of 10 or more. Most astronomers will claim that the mass of the cluster must be increased in order to stabilize the cluster, thus the missing mass problem.

ANSWERS TO CHAPTER 24 REVIEW QUESTIONS

1. Elliptical galaxies have a stellar content remindful of the halo of our galaxy. The stars are generally low mass and old. Their distribution more resembles our halo too; ellipticals probably have a prolate shape and some may even be spherical. There is no observed gas or dust in either the elliptical galaxies or in our halo.

2. Radar ranging is used to establish distances within the solar system and gives us the size of the A.U.

   Parallax uses triangulation to measure distances to the nearest stars. The radius of the Earth's orbit, 1 A.U. is one side of the triangle. Distances are good out to about 100 pc.

   Spectroscopic parallax utilizes the properties of stars in the H-R diagram. Using parallax, the absolute luminosities of some types of stars are established. When identified in the H-R diagram, similar stars at unknown distances can have their distances determined by comparing their apparent luminosities with those that are known. Distances can be determined to at least 1,000 pc.

   Pulsating variable stars such as Cepheids have a strong relationship between the period of their pulsations and their absolute luminosities. Once established using nearby Cepheids, this method can be extended to the nearest galaxies. Distances to at least 5 Mpc are possible.

3. The Local Groups of galaxies is about one million parsecs (1 Mpc) in diameter. The 20 or so galaxies making up this group fill very little of the space; only 3 of the galaxies are of full size, the others are dwarf irregulars or ellipticals.

4. The Tully-Fisher relation is a correlation between a galaxy's luminosity and its rotational velocity. The rotational velocity is determined from the broadening of the 21-cm line width. Here is a way in which a galaxy's total luminosity can be independently determined and, when compared to its apparent luminosity, the distance can be calculated. This relation is also independent of many of the other methods in its calibration.

5. The Virgo Cluster is one of the nearest rich clusters of galaxies. It contains about 2500 galaxies and is about 20 Mpc distant.

6. The mass of a galaxy can be determined in several different ways. The rotation curve is the most accurate method. By measuring the velocity of rotation, Kepler's third law can be applied to calculate the mass. If the galaxy is part of a binary galaxy system, Kepler's third can be applied again, but now to the orbit of the galaxies around each other. There are some uncertainties in this method and it is best applied to a large number of binaries in order for a statistical result to be obtained.

7. The motion of galaxies within a cluster must be balanced by the total gravitational field produced by all the mass in the cluster. When traditional methods are applied to determining the total mass of the galaxies in a cluster it always results in total masses that are 10 to 100 times too little compared to the mass necessary to hold the cluster together. But because the cluster is a cluster, it must be held together by is own gravity. The question arises; where is the extra mass?

8. Galaxies are observed to have redshifted spectra, which is interpreted as meaning that all galaxies are receding from us. Hubble discovered that the recessional velocity is proportional to the distance for all galaxies. This is known as the Hubble Law.

9. Once the Hubble Law is known, it is almost trivial to use for determining distances to galaxies. The spectrum of a galaxy will reveal its recessional or radial velocity. The Hubble Law states how this velocity is proportional to the distance; the distance is immediately determined once the velocity is known.

10. The Hubble constant appears to be in the range of 60-90 km/s/Mpc. In order to establish the Hubble Law, each galaxy observed must have its velocity and distance determined. The velocity is relatively easy to determine because it comes directly from the spectrum of the galaxy. The distance, however, is much more difficult and uncertain. The Hubble constant is the constant of proportionality between the distance and the velocity of galaxies. With distances uncertain, the Hubble constant remains uncertain too.

11. It now appears that large galaxies grow through repeated mergers or collisions with smaller galaxies. This process is not at all like star formation but in many ways is more similar to planetary formation. We do not know how this process affects the type of galaxy that results. Certainly this process continues today; interacting galaxies are relatively common.

12. Collisions between galaxies can be partly evolutionary. The large central galaxies found clusters certainly share an evolutionary history; they have cannibalized many smaller galaxies in their cluster. But collisions and close encounters are random processes, each case being a little or a lot different from the next. The re-

sult is that each galaxy may have, to some degree, a uniqueness to it—a structure unlike any other—that disallows any discussion of evolution. The evolution of a one solar mass star will be just like any other star of the same mass and composition; this can not be said for any Sb, E3, or any other type of galaxy.

ANSWERS TO PROBLEMS

1. Apparent luminosity is related by the inverse square law to the distance and is proportional to the true luminosity.

$$L_{app} \alpha \frac{L}{r^2}$$

For two objects observed by the same telescope, the apparent luminosity is the same in both cases. Set up a proportion for each case and set them equal to each other.

$$\frac{1}{10,000^2} = \frac{10^9}{r^2}$$

$$r = 3.2 \times 10^8 \text{ pc}$$

$$r = 320 \text{ Mpc}$$

2. The Hubble Law can be expressed as follows:

$$v_{rec} = H_0 \times D$$

For a galaxy at 200 Mpc, the recessional velocity will be $75 \times 200 = 15,000$ km/sec.

For a galaxy whose recessional velocity is 4,000 km/sec, its distance will be $4,000/75 = 53$ Mpc.

If the Hubble constant changes to 50 km/sec/Mpc then these answers will be 10,000 km/sec and 80 Mpc, respectively.

3. Convert 500 kpc to A.U. as follows: 500 kpc × 1,000 pc/kpc × 206,000 A.U./pc = 1.03×10^{11} A.U. Set up Kepler's third law as usual.

$$(3 \times 10^{10})^2 = \frac{(1.03 \times 10^{11})^3}{M}$$

$$M = 1.2 \times 10^{12} \text{ solar masses}$$

4. Convert 500,000 pc to kilometers. 500,000 pc × 3.09 × 10^{13} km/pc = 1.5×10^{19} km. Dividing this distance by the velocity will give the amount of time. 1.5×10^{19}

km / 1000 km/s = 1.5×10^{16} s. A year has 3.2×10^7 s/yr. Making the conversion to years gives 1.5×10^{16} s / 3.2×10^7 s/yr = 4.8×10^8 yr or 480 million years.

SUGGESTED READING

Burbidge, G. "The Cult of the Missing Mass." *Sky and Telescope* (June 1990). An outspoken extragalactic astronomer presents an alternative view of the mass of the universe.

Cown, R., "The Little Bang." *Science News* (June 24, 1995). Collisions among galaxies in the Local Group.

Croswell, K., "Intruder Galaxies." *Astronomy* (November, 1993). The Andromeda galaxy's influence on the Local Group of galaxies.

Eicher, D. J., "Galaxy Time Machine." *Astronomy* (April, 1995). Elliptical and spiral galaxies as they appeared in the past.

Elmegreen, D. M. and Elmegreen, B. "What Puts the Spiral in Spiral galaxies?" *Astronomy* (September, 1993).

Freeman, M. "Galaxies." *Smithsonian* (January 1989). Popular article about the variety of galaxies.

Gallagher, J. and Keppel, J., "Seven Mysteries of Galaxies." *Astronomy* (March, 1994). Formation and evolution of galaxies.

Geller, M. J., and J. P. Huchra. "Mapping the Universe." *Sky and Telescope* (August 1991). Researchers explain how they probe the three-dimensional structure of the universe.

Hodge, P. W. *Galaxies.* Cambridge, MA: Harvard University Press, 1986. Good basic information about most of the topics discussed in this chapter.

Hodge, P., "Our New! Improved! Cluster of Galaxies." *Astronomy* (February, 1994). Dark matter in the Local Group.

_ "The Extragalactic Distance Scale: Agreement at Last?" *Sky and Telescope* (October 1993). A survey of recent progress in efforts to determine the Hubble constant.

Shapley, H. *Galaxies.* Cambridge, MA: Harvard University Press, 1943, 1961, 1972. Engaging, readable, and classic book by one of the world's foremost galaxy pioneers.

Steiman-Cameron, T., "A Peculiar Twist." *Astronomy* (June, 1993). Dark matter revealed by a galactic twisted disc.

Chapter 25

ACTIVE GALAXIES AND QUASARS
Limits of the Observable Universe

Energy From A Black Hole

Of fundamental importance to this entire chapter is the energy derived from matter "falling" into a black hole. The matter actually spirals into the hole and this is important in converting the energy into a form that can be radiated away. The primary questions are: "Where does this energy come from?" and "How much energy is produced?" Both of these questions can be rather easily answered using simple physics already presented in previous chapters.

Showing students the following explanations can help them gain insight to a very important astrophysical process. If your students are not able to understand the mathematics, you may still be able to present some of the ideas to them in a general way. The entire principle is based on circular orbits and what we already know about black holes.

We know from circular orbits that the gravitational force provides the centripetal force.

$$-\frac{GMm}{R^2} = -\frac{mv^2}{R}$$

The mass being orbited is M, the mass doing the orbiting is m and has a velocity v. M and m are separated by a distance R. I have retained the minus signs because they are important to the following discussion. Multiplying out an R on both sides gives

$$-\frac{GMm}{R} = -mv^2$$

The term on the left side is just the gravitational potential energy, PE. On the right side is twice the kinetic energy, KE, with a negative sign in front.

$$PE = = -2KE \text{ or }$$

$$KE = -\frac{1}{2}PE$$

The total energy, E, of an orbiting body is just the sum of the kinetic and potential energies. Substituting for the kinetic energy, we can get the total energy in terms of the potential energy.

$$E = KE + PE$$

$$E = -\frac{1}{2}PE + PE$$

$$E = \frac{1}{2}PE$$

$$E = -\frac{1}{2}\frac{GMm}{R}$$

Now consider a mass, m, very far away from a black hole moving into an orbit very near to it. At a great distance the potential energy is about zero because R is very large and so the total energy is also zero. Very near the black hole the total energy is what is shown above, where M is the mass of the black hole and R is the distance between the black hole and m. If we look at the *change* in energy, ΔE, going from very far away to very close, this will be 0 - E or

$$\Delta E = \frac{1}{2}\frac{GMm}{R}$$

If the mass gets very close to the black hole then R is just the Schwarzschild radius $R = 2GM/c^2$ (from Chapter 22). Substituting in this value for R gives

$$\Delta E = \frac{mc^2}{4}$$

Einstein told us that the energy equivalent of an object's rest mass, m, is $E = mc^2$. So, an object spiraling into a black hole could potentially give up as much as one quarter of its rest mass energy before entering the black hole. Through collisions with other material in the disc surrounding the black hole it will give up a substantial fraction of this but not all of it. But 25% of its rest mass energy is available. For a one solar mass object this is equivalent to 5 $\times 10^{46}$ J or enough to power an average quasar for about a year. Keep in mind that the fusion of hydrogen into helium converts only 0.7% of the rest mass of hydrogen into energy. Allowing matter (and it could be hydrogen or old cars) to spiral into a black hole is much more energy productive.

Although the above discussion uses only classical physics and is therefore very approximate, as in the case of deriving the Schwarzschild radius from a simple expression for escape velocity, the result is conceptually correct and surprisingly close to what detailed calculations will show.

Our two initial questions have been answered. The energy comes just from gravitational potential energy and the amount of energy that is available is up to one quarter of the rest mass energy. Notice too, that the result does not depend on the mass of the black hole! Indirectly, the result does depend on the mass of the black hole. If the black hole has low mass, then r is very small. The mass m will experience a small gravitational potential energy and will have to fall farther to reach the Schwarzchild radius r. For a super massive black hole, r will be much larger but so is the gravitational potential energy. So mass m will not have to fall as far. Either way, the same amount of energy is given up whether the black hole has a high or low mass.

Quasars

The discovery of quasars as extragalactic objects is interesting because of the series of events that led to it. Through lunar occultations, the positions of several unidentified radio sources were refined to the point that optical astronomers could look precisely at the locations in an attempt to identify these objects. What they found were objects that looked like stars! In fact, they were referred to as "radio stars." That name, as it turned out, was important and highly misleading.

When Matthews and Sandage took the first spectrum, it contained emission lines that were unrecognizable. Thinking in terms of stars, they knew that stars could not have highly shifted (blue or red) spectra because their motions in the Galaxy are relatively slow. In fact, the escape velocity from the Galaxy, in the vicinity of the Sun, is about 350 km/sec. So the lines they saw in the spectrum might be shifted a little but not by much if they were stars. Of course, everyone called them radio stars and they looked like stars, so they must be stars, right? Astronomers remained baffled by these new objects for about 2 years.

Maarten Schmidt made his breakthrough when he stopped thinking of them as stars, but rather, as possible extragalactic objects. Such objects could have high redshifts, so high that the visible spectrum is shifted into the near infrared, and the ultraviolet, which normally can not be seen, is shifted into the visible. Schmidt made his discovery because he stopped thinking of these objects as "stars."

There is a lesson to be learned here, both in science and in many other areas. We sometimes think we know or understand something by the label that is attached to it. But we, or others, are the ones making the labels. We can easily fool ourselves. Because someone called these objects radio "stars" they could not think of them being anything else but stars. The label was wrong and some very bright scientists struggled for two years with the problem.

ANSWERS TO CHAPTER 25 REVIEW QUESTIONS

1. Active galaxies are different from normal galaxies in at least two ways. First, they emit much more radiation than normal galaxies, up to thousands of times more. Second, the nature of the radiation is different. Normal galaxies emit most of their radiation around and near the visible part of the spectrum. This is because they are composed of stars which are all emitting light at various wavelengths of the visible spectrum. But active galaxies emit most of their radiation at in-frared or radio wavelengths. The source of these emissions must be other than stars and this radiation may be referred to as nonstellar radiation.

2. Seyfert galaxies emit most of their radiation from a small central region called a galactic nucleus. The radiation coming from the nucleus is nonstellar. The spectrum of the nucleus is also nonstellar, with many strong, wide emission lines of highly ionized heavy elements. The line widths indicate high internal motions on the order of 1,000 km/sec.

3. A core-halo radio galaxy emits radio radiation from its nucleus and from a large halo surrounding the galaxy. A lobe radio galaxy has typically two regions of radio emissions on opposite sides of the galaxy. The nucleus often emits radio waves too.

4. The lobes of a radio galaxy are aligned on either side of the nucleus; a straight line joining the lobes would always pass through the nucleus. In some lobe radio galaxies a filament of radio-emitting material can be traced connecting the lobes to the nucleus.

5. A head-tail radio galaxy is formed by a galaxy moving through the intergalactic gas of the cluster of which it is a part. In doing so, the gas forming the lobes is pushed against by the intergalactic gas and a tail is formed as the galaxy continues to move.

6. In the nucleus of an active galaxy is a massive black hole surrounded by an accretion disc. Gas moving in this disc emits large quantities of radiation before entering the black hole. Up to 20% of the rest mass of the gas can be emitted before entering the black hole. This model can also account for the small size of the central engine, the rapid motions, and possibly jets coming out of the disc.

7. Radio lobes emit synchrotron radiation which is produced by fast moving electrons in a magnetic field. As the electrons spiral around the magnetic field lines, they lose energy and radiate it away in the form of radio waves. The electrons and magnetic fields are ejected out of the accretion disc surrounding the supermassive black hole at the center of active galaxies. This jet of material is ejected in opposite directions.

8. The spectra of quasars have highly redshifted lines. The redshift is so high, lines normally found in the ultraviolet are shifted into the visible; visible lines are shifted out into the infrared. This is what caused so much confusion in understanding their spectra. Astronomers were expecting to see normal visible lines that were slightly shifted. The high redshifts also implied very large distances, much farther away than ever seen in any other type of objects.

9. The apparent reason quasars are much more luminous than active galaxies is that their black hole is being

"fed" at a higher rate. More matter is falling into it than for active galaxies. This is probably a natural consequent of there being much more matter available to the quasar black hole; the active galaxies have used up much of that matter and little is now available to fall into the black hole.

10. Clouds of gas between quasars and us will produce absorption lines in the spectrum of the quasar. These can be distinguished from the quasar absorption lines (if any exist) by their different redshifts, corresponding to their respective distances. The quasar can also be gravitationally lensed by a galaxy or cluster of galaxies lying between it and us. Study of the lensing pattern can provide information regarding the mass and mass distribution of the galaxy or cluster.

11. BL Lac objects are intermediate in energy output between quasars and radio galaxies. They have spectra that show little else other than nonthermal radiation coming from the central engine. It is also possible that BL Lac objects are actually radio galaxies in which the radio jet is pointing directly at us.

12. Although the lifetime of quasars is unknown we know it can neither be very short nor very long. If quasars existed for just a few years, we probably would not see any. Records indicate quasars on old photographs dating back many decades. If quasars last billions of years then there are two problems. First, where would they get all the mass to feed their energy needs. Some quasars are using between 10 and 100 solar masses a year. Over 10 billion years would require between 10^{11} and 10^{12} solar masses, in other words, the mass of entire large galaxy. Second, if quasars lasted this long, we should see many more of them near to us, which we do not. It is reasonable to expect that quasars lasted just a few tens of millions of years; it is consistent with the numbers and distances of quasars.

ANSWERS TO PROBLEMS

1. Use the usual ratio for comparing the object to the circumference of a circle.

$$\frac{1}{2\pi \times 4} = \frac{X}{360°}$$

$$X = 14°$$

This is about 28 times larger than the Moon, which is half a degree in diameter.

2. In calculating a rate at which a black hole must be fed, this is just m/t where m will be in units of solar masses and t will be in years. However, the equation we will use is in mks units, so it will be necessary to convert our units from solar masses to kg and from years to seconds. Remember, the efficiency of matter-to-energy conversion using a black hole is about 20% or 0.20.

$$0.2 \times \frac{mc^2}{t} = L \ J/sec$$

Use one Earth mass, 6×10^{24} kg, and one day, 86,400 sec.

$$0.2 \frac{6 \times 10^{24} \, kg \times (3 \times 10^8)^2}{86,400 \, sec} = L \ J/s$$

$$L = 1.3 \times 10^{36} \, J/s$$

The luminosity of the Sun is 3.9×10^{26} J/s, making the above luminosity equal to 3 billion solar luminosities.

3. The Hubble law is

$$v_{rec} = H_0 \times D$$

$$60,000 = 75 \times D$$

$$D = 800 \ Mpc$$

Use how the apparent luminosity depends on the absolute luminosity and distance (see Problem 1 in Chapter 24) and convert 1 kpc to 0.001 Mpc.

$$L_{app} \alpha \frac{L}{r^2}$$

$$\frac{1}{(0.001 \, Mpc)^2} = \frac{L}{(800 \, Mpc)^2}$$

$$L = 6.4 \times 10^{11} \ \text{solar luminosities}$$

$$L = 6.4 \times 10^{11} \times 3.9 \times 10^{26} \ J/sec$$

$$L = 2.5 \times 10^{38} \ J/sec$$

4. Use the equation for the velocity in a circular orbit from Chapter 2.

$$v = \sqrt{\frac{GM}{R}}$$

Use mks units, remembering to convert 1 pc into meters and kilometers into meters. In the end, convert kilograms back into solar masses.

$$10^6 = \sqrt{\frac{6.67 \times 10^{-11} M}{3.09 \times 10^{16}}}$$

$$M = 4.6 \times 10^{38} \ kg$$

$$M = 4.6 \times 10^{38} \ kg \ / \ 2 \times 10^{30} \ kg/\text{solar mass}$$

$$M = 2.3 \times 10^8 \ \text{solar masses}$$

$$M = 230 \ \text{million solar masses}$$

SUGGESTED READING

Burbidge. G. and Hewitt, A. "A Catalog of Quasars Near and Far." *Sky & Telescope* (December, 1994).

Burns, J. O. "Chasing the Monster's Tail." *Astronomy* (August 1990). Good article discussing new views of cosmic jets.

Croswell, K., "Have Astronomers Solved the Quasar Enigma?" *Astronomy* (February, 1993).

Courvoisier, T. J.-L. "The Quasar 3C273." *Scientific American* (June 1991). One of the most luminous objects in the universe and the nucleus of an active galaxy.

Djorgovski, S. G., "Fires at Cosmic Dawn." *Astronomy* (September, 1995). Quasars may reveal how galaxies formed.

Mercury (January–February 1988). Special issue commemorating the twenty-fifth anniversary of the discovery of the red shift and bizarre properties of quasars.

Miley, G. K. and Chambers, K. C. "The Most Distant Radio Galaxies." *Scientific American* (June, 1993).

Preston, R. *First Light*. The Atlantic Monthly Press, 1987. Insider's look at research at Palomar Observatory. Good section about early work on quasars.

Sheldon, E. "Faster Than Light?" *Sky and Telescope* (January 1990). A discussion of superluminal quasars.

Wilkes, B. "The Emerging Picture of Quasars." *Astronomy* (December 1991). What many of today's astronomers believe about quasars and their relation to active galaxies.

Chapter 26

COSMOLOGY
The Big Bang and the Fate of the Universe

The Hubble Constant

In cosmology one of the most fundamental and important pieces of observational information is the Hubble constant. The text uses a value of 75 km/sec/Mpc. Students should be strongly reminded that this number, based on numerous observations, has an uncertainty of approximately ± 25 km/sec/Mpc. In a sense, the value of 75 is no better than a value near 50 or 100. The uncertainty tells us that the true value of the Hubble constant is probably in this range; 75 is used in calculations because it is the midrange value.

Although the Hubble constant is determined by observing galaxy redshifts and distances (the latter having large uncertainties at large distances), its value should not be viewed in such an isolated environment. Because the Hubble constant provides information about the (maximum) age of the universe, many other areas of astronomy provide information on what the value of the Hubble constant *can not be*. To pick an obvious example, we are quite certain that the age of the Earth and the rest of the solar system is about 4.6 billion years old. This immediately tells us that the Hubble constant can not be more than about 210 km/sec/Mpc, else wise the universe would be younger than the solar system. (An easy way of relating the Hubble constant with age is the following; Age = $975/H_0$, where H_0 is given in units of km/sec/Mpc and age is in billion of years.)

Many astronomers believe we understand the principles of stellar evolution far better than most of cosmology. Globular clusters are consistently found to have ages of 12 to 14 billion years; some might say even a little older. This would imply that H_0 can not be larger than 70 or else the universe ends up being younger than some of the globular clusters.

Students should remember that H_0 is probably not 75 but 75 is often used as a convenience. They should also remain highly suspect of values of H_0 that imply a low age for the universe; there are strong arguments outside of cosmology that suggest the value of H_0 is significantly lower than 75. Let us all hope that with the new generation of large telescopes this problem will be resolved.

Age of the Universe From H_0

Even my least mathematically oriented students know that velocity = distance / time. So I start with this concept when discussing the Hubble Law. They usually don't mind me changing this around to time = distance / velocity; I still do an example or two. You drive 120 miles and average 60 mph. How long does it take? Just as is done in the text, I relate time to the inverse of H_0.

I also like to pose the question "What if you drove faster than 60 mph when you began your trip and eventually slowed down to 60 mph at the end of the trip. Would the trip take more or less time?" They almost always will tell me that the time is less, which is correct. Now they are ready to understand why the Hubble constant gives a maximum age and not the true age. The universe was expanding faster in the past and only now is going at the slower observed rate.

The Big Bang

Of all demonstrations used in an astronomy class, the balloon model of the Big Bang and curved space is a classic and, I believe, an absolute must to do. Use as large a balloon as is convenient to blow up and deflate several times during class. You can paint some galaxies on it with a pen but these have a habit of expanding along with the universe and then you have to explain why this doesn't actually happen. Use stick-on stars (my favorite) or dots to represent the galaxies. They usually stay on although on occasion I experience a "falling star." (My students don't appreciate the joke either!)

There are so many concepts you can show with the balloon: isotropy, homogeneity, curvature of space, no edge to the universe, the Hubble Law, no center to the universe, play back the universe to the Big Bang, the expansion of space rather than motion of galaxies through space. A good Hubble Law can be derived using this demonstration and a cloth or paper measuring tape. Inflate the balloon and measure a few distances from a "home" galaxy. Inflate the balloon some more and remeasure the distances. Calculate a "velocity" by dividing the change in distance by some arbitrary amount of time. Plot these velocities against the new distances and a Hubble Law will be seen.

Critical Density

The critical density plays an important role in much of cosmology and in related areas such as dark matter. We can once again use some of the very simple physics used in previous chapters to actually calculate the value of the critical density, and it is surprisingly simple.

The critical density occurs when the motions of the galaxies are essentially moving with exactly the right velocity to just escape the gravitational pull of the matter in the universe. We know that the escape velocity is

$$v_{esc} = \sqrt{\frac{2GM}{R}}$$

Now express the mass in terms of a density, using a spherical volume.

$$M = \frac{4}{3}\pi R^3 \rho$$

Substituting for M and squaring both sides gives

$$v_{esc}^2 = \frac{8}{3}\pi GR^2 \rho$$

But the velocity can be given by using the Hubble Law. Note that the distance R is just any arbitrary distance and the Hubble Law can be written as $v = H_0 R$. This velocity is also the same as the escape velocity because that is how fast the galaxies are moving in this case.

$$H_0^2 R^2 = \frac{8}{3}\pi GR^2 \rho$$

Finally, solving for the density we get

$$\rho = \frac{3}{8\pi G} H_0^2$$

Putting in a value for H_0 of 75 km/sec/Mpc, the density is 1.2×10^{-26} kg/m^3. Notice that the density depends strongly on the Hubble constant. If the Hubble constant is smaller than 75 then the critical density is significantly less, although not small enough to solve the dark matter problem.

I never cease to be amazed that, from the simple concept of the escape velocity which was derived in an early chapter, we have succeeded in computing the critical density of the universe. A little physics can be a powerful tool. I hope your students come to appreciate this.

An example of calculating the actual density of matter is interesting because there is one easy example available and the results may not be expected. The Local Group has a diameter of about 1 million pc. Its (spherical) volume calculates to be 1.5×10^{67} m^3. The Andromeda and Milky Way galaxies dominate with masses about 3×10^{11} solar masses. M33 has a bit less mass at 1×10^{11} solar masses and the other 18 galaxies combined are probably another 1×10^{11} solar masses. The total mass is 8×10^{11} solar masses or 1.5×10^{42} kg. Dividing mass by volume gives a density of 10^{-25} kg/m^3 for the Local Group. This is 10 times the critical density and it doesn't even include dark matter! Have we over-estimated the mass? Not really; for the answer to equal the critical density would mean there could only be 1×10^{11} solar masses in this volume and we know the Milky Way is more massive than this. Possibly we have underestimated the volume. This is much more likely. The critical density requires calculating an *average* density for the universe. The Local Group is a small cluster or concentration of matter; this is probably not at all average for the universe. By increasing the radius of the Local Group by a factor of 2 (which would encompass little additional mass), the density would be the same as the critical density. This example demonstrates the difficulty astronomers encounter when trying to determine the actual density of matter in the universe.

ANSWERS TO CHAPTER 26 REVIEW QUESTIONS

1. Pencil-beam surveys extending to a distance of 2000 Mpc suggest that the universe is uniform on a large scale. There does not appear to be any structures larger than about 200 Mpc.

2. The cosmological principle is made up of two assumptions fundamental to cosmology. They are homogeneity and isotropy. At a large enough scale, the universe is homogeneous; one part is pretty much like any other

part. Isotropy means that it looks the same in all directions.

3. According to the cosmological principle, the universe is homogeneous and isotropic. If it is also infinite in extent and unchanging in time, then the universe is uniformly populated with galaxies filled with stars. In that case, when you look at the night sky, your line of sight must eventually encounter a star; the sky should appear as bright as the surface of the Sun. This was first proposed by Olber and is known as Olber's paradox. Since this is not what is observed, however, something must be different than what was assumed. The universe is, in fact, not infinite and it is also expanding. The expansion redshifts the radiation to longer wavelengths, so distant stars would not be seen in the visible part of the spectrum.

4. Hubble's law is a relationship between velocity of recession of objects in the universe and their distance, v = H_0d. Since we know that velocity is distance divided by time, the Hubble constant, H_0, is a measure of one divided by time, the time of the expansion of the universe to its present size. It turns out that this time gives a maximum age for the universe.

5. Although we appear to be at the center of the Hubble flow, it turns out that all other locations in the universe appear to be at the center too. This is due to the fact that the Hubble flow is not due to the motion of objects into the universe, rather, it is an expansion of the universe itself. Space, itself, is expanding.

6. Since the Hubble flow is an expansion of space itself, galaxies are not rushing outward into unoccupied parts of the universe. The universe is evenly filled with matter but space is expanding, which gives rise to an appearance of galaxies flying outward from us.

7. Where did the Big Bang occur? In a word, everywhere. It was an explosion of all of space and time, not an explosion in space.

   What happened before the Big Bang? In a word, nothing. Time started when the Big Bang started. Time is essentially undefined before the Big Bang so there is no meaning to "before" the Big Bang.

8. A wave of electromagnetic radiation, as it moves through the universe, will experience the same expansion of the space experienced by the universe. As the wave travels farther and farther, it expands more and more. By the time it is observed, it appears redshifted in proportion to the distance it has traveled.

9. The density of matter in the universe determines whether it will expand forever or not.

10. There is not enough luminous matter known in the universe to stop its expansion. In fact, there appears to be about 100 times too little of this matter to stop the expansion.

11. The amount of dark matter in the universe is still not well known. There may be enough to produce the critical density; maybe there is even more. There are other arguments that suggest the total density of matter (luminous and dark) must be at the critical density.

12. Just after the Big Bang occurred, the universe was filled with X-ray and gamma-ray radiation. Since that period, it has traveled through the universe, its wavelength expanding as the universe has expanded. It is now observed in the microwave part of the spectrum. It proves us with information about the very early universe; it is the light from the very oldest object visible in the universe—the universe itself!

13. The cosmic microwave background radiation is black body radiation. As its wavelength expands, so must the representative temperature drop, according to Wien's law.

14. This is an open-ended question and depends on the personal preference of the person answering it. In answer to the last part of the question, YES, scientists definitely do have their preferences.

15. Astronomers do not yet understand why some values of the Hubble constant are in such strong disagreement with the ages of globular clusters, which appear to be very well determined. The problem(s) will be resolved by doing more and better observations and possibly having better theory to which the observations can be compared.

ANSWERS TO PROBLEMS

1. The maximum age of the universe is given by $1/H_0$. But units must be resolved because of the mixture of km and Mpc, seconds and years. From the Appendix 1 Mpc = 3.09×10^{19} km and 1 yr = 3.2×10^7 s.

$$Age = \frac{1}{H_0} = \frac{3.09 \times 10^{19}\, km/Mpc}{H_0 \times 3.2 \times 10^7\, s/yr}$$

$$Age = \frac{9.7 \times 10^{11}\, yr}{H_0}$$

$$Age = \frac{970}{H_0}\ billion\ years$$

For the three values of the Hubble constant given, the ages are 19, 13, and 10 billion years old, respectively.

2. 1 A.U.^{3} = 3.35×10^{33} m^3. Multiplying this times the density gives 3.35x 10^7 kg.

   The mass of the Earth is 1.99×10^{30} kg. Dividing this by the density will give the volume, 1.99×10^{56} m^3. This is a cube with sides of 5.8×10^{18} m. This distance is about 190 pc!

3. From Interlude 25-1 take the "radius" of the universe to be 7746 Mpc. 1 Mpc = 3.09×10^{22} m, so this distance is equal to 2.39×10^{26} m. Assuming a spherical volume to the universe, $4/3\pi r^3$ gives 5.74×10^{79} m^3.

   (a) For a critical density of 10^{-26} kg/m^3, the total mass will be 5.74×10^{53} kg.

   (b) One solar mass is 1.99×10^{30} kg. The above mass of the universe is therefore 2.89×10^{23} solar masses.

   (c) For a galaxy mass of 10^{11} solar masses, the above mass is equal to 2.89×10^{12} galaxies. That is over a trillion galaxies; certainly more than can be seen with modern telescopes.

4. The density given is 100 times smaller than the density given in Problem 2. for a Hubble constant of 75 km/s/Mpc. Because the density depends on the Hubble constant squared, and this density is 100 times smaller, then the Hubble constant must be 10 times smaller or 7.5 km/s/Mpc.

SUGGESTED READING

Brush, S. G., "How Cosmology Became a Science." *Scientific American* (August, 1992).

Croswell, K., "How Far to Virgo?" *Astronomy* (March, 1995). Cepheids give the distance to the Virgo cluster.

Davies, P. "Everyone's Guide to Cosmology." *Sky and Telescope* (March 1991). Good basic article on cosmology by a prolific author.

Finkbeiner, A. "A Universe in Our Own Image." *Sky and Telescope* (August 1984). Is the presence of conscious beings such as ourselves crucial to the observed structure of the entire universe?

Freedman, W. L., "The Expansion Rate and Size of the Universe." *Scientific American* (November, 1992). New results from the Hubble Space Telescope, using Cepheid variable stars, give distances to nearby galaxies and new determinations of the Hubble Law.

Kanipe, K., "Beyond the Big Bang." *Astronomy* (April, 1992). New observations suggest that current theories of how the universe formed need revision.

Lightman, A. *Ancient Light*. Cambridge: Harvard University Press, 1991. Big Bang cosmology presented on a popular level.

Odenwald, S. "Einstein's Fudge Factor." *Sky and Telescope* (April 1991). After 75 years, Einstein's "greatest blunder" keeps turning up in cosmologists' discussions about the origin, evolution, and fate of the universe.

Osterbrock, D. I. et al., "Edwin Hubble and the Expanding Universe." *Scientific American* (July, 1993).

Overbye, D. *Lonely Hearts of the Cosmos*. New York: Harper Perennial, 1991. Personal narrative on research at the front lines of modern cosmology.

Silk, J. "Probing the Primeval Fireball." *Sky and Telescope* (June 1990). Early article about *COBE*'s exploration of the cosmic microwave background.

Chapter 27

THE EARLY UNIVERSE
Toward the Beginning of Time

Introductory Comment

This may by the most difficult chapter to teach from the entire text. Students, who for the first time have encountered protons, neutrons, and electrons, may find the material far removed from their prior experiences and may have difficulty grasping some of the central ideas.

This material, much of which is highly theoretical, does not lend itself well to additional physical insights like I have given in many of the previous chapters. Grand unified theories do not lend themselves easily to simple, classical approximations! Depending on the backgrounds of students taking your course, you may have to settle for various degrees of understanding.

Table 27-1 is an excellent place to start for everyone. The sequence of events in the major eras and epochs should be understandable to most students. Normally a table like this might be presented in a scaled time-line. But even by using a logarithmic scale, it is not easy to show events from 10^{-43} sec to 10^{10} years. Continue to refer back to this table while discussing the chapter. Have this table put on to a transparency and have it projected during lecture. While discussing a specific epoch, seeing the table will remind students of the era, time, and temperature of that epoch and its position relative to the other epochs.

Observational Basis as a Link

Students often are able to relate to observational material better than theory. Much of the content of this chapter attempts to explain specific observations discussed in previous chapters. Some new observations are also introduced.

There is a surprising number of observations that guide our understanding of the early universe. Here is a list that comes quickly to mind.

1. The Hubble Law,
2. 2.7 K microwave background radiation,
3. Isotropy of the microwave background radiation,
4. Fluctuations in the microwave background radiation,
5. The primordial helium abundance,
6. The primordial deuterium abundance,
7. The ratio of the average mass density to the critical density (Ω_0),
8. The large scale structure of the universe,
9. The times of formation of quasars and galaxies,
10. Particle physics (most of which is not familiar to students but is critical to the discussion),
11. The basic forces of nature.

In each section, try to relate the material directly to one or more of the above observations. The theories are trying to reproduce and interpret what is seen observationally. Here are some of the sections and the observations (by number) which are related to them.

Radiation Era	2, 3, 4, 10
Primordial Nucleosynthesis	5, 6, 7, 10
Formation of Atoms	2, 5
Cosmic Inflation	1, 3, 7, 10, 11
Growth of Perturbations	4, 8, 9

ANSWERS TO CHAPTER 27 REVIEW QUESTIONS

1. A few thousand years after the Big Bang, the amounts of radiation and matter were equal. Before that time, the universe was dominated by radiation; since then, it has been dominated by matter. The temperature was about 60,000 K.

2. The Planck epoch requires a theory of quantum gravity, which does not exist today. There is also nothing known observationally about that period of time.

3. Matter was formed in the order of neutrons and protons, then electrons, and finally helium and deuterium. This occurred as the universe expanded and cooled. When it finally cooled to about 4500 K, electrons recombined with atomic nuclei, forming atoms. This produced the event known as decoupling and it occurred when the universe was about 200,000 years old.

4. By the end of the galactic epoch, matter was no longer distributed smoothly throughout the universe. Large-scale structure had formed. Quasars were already shining brightly and the first stars had started to form. This was about one billion years after the Big Bang.

5. When the universe was about 100 seconds old, conditions such as temperature and density were just right for the fusion of protons and neutrons to form helium. 25% of matter by mass was converted in helium at that time. Not until stars started nucleosynthesis did hydrogen fuse into helium again. But all matter in the universe contains at least this 25% helium; any more than this is due to stellar nucleosynthesis.

6. To form elements heavier than helium requires temperatures and pressures greater than that needed to form helium. But the universe was expanding; temperature and pressure were dropping. So, after helium was formed, heavier elements could not form because temperature and pressure were too low.

7. Virtually all the deuterium was used in the formation of helium; little remained from this time.

8. The amount of deuterium that remains today depends on the amount that remained after helium was formed. That amount was very sensitive to the conditions of the universe at that time, particularly the density. The greater the density, the less deuterium that should have been left over. The deuterium abundance suggests that $\Omega_0 \approx 0.1$.

9. When the universe cooled to the point where electrons could recombine with nuclei, neutral atoms started to appear. Radiation no longer interacted strongly with matter and the universe became transparent. The universe was a few hundred thousand years old at the time.

10. GUTs are Grand Unified Theories. These theories unify the three non-gravitational forces—electromagnetic, strong, and weak forces— into one superforce.

11. The horizon problem is solved by inflation by taking points that were close together and in communication with each other and quickly separating them. They are the same today because they were the same then.

12. The flatness problem is solved by inflation. Although space was curved, at the time of inflation the universe grew so large, the curvature is now no longer significant.

13. Hot dark matter is composed of lightweight particles—much less massive than the electron. The neutrino is an example of hot dark matter. Cold dark matter is composed of massive particles formed during the GUT era.

14. Fluctuations in baryonic matter could not have formed large-scale structures in as short a time as is observed. Dark matter decoupled very early from normal matter and its fluctuations had time to grow. Gas was later attracted to these regions, producing the large-scale structure now observed. Hot dark matter can produce large-scale structures but not small-scale structures. Cold dark matter can produce both.

15. Although dark matter are consistent with a high degree of isotropy in the background radiation, it does produce slight variations due to gravitational interaction with the radiation. This was predicted by models and discovered by COBE.

16. The microwave background, fluctuations in the background, deuterium abundance, dark matter—they have all help support and improve on the assumptions of the cosmological principle.

ANSWERS TO PROBLEMS

1. The following equation must be solved: $2^x = 10^{50}$. The easiest solution is by using logarithms.

$$x\text{Log}(2) = 50$$

x = 166 The universe doubled 166 times in order to expand by 10^{50} in size.

2. Since two particles of equal mass are formed, m = 1.82 × 10^{-30} kg.

$$E = 1.82 \times 10^{-30} \times (3 \times 10^8)^2$$

$$E = 1.64 \times 10^{-13} \text{ J}$$

$$f = \frac{1.64 \times 10^{-13}}{6.63 \times 10^{-34}}$$

$$f = 2.47 \times 10^{20} \text{ Hz}$$

Now find the wavelength corresponding to this frequency.

$$\lambda = \frac{3 \times 10^8}{2.47 \times 10^{20}}$$

$$\lambda = 1.21 \times 10^{-12} \text{ m} = 1.21 \times 10^{-10} \text{ cm}$$

Apply Wien's Law but solve for T.

$$T = \frac{0.29}{1.21 \times 10^{10}}$$

$$T = 2.4 \times 10^9 \text{ K}$$

The text gives 6×10^9 K.

3. Working backward, find how T depends on the mass of the particle.

$$T \propto \frac{1}{\lambda} \propto \frac{f}{1} \propto E \propto m$$

So, for a particle that is 1800 times that of the electron, a temperature 1800 higher is required for production. For proton-antiproton pair production, this temperature is 6×10^9 K $\times 1800 = 1 \times 10^{13}$ K, just as is given in the text.

SUGGESTED READING

Alpher, R. A., and R. Herman. "Reflections on Early Work on 'Big Bang' Cosmology." *Physics Today* (August 1988). A historical exposition on the physics of the Big Bang cosmological model.

Cornell, J., ed. *Bubbles, Voids and Bumps in Time: The New Cosmology.* Cambridge: Cambridge University Press, 1989. Based on a series of popular lectures by various experts, this book includes a chapter called "Starting the Universe: The Big Bang and Cosmic Inflation."

Cowen, R., "The Debut of Galaxies." *Astronomy* (December, 1994). Galaxies from tiny ripples in space-time.

_. "Eyeing Evidence of Primordial Helium." *Science News* (June 17, 1995).

Davies, P. *Superforce.* New York: Simon and Schuster, 1984. The search for a Grand Unified Theory of nature.

Flam, F. "Giving the Galaxies a History." *Science* (February 28, 1992). Astronomers discover one of the first galaxies.

Hawking, S. *A Brief History of Time.* New York: Bantam Books, 1988. On the best-seller list for many weeks, this book explores many basic ideas—and a few obscure ones—related to the physics of the early universe.

Linde, A., "The Self-Reproducing Inflationary Universe." *Scientific American* (November, 1994).

Monda, R., "Shedding Light on Dark Matter." *Astronomy* (February, 1992).

Peterson, I., "Making universes, constants out of nothing." *Science News* (February 18, 1995).

Schramm, D. N. "Dark Matter and the Origin of cosmic Structure." *Sky & Telescope* (October, 1994).

Spergel, D. N. and Turok, N. G., "Textures and Cosmic Structure." *Scientific American* (March, 1992).

Talcott, R. "COBE's Big Bang." *Astronomy* (August, 1992).

Weinberg, S. *The First Three Minutes.* New York: Basic Books, 1977.

Chapter 28

LIFE IN THE UNIVERSE
Are We Alone?

Chemical Evolution

In the 1950s it was believed that the Earth started out with no organic molecules. This is the reason Urey and Miller did their experiments, to see if it was possible to produce organic molecules from an inorganic environment. They succeeded but the results still allowed for the possibility that Earth was unique in this respect, that organic life was possible only here and maybe no where else.

The discovery of complex organic molecules in interstellar space (mostly in the 1970s and 1980s) completely changed much of the thinking about the origin of life on Earth. Life on Earth is based on organic chemistry, not because of special or even unique conditions that exist on Earth, but because this is the raw material that was present on the surface of the Earth when it formed. Molecular clouds out of which stars and solar systems form have significant amounts and varieties of organic molecules. Amino acids and genetic bases found in meteorites tell us that some very complex organic chemistry took place in space *before* life developed on Earth. Organic chemistry is very likely one common link we may have with other alien life forms.

The original intent of the Miller-Urey experiments was to produce basic organic molecules from inorganic molecules. Although this chemistry may have taken place on Earth, it is no longer believed essential to the chemical evolution of life. These experiments are now seen as a way very complex organic molecules could further develop from the organic molecules already present.

It was never the intent of Miller-Urey experiments to produce, from inorganic molecules, life. This is a common mistake made by many students, that, until these experiments produce a living organism, they have failed to "prove" chemical evolution of life. One must remember that even if one of these experiments exactly reproduces the conditions on Earth, there will always be one ingredient missing—-a few hundred million years. That is how long the "original" Miller-Urey experiment ran in order to produce life.

Biological Evolution

There is some evidence that life dates back to at least 3.8 billion years ago. These microfossils are found in some of the oldest Earth rocks known. Certainly the 3.5 billion year old blue-green bacteria are well-recognized inhabitants of the youthful Earth. These bacteria form large mats known as stromatolites and were once thought to be algae. They exist even to this day. Early single cell life forms were prokaryotes, meaning non-nucleated cells. They are a much simpler type of cell as opposed to eukaryotes, nucleated cells, which make up most of life today. Although DNA may have been present in these cells it is very possible that RNA was the original genetic molecule.

But life dates back farther than either of the two dates given above. The earliest evidence of life shows a sufficiently complex structure that it must have had many predecessors. The earliest life forms may have arisen when the Earth was no more than 500 million years old. This would have been at the end of the age of bombardment, after the Earth's surface had been heavily impacted by the leftover material from the formation of the solar system.

Viruses

Viruses are believed to be the simplest type of life-like structure. Small and compact, they lack many of the mechanisms needed by even the simplest of cells. Viruses can be completely inert, only to come alive when placed in a cellular environment. But did virus-like organisms develop before even the first single cell life form? This presents us with an interesting "chicken and egg" problem. Viruses are parasitic to cells. Viruses need the cellular environment to grow and reproduce. Could any virus have existed before cells evolved? Which came first, the virus or the cell? Although we can not be certain, it would appear that viruses had to develop at a later time than cells, at least viruses as we now know them.

Extinction of the Dinosaurs

This topic is very popular today and I find students really enjoy hearing about the impact theories. You can easily calculate the energy released by an asteroid or comet striking the Earth. Here is a simple example. Take a 1 km diameter spherical rock. Its radius is 500 m and has a density of about 3000 kg/m^3. From mass = volume times density, the mass = 1.6×10^{12} kg. Most of its energy will be in the form of kinetic energy (gravitational potential energy contributes little to the energy). If the velocity on impact is 30 km/sec, then the total amount of kinetic energy is 7×10^{20} J. One ton of TNT yields 4.2×10^9 J, so this one kilometer rock yields the equivalent energy of 170,000 megatons.

Although this would be devastating to any population within hundreds of kilometers of the impact, it would not produce "global" effects. Global damage to life usually is said to occur for impacts from objects 10 km or larger. Since the mass scales as the cube of the radius, a 10 km object would release 1,000 times more energy, or 170 million megatons. As the text notes, this impact would inject an enormous cloud of obscuring dust into our atmosphere. But what if it hit an ocean instead? There is about an 80% probability that it would. A 10 km object has the potential to put the equivalent of almost one meter of *salt* water into the atmosphere, averaged over the entire Earth! Imagine the damage to plant life everywhere on Earth from 30 inches of salt water rain. The tsunami (tidal wave) created by an impact in the ocean could be well over one kilometer high and have the capability to wash back and forth several times in the ocean. This would be very devastating to all coastal communities and others miles inland.

Astronomers predict that a 10 kilometer object strikes the Earth every 10 to 50 million years. Although some might call this a rare event, astronomically speaking it is a frequent event. If the dinosaurs existed on Earth for about 100 million years then they, as a species, should have experienced from 2 to 10 impacts producing global damage. Why did the impact from 65 million years ago cause their extinction and the others didn't? Shouldn't there have been 1 to 3 more impacts since that time? These are good questions to ask students as topics for further discussion.

Your students may also appreciate this statistic. If a large impact occurred today, it could literally wipe out the entire human race; 5 billion people. If that sort of event happens every 10 million years, then statistically speaking, on the average the Earth loses 5 billion people / 10 million years = 500 people per year to impacts. Fewer people die each year in airplane crashes, so you have a higher probability of dying from a large asteroid impact than from flying!

Life in the Solar System

We have landed on only three solar system bodies; the Moon, Venus, and Mars. The Moon and Venus are very poor candidates for having life; Mars, as the text notes, is one of the best places, particularly during its past. Do fly-by missions of the other planets and moons really have the potential to tell us much about life in those environments? Ask your students what those fly-by missions might have detected of life if they had passed by Earth instead. Would the rain forests be obvious? Giant redwood trees, blue whales, elephants, bacteria, and plankton in the oceans? How close to the Earth do you have to get before life is obvious? If we observed Earth from Mars would there be detectable signs of life on Earth?

Explore with your students places on Earth where life exists under difficult conditions. Where else in the solar system might such conditions exist that would also allow life? Life on Earth exists in some rather inhospitable places; under tremendous pressures and in darkness at the bottom of the ocean around superheated volcanic vents, in the frozen Antarctic, in the driest, hottest, most remote deserts. The enormous ocean of atmospheric hydrogen and helium of Jupiter, which contains some organic molecules, might seem pleasant compared to these places on Earth. What about the interior oceans of water of Europa, Ganymede, and Callisto? It may be a long time before we can penetrate their icy crusts to look for the existence of life in those environments. We can eliminate the very hottest and coldest places in the solar system as being inappropriate for life but there remains many places that are more temperate and which contain all the building blocks of life that have yet to be explored.

Alternative Biochemistries

If you want to see trees, you go to a forest. If you want a lot of water, the ocean is just the place. If you want life based on organic chemistry, shouldn't you go someplace where there is a lot of carbon? Well, we know life on Earth is based on organic chemistry but carbon is relatively uncommon on the surface of the Earth, compared to other elements. Indeed, if you want to find a place where life might be based on silicon instead of carbon, the Earth should be just the place! The Earth is made of 14% silicon and its crust is 28%. Possibly the temperature isn't correct for silicon-based life? But Earth has an enormous range in temperatures if one considers its interior conditions. Remember, molten lava is common on the surface, and was even more common in the past.

All life forms on Earth are 99% hydrogen, oxygen, carbon, and nitrogen, in order of decreasing abundance. This certainly is not the makeup of the Earth's crust or atmosphere. What object(s) have a composition similar to this? It is a good question to ask your students because they have the information to answer it. It is the Sun (and typical stars and interstellar clouds of gas and dust). With the exception of two inert gases, helium and neon, life's elemental abundance reflects that of stars and interstellar matter from which they all formed! This is hardly a coincidence and a good topic for discussion.

When discussing the varieties of life on Earth, amino acids and proteins are a good place to begin. Proteins determine much of the structure, organization, and functions of an organism. Proteins are formed out of hundreds of amino acids strung together in a specific sequence. But there are only 20 amino acids that are used in forming all of life on Earth. (Other amino acids exist but are not used.)

Here is a good analogy of a protein with its amino acids. Think of a train made up of 20 types of cars; engines, flat cars, tankers, box cars, etc. The train, though, isn't just 20 cars long, it may be hundreds of cars in length. Thus there are many box cars in different locations as there are tankers in other locations and so forth. A protein is like the entire train and is composed of hundreds amino acids in a variety of locations.

Different proteins have both different sequences of these amino acids and different numbers of amino acids. For simplicity, let us say that proteins are formed out of 200 amino acids. How many different combinations or arrangements are possible with 20 amino acids linked to form a sequence of 200? It is simply 20^{200}. For proteins with 500 amino acids in sequence it would be 20^{500}. These numbers are virtually infinite in size.

This suggests that there may be an infinite number of varieties of life possible for just the Earth. (Once a life form becomes extinct, there is essentially zero probability that it will ever occur again on Earth or anywhere in the universe!) Each life form, including human, is unique, not only on Earth but in the universe. Imagine the possibilities for the varieties of alien life, even if they are all based on organic chemistry. The diversity may truly be unimaginable!

Drake Equation

When going through the Drake Equation, have the students come up with their own estimation for each value. You can present the "liberal" view given in the text; students typically enjoy being very conservative with some of their estimates. Have a discussion on each of the factors and let the students provide the pros and the cons. Let the lifetime, L, remain an open question after it has been thoroughly discussed (and this term usually produces the liveliest discussion). Putting all the factors together, the number of technical civilizations in the galaxy, N, will be N = L from the text and maybe something like N = 0.000000001 L from your students (depending on how unlikely they feel some of the factors are).

Now put in a conservative value for L, like L = 100, which is about where we are, at this time. In the case of the text, N = 100 but for the students, N = 0.0000001. But this can not be right because they have not managed to predict their own existence! N = 1 should be a minimum result. Remember, the Drake Equation gives us the average number over time and certainly at this time the average is at least one. The Drake Equation can not, at this time, tell us N because the value of L has such an enormous potential range, i.e. 100 less than L < 10^{10}.

The Search for Extraterrestrial Intelligence (SETI):

The acronym SETI is now used a lot and so it is helpful to introduce the students to its use. What is the value in conducting SETI with, say, radio telescopes, as currently funded by NASA? What does society get out of this search and any potential discoveries? Would the discovery of ETI be beneficial to society? These are excellent questions to pose to your students.

What would we immediately know, once the first ETI is discovered? Phillip Morrison is known to have said, and I paraphrase, "Once you find the first one, you can do statistics." What did he mean by this? The first ETI discovered is likely to be the nearest to us. Astronomers should be able to determine the distance rather easily. For example, let this distance be 50 pc. If we assume this distance is also the average distance between civilizations in the Galaxy, then we can immediately say there should be about 1 million civilizations in the Galaxy, i.e. N = 1 million. From the Drake Equation this tells us that L = 1 million. SETI doesn't have to find a million civilizations, all it needs to do is find the first one and simple math tells us the rest.

If SETI does not find a ETI within about 1,000 pc then the search is not worth continuing. Why? Because at this distance N = 3,000 = L and so civilizations do not last long enough to communicate over interstellar distances. Although the Galaxy may contain a couple of thousand civilizations, they and we are all so isolated from one another that we, in effect, are all alone!

Space Flight

I like to emphasize the dangers of interstellar flight and how space flight is portrayed in movies. Discuss with students the energy requirements for space flight and/or the time necessary for such trips. Obviously to resolve the problem of time, flight velocities must be very high, in fact they must be relativistic. If such flights are possible, and the energy requirements are truly astronomical, time dilation allows onboard crews to survive lengthy journeys. However, point out that time still passes at the same rate on Earth, so the crew returns to a much older Earth than they left; maybe hundreds or thousands of years older!

To emphasize interstellar flight hazards I bring to class a one gram mass. It is small but that's OK because I want to remind the students that one gram of metal or rock is small. I pose the following question: "What is the result of a spacecraft moving at 99% the speed of light hitting this one gram mass?" It is, of course, the same as the one gram mass moving at 99% the speed of light hitting a stationary spacecraft. At this speed, special relativity tells us its mass is equivalent to about 7 grams. Using $E = mc^2$ the energy is calculated to be 6.4×10^{14} J or 150 kilotons of TNT (which is the size of a typical nuclear explosive). Hit many of these and you don't have a spacecraft! Hit lots of interstellar dust grains, which you will, and the effect is the same! You quickly "erode" the spacecraft away!

First Contact

The first time we have definitive proof that ETI exists, this is referred to as First Contact. Will they be more advanced than us? You can ask your students, but the answer is a definite Yes. Why? Suppose L = 1 million years. We have been technical for only about 100 years but civilizations in general last one million years. The "technological ladder" is one million years long and we are barely on the first rung of a very lengthy ladder. Odds are that any civilization we encounter will be thousands, even hundreds of thousands, of years in advance of us. I wonder what that will be like?

ANSWERS TO CHAPTER 28 REVIEW QUESTIONS

1. Characteristics of life are reaction, growth, reproduction, and evolution. Although other characteristics might be listed, most life have these four in common. Life is difficult to define because not all forms of life share the same characteristics.

2. Chemical evolution is a process by which life develops from the natural environment of the Earth (or any place else, for that matter). The chemistry of life, to some degree, depends on the material present on the Earth's surface and on the environment of the surface.

3. The Urey-Miller experiment tries to recreate the conditions on Earth before life existed, with the purpose of producing molecules necessary for life. Using ingredients like water, methane, ammonia, and carbon dioxide, and by adding energy, essential organic molecules for life, such as amino acids and nucleotide bases have been formed.

4. The basic ingredients are water, methane, carbon dioxide, and ammonia.

5. The fossil record dates back to at least 3.5 billion years ago, when the Earth was just over one billion years old. The fossil record, although at times is unclear, is continuous up to the present time.

6. Language may be the direct result of the development of human intelligence. With language, information could be passed on from generation to generation. Ideas could be developed and exchanged. Cultural evolution are the changes in ideas and behavior of society and are likely linked to the appearance of language.

7. Organic molecules have been found in meteorites and in molecular clouds of interstellar matter. Comets and the surface of Triton likely contain some organic molecules. Many other solar system objects may also, but have not been sufficiently explored.

8. The possibility of life can not be excluded from places such as Jupiter's atmosphere, Europa's liquid ocean, or the surface of Triton.

9. The *Viking* landers on Mars found no evidence of life as we know it. However, several possibilities remain before anyone can say for certain that life does not exist on Mars. The landers were in very desolate, mid-latitude sites that may be quite inhospitable for life. Better locations might be near the poles where water, mostly frozen, exists in greater abundance. Life might also exist below the immediate surface of Mars, deeper in the soil where water may be abundant and life is shielded from the harsh surface environment. The landers could only look for life as we know it to be and could not look for alternate forms of life. Fossil evidence of life might also exist, telling of times in the past when the Martian environment was favorable for life. These questions have yet to be investigated.

10. "Life as we know it" means life based on organic molecules in a mostly water environment. When searching for life we must remember that "Life as we know it" may not be the only possibilities for life to have. Life might be based on other atoms than carbon or it may have a carbon base but function radically differently than our own forms of life.

11. The Drake equation has been devised as a way to estimate the abundance of life outside of the solar system. The result depends on 7 factors: (1) rate of star formation, (2) fraction of stars having planetary systems, (3) number of planets in a solar system with a suitable environment for life, (4) fraction of suitable planets on which life actually develops, (5) fraction of life-bearing planets on which intelligence evolves, (6) fraction of intelligent life planets that develop a technology, and (7) average lifetime of a technological civilization.

    Referring to the previous answer and the 7 factors of the Green Bank equation, factors 1 and 2 are fairly well known. Factor 3 could also be included in this group although it is not as well known as 1 and 2. Factors 4, 5, and 6 really require some guess work. We really have no other examples other than ourselves. Factor 7 has the widest range of values possible and is therefore the least well-known.

12. When the lifetime of a civilization approaches the time it takes for one two-way communication, then such communication becomes impractical if not impossible. This occurs for lifetimes of less than about 3000 years. If these civilizations were separated by 1500 light years, then one two-way communication would require 3000 years. By the time one of the civilizations sent a message by radio waves to the other and receives a reply, it would be just dying out.

13. Radio transmissions from Earth would vary significantly over a 24 hour period. This is the result of the Earth's rotation and various groups of transmitters coming into view. Most of the transmissions would be in the FM and television frequencies.

14. The advantages of radio waves for interstellar communication are several. Radio waves travel just as fast as all other electromagnetic waves—the speed of light. They can penetrate dust clouds and can reach anywhere in the Galaxy. Being the lowest energy waves, they are cheap to produce and do not require a high level of technology to produce or receive. The background noise level at radio wavelengths is minimal, allowing signals to be detected over large distances.

15. The water hole is a section of radio wavelengths between 18 and 21 cm. This region of the radio spectrum would be the best for interstellar communications because it has the least amount of naturally occurring radio noise. These wavelengths also pass easily through interstellar dust clouds and are least affected by planetary atmospheres.

ANSWERS TO PROBLEMS

1. (a) $N = 20 \times 0.1 \times 1 \times 0.1 \times 0.1 \times 0.1 \times 100$

    $N = 0.2$ technological civilizations

   (b) $N = 20 \times 0.1 \times 1 \times 0.1 \times 0.1 \times 0.1 \times 10,000$

    $N = 20$ technological civilizations

   (c) $N = 20 \times 0.1 \times 1 \times 0.1 \times 0.1 \times 0.1 \times 1,000,000$

    $N = 2000$ technological civilizations

2. Use an age of 20 years for an example. In 45 years there are $45 \times 3.2 \times 10^7$ s = 1.44×10^9 s. Dividing this by the 4.5 billion year age of the Earth gives 0.32 s/yr. For a 20 year old person, this would be equivalent to 6.4 s.

3. 10,000 stations $\times$ 50,000 W/station = 5×10^8 W. This is 5×10^8 W / 10^6 W = 500 times more power radiated than the Sun in this same frequency range.

4. The water hole ranges from 18 to 21 cm in wavelength. $c = \lambda f$, so 3×10^{10} cm / 18 = 1.7×10^9 Hz and 3×10^{10} cm / 21 = 1.4×10^9 Hz. Subtracting these two frequencies gives 0.3×10^9 Hz. Dividing by a 100 Hz per channel gives 3,000,000 channels. This is how many channels have to be searched when observing throughout the water hole. Talk about channel surfing!

5. 20,000 hours is the equivalent of 833 days or 2.3 years. 20,000 days is the equivalent to 54.8 years. This suggests that such a search must be conducted in such a way that each star can be searched in under an hour, otherwise the search would take too long.

SUGGESTED READING

Goldsmith, D., ed. *The Quest for Extraterrestrial Life.* Mill Valley, CA: University Science Books, 1980. A variety of fascinating readings.

Goldsmith, D., and Owen, T. *The Search for Life in the Universe,* 2nd ed. Menlo Park, Calif.: Benjamin/Cummings, 1993.

Kutter, G. S. *The Universe and Life: Origins and Evolution.* Boston: Jones and Bartlett, 1987. A readable treatise on both the physical and biological aspects of cosmic evolution.

Miller, S. L., and C. Chyba. "Whence Came Life?" *Sky and Telescope* (June 1992). Two researchers present modern alternative views on the origin of life on Earth.

Naeye, R. *SETI at the Crossroads.* NASAs latest foray into the search for extraterrestrial intelligence.

Paque, J., "A Friend for Life?" *Astronomy* (June, 1995). Could life arise elsewhere?

Pendleton, Y. J. and Cruikshank, D. P., "Life from the Stars?" *Sky & Telescope* (March, 1994).

Regis, E. *Extraterrestrials: Science and Alien Intelligence.* Cambridge: Cambridge University Press, 1985. Over a dozen scientists present their views on the subject.

Sagan, C. *The Cosmic Connection.* New York, Dell, 1973. Short, visionary book presenting life from a cosmic perspective.

Shklovskii, I. S., and C. Sagan. *Intelligent Life in the Universe.* New York: Dell, 1968. This classic book is a translation, extension, and revision of Shklovskii's earlier work called *Universe, Life and Mind.* It presents many of the basic questions concerning life in the universe.

Sullivan, W. T., S. Brown, and C. Wetherill. "Eavesdropping: The Radio Signature of the Earth." *Science* (January 27, 1978). Classic article describing how Earth's radio emissions would appear to extraterrestrial civilizations.

DENNIS HOPELESS
SERG ACUÑA
DOUG GARBARK

VOLUME TWO

LUNATIC FRINGE

BOOM!
STUDIOS

WWE

WWE
BOOKS

Relive
Explore
Adventure
Discover

WWE Volume Two, January 2018. Published by BOOM!
Studios, a division of Boom Entertainment, Inc. WWE is ™ &
© 2018 WWE. All WWE programming, talent names, images,
likenesses, slogans, wrestling moves, trademarks, logos
and copyrights are the exclusive property of WWE and its
subsidiaries. All other trademarks, logos and copyrights are
the property of their respective owners. © 2018 WWE. All
rights reserved. Originally published in single magazine form
as WWE No. 5-8. ™ & © 2017 WWE. All rights reserved. BOOM!
Studios™ and the BOOM! Studios logo are trademarks of
Boom Entertainment, Inc., registered in various countries and
categories. All characters, events, and institutions depicted
herein are fictional. Any similarity between any of the
names, characters, persons, events, and/or institutions in this
publication to actual names, characters, persons, events, whether
living or dead, events, and/or institutions is unintended and
purely coincidental. BOOM! Studios does not read or accept
unsolicited submissions of ideas, stories, or artwork.

BOOM! Studios, 5670 Wilshire Boulevard, Suite 450, Los
Angeles, CA 90036-5679. Printed in China. First Printing.

ISBN: 978-1-68415-062-5, eISBN: 978-1-61398-739-1

LUNATIC FRINGE

WRITTEN BY
DENNIS HOPELESS

ILLUSTRATED BY
SERG ACUÑA

WITH PENCILS BY
TIM LATTIE
(CHAPTER 7 PAGES 16-20, CHAPTER 8 PAGES 1-7)

COLORED BY
DOUG GARBARK

LETTERED BY
JIM CAMPBELL

COVER BY
DAN MORA

DESIGNER
GRACE PARK

ASSOCIATE EDITOR
CHRIS ROSA

EDITORS
**JASMINE AMIRI
& ERIC HARBURN**

SPECIAL THANKS TO
**STEVE PANTALEO
CHAD BARBASH
BEN MAYER
JOHN JONES
STAN STANSKI
LAUREN DIENES-MIDDLEN**
AND EVERYONE AT **WWE**

CHAPTER
FIVE

ME SINCE BEFORE I WAS EVEN OLD ENOUGH TO DRIVE HER.

AND PEOPLE HAVE BEEN UNDERESTIMATING HER FROM THE VERY BEGINNING.

UNDERESTIMATING THE BOTH OF US.

GUY AT THE JUNKYARD THOUGHT I WAS JOKING WHEN I PICKED HER OUT.

SHE HAD A DATE WITH THE CRUSHER THAT NEXT WEEK.

DID I HAVE ANY IDEA WHAT I WAS GETTING MYSELF INTO?

BUT HARD WORK DIDN'T SCARE ME. NOT EVEN AT FIFTEEN.

I COULD SEE THROUGH ALL THE RUST AND DENTS.

CLASSIC AMERICAN MUSCLE. ALL THE POTENTIAL IN THE WORLD.

WAITING FOR THE RIGHT LUNATIC TO COME ALONG--

--AND BRING HER BACK FROM THE DEAD.

LOOK, I GET PAID TO BEAT PEOPLE UP.

ON TELEVISION.

I CAN AFFORD SOMETHING NEWER. SOMETHING MORE RELIABLE.

BUT I KNOW SHELLY. I TRUST SHELLY.

THERE'S NOTHING ON THIS CAR I HAVEN'T FIXED AT LEAST ONCE.

WHICH MEANS THERE'S NOTHING I CAN'T FIX AGAIN.

COMFORT LIKE THAT IS WORTH A LITTLE ELBOW GREASE EVERY NOW AND AGAIN.

ALTERNATOR'S SHOT.

RAN MY BRAND NEW BATTERY DOWN TO NOTHING.

SIMPLE ENOUGH TO FIX BUT...

I'M GONNA NEED ANOTHER ALTERNATOR.

IT'S TOO BAD THERE'S NOT--

--SOME BIG MUSCLE-HEAD--

--COCKY ENOUGH TO ALWAYS LEAVE HIS TRUCK UNLOCKED--

--AND WITH DEEP ENOUGH POCKETS FOR A CAR SERVICE HOME.

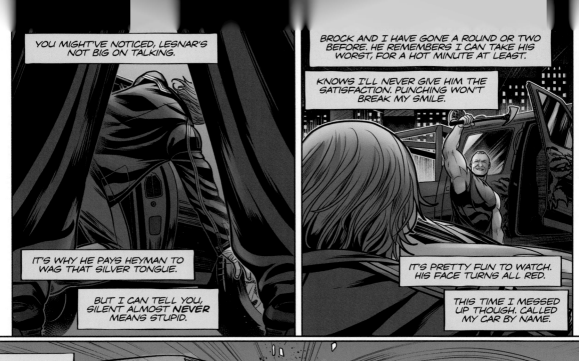

YOU MIGHT'VE NOTICED, LESNAR'S NOT BIG ON TALKING.

IT'S WHY HE PAYS HEYMAN TO WAG THAT SILVER TONGUE.

BUT I CAN TELL YOU, SILENT ALMOST *NEVER* MEANS STUPID.

BROCK AND I HAVE GONE A ROUND OR TWO BEFORE. HE REMEMBERS I CAN TAKE HIS WORST, FOR A HOT MINUTE AT LEAST.

KNOWS I'LL NEVER GIVE HIM THE SATISFACTION. PUNCHING WON'T BREAK MY SMILE.

IT'S PRETTY FUN TO WATCH. HIS FACE TURNS ALL RED.

THIS TIME I MESSED UP THOUGH. CALLED MY CAR BY NAME.

NOW THE BEAST HAS SEEN MY BELLY--

KROOSH

--AND HERE COME...

TOONCH

THOK

...HIS TEETH.

MOVE IT OR LOSE IT, LESNAR.

I'VE ALWAYS FIGURED IF YOU'RE LUCKY ENOUGH TO FIND THE THING YOU'RE GOOD AT IN LIFE AND SOMEBODY WILL PAY YOU FOR IT--

--JUST DO THAT THING EVERYDAY 'TIL THEY MAKE YOU STOP.

HEY. HEY. HEY. EASY, WE'LL GET HIM NEXT TIME.

GOOD CHOICE.

CLIMB INTO THE RING, KNUCKLE UP AND GET TO WORK. WHAT ELSE IS THERE?

NOBODY'S ITCHING TO HAND DEAN AMBROSE A CHAMPIONSHIP MATCH.

SO WHAT ELSE IS NEW?

--I REACHED OUT AND TOOK.

I JUST THUMPED THE BADDEST BULLY ON THE ROSTER.

--FROM SNATCHING THAT GOLDEN BRIEFCASE?

NEVER BEEN HANDED MUCH OF ANYTHING. EVERYTHING I HAVE--

WHO DO THEY HAVE THAT CAN STOP ME--

VRRRRRMM

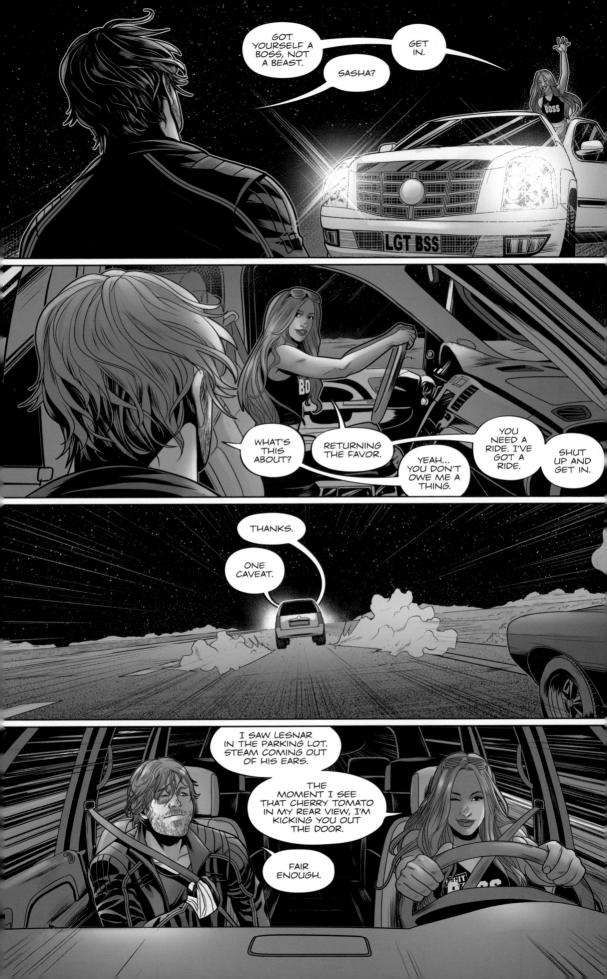

CHAPTER
SIX

GAH!

Heh Heh Heh.

I HATE STUPID CLOWNS.

OMG. WHY?

CLOWNS. MIMES. JESTERS. THOSE AWFUL HUMAN STATUES.

ANYBODY WHO PUTS ON A CLOWNFIT AND PRANCES ABOUT TRYING TO BE THE CENTER OF ATTENTION.

THAT'S RICH COMING FROM A DUDE WHOSE JOB TITLE IS SUPERSTAR. WHAT'S THE DIFFERENCE BETWEEN THAT GUY'S COSTUME AND YOURS?

YOU MIGHT NOTICE I FIGHT IN JEANS AND A TANK TOP.

YOU KNOW...

THE AMBROSE ASYLUM THING IS WHAT YOU DO BEST. NEVER SAY QUIT. CRAZY DUDE. THAT'S OBVIOUSLY YOUR STRENGTH, RIGHT?

BUT FOR SOME REASON YOU ALSO GOTTA BE THE BAD BOY TOUGH GUY ALL THE TIME.

ANYTHING EVEN REMOTELY FUN OR WEIRD OR EMBARRASSING... YOU GO ALL STONE-FACED.

MAKES YOU WONDER WHY THE LUNATIC HAS SO MANY STIPULATIONS TO HIS CRAZY.

WHERE ARE WE GOING?

DEMOLITION DERBY.

GREAT...

SO A BUNCH OF IDIOTS CRASHING THEIR BUSTED CARS TOGETHER?

LATER.

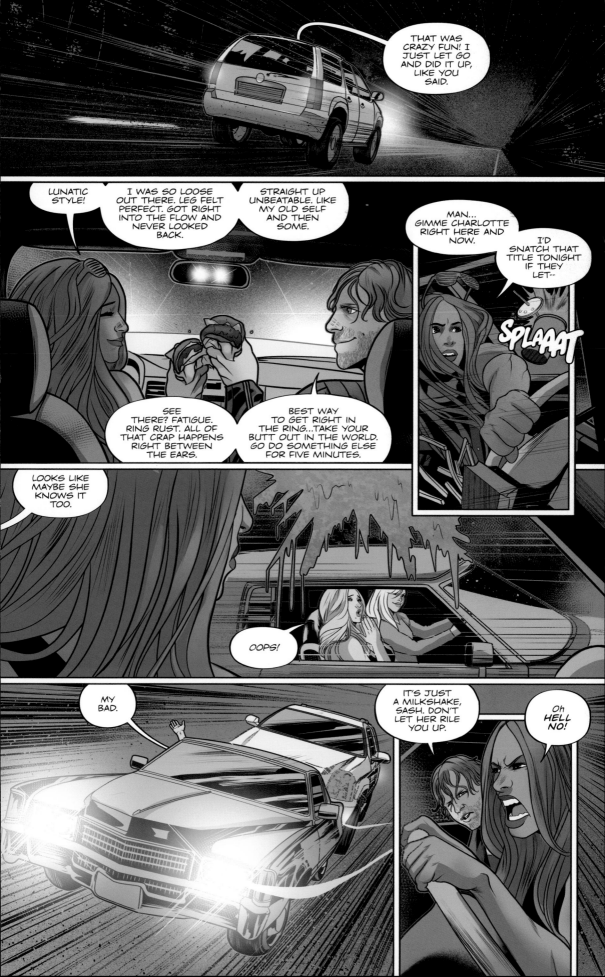

BEEN FINE LIKE THAT MOST OF MY LIFE.

MY CAR.

DON'T SWEAT IT. WE'RE DANGEROUSLY CLOSE TO MY OLD STOMPING GROUNDS. MY BUDDY JERRY HAS A SHOP NOT FAR. HE'LL GIVE US A TOW IN THE MORNING.

THAT KIND OF FINE WILL GET YOU IN ALL SORTS OF TROUBLE.

THIS IS STUPID. WHY DON'T WE JUST GO TO A HOTEL?

BECAUSE DEANO ALWAYS TRAVELS WITH CAMPING GEAR... AND WE'LL WANT TO BE RIGHT HERE IN THE MORNING SO WE CAN GET A TOW FIRST THING.

MEANS SHE'S SO ANGRY THEY DON'T MAKE WORDS FOR IT.

THEY SELL THAT STUFF IN LITTLE BUNDLES, YOU KNOW. PRECHOPPED.

YEP.

TH'WAK

THEY SELL LOTS OF STUPID THINGS.

AND IF SHE'S STILL FINE TWO NIGHTS FROM NOW--

--CHARLOTTE'S GONNA WIPE THE MAT WITH HER.

SO, CAMPING IS LIKE TWO HOURS OF SUPER UNNECESSARY WORK...

...AFTER WHICH YOU GET TO SMELL LIKE SMOKE AND SLEEP ON THE GROUND?

WORST HOTEL ROOM EVER.

Nah, MAN.

YOU JUST GOTTA EARN THAT VIEW.

...WHATEVER.

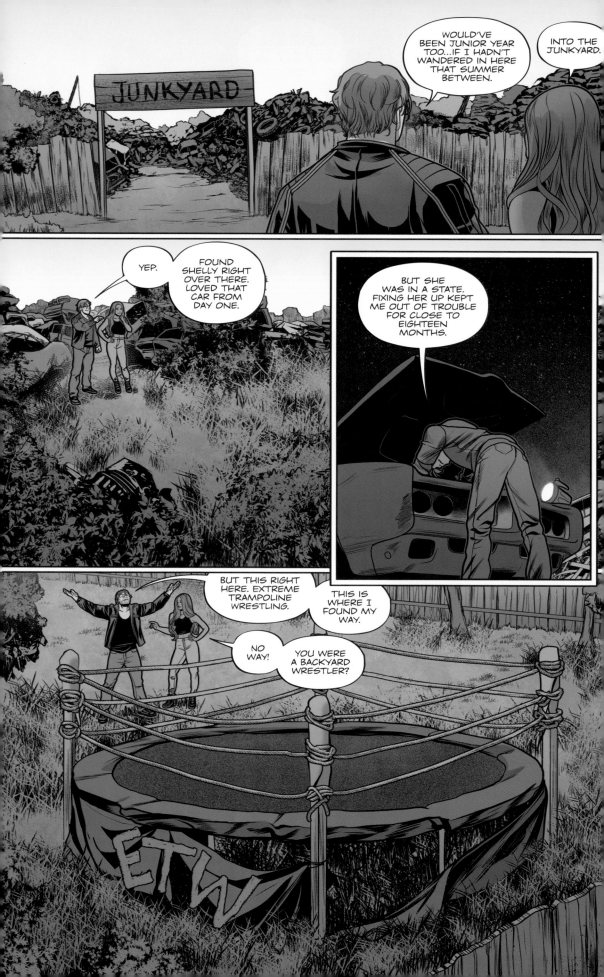

CHAPTER
SEVEN

GOTCHA...

THAT'S ERIC ROWAN, AND HE DID. HE GOT ME.

SHOULD'VE SEEN THAT COMING--

--THESE HILLBILLIES ALWAYS TRAVEL IN PAIRS.

THNNNK

THUNK
KRAK
WHAK
WUNNK

I WAS REALLY LOOKING FORWARD...

...TO THAT...

FLMMMP

...DONUT.

CAN YOU FELLAS POINT ME IN THE DIRECTION OF THE WAFFLE HOUSE?

IF I DON'T GET SOME HASH BROWNS IN ME...

WH/AK

...I MIGHT JUST HAVE TO HURT SOMEBODY.

SMOTHERED.

COVERED.

SCATTERED AND CHUNKED.

OUR GUEST HAS HAD HER FILL, BOYS.

TAKE HER TO HER ROOM.

YOU SAID THIS WAS BUSINESS, WYATT!

YOU SAID IT WAS MY CHOICE.

YOUR CHOICE. YES INDEED.

WHAT WE HAVE HERE IS A FAMILY AFFAIR. COULDN'T FORCE YOU IN IF I TRIED. NO MA'AM.

FREE WILL RULES THE ROOST. PIT TO PULPIT AND BACK AGAIN.

BUT THAT DON'T MEAN YOU GET TO UP AND LEAVE US.

NOM

TOMORROW MORNING BRINGS ANOTHER MEAL.

ANOTHER CHAT.

ANOTHER--

VROOOM

WOULD IT HAVE KILLED YOU TO RING THE DINNER BELL?

YOUR MISTAKES ARE PILING HIGH TONIGHT, LUNATIC.

LIKE DRY LOGS STACKED *FAR TOO NEAR* MY DANCING FLAME.

AND SOON WE'LL DANCE TOGETHER!

YEAH, SORRY... DEAN DON'T DANCE.

I'LL DANCE WITH YOU THOUGH.

JUST HOLD ON TIGHT--

TH*NNK*

--AND FOLLOW MY LEAD.

CHAPTER
EIGHT

PEOPLE HAVE BEEN CALLING ME CRAZY MY WHOLE LIFE.

LET US CHASE THE FRIGHTENED RABBITS... SCAMPER!

RUN!

RUN!

RUN!

NEVER BOTHERED ME TOO MUCH.

SASH, UP AHEAD. GOT SHEEP MASKS IN THE TREES.

I KNOW BETTER.

ON IT. THANKS.

EVER SEE A FIREFLY--

--GO SPLAT?

TWAANG

BUT IF YOU POKED YOUR HEAD IN HERE RIGHT NOW AND TOLD ME THAT NONE OF THIS IS REAL--

--THAT THE WYATT FAMILY TRACTOR PULL DEATH RACE--

DELUSION OR DESTINY?

I COULD GIVE A DAMN.

WOOOOM

KROOOOOSH

TEAMWORK.

NAILED IT.

ARE WE THERE YET?

THERE'S A GOLDEN BRIEFCASE IN THEM THERE HILLS.

DEAN, NO! GOTTA FIGHT SMART, REMEMBER?!

THAT'S NOT SMART.

Nah, BUT IT MIGHT BE FUN.

AND I'M NOT STOPPING, NOT EVEN SLOWING DOWN--

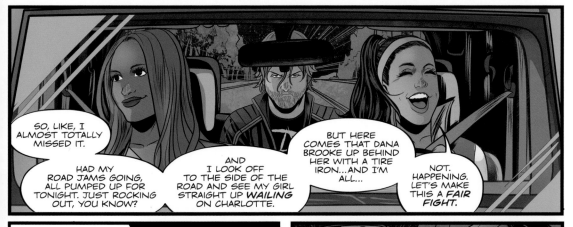

SO, LIKE, I ALMOST TOTALLY MISSED IT.

HAD MY ROAD JAMS GOING, ALL PUMPED UP FOR TONIGHT. JUST ROCKING OUT, YOU KNOW?

AND I LOOK OFF TO THE SIDE OF THE ROAD AND SEE MY GIRL STRAIGHT UP *WAILING* ON CHARLOTTE.

BUT HERE COMES THAT DANA BROOKE UP BEHIND HER WITH A TIRE IRON...AND I'M ALL...

NOT. HAPPENING. LET'S MAKE THIS A *FAIR FIGHT.*

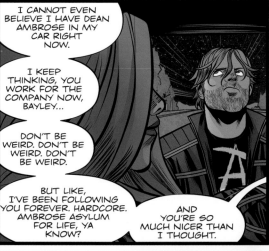

I CANNOT EVEN BELIEVE I HAVE DEAN AMBROSE IN MY CAR RIGHT NOW.

I KEEP THINKING, YOU WORK FOR THE COMPANY NOW, BAYLEY...

DON'T BE WEIRD. DON'T BE WEIRD. DON'T BE WEIRD.

BUT LIKE, I'VE BEEN FOLLOWING YOU FOREVER. HARDCORE. AMBROSE ASYLUM FOR LIFE, YA KNOW?

AND YOU'RE SO MUCH NICER THAN I THOUGHT.

I ALWAYS THOUGHT MY ENTHUSIASM WOULD DRIVE THE LUNATIC FRINGE *NUTS.*

YEAH... TURNS OUT HE'S A *REAAAL* PEACH.

OMG, SASHA!

I'M GONNA BE RINGSIDE FOR MONEY IN THE BANK!

HUG LIFE

YEP... PRETTY COOL.

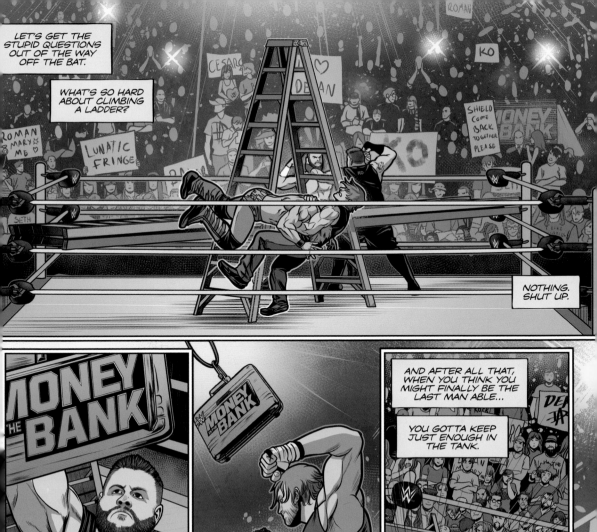

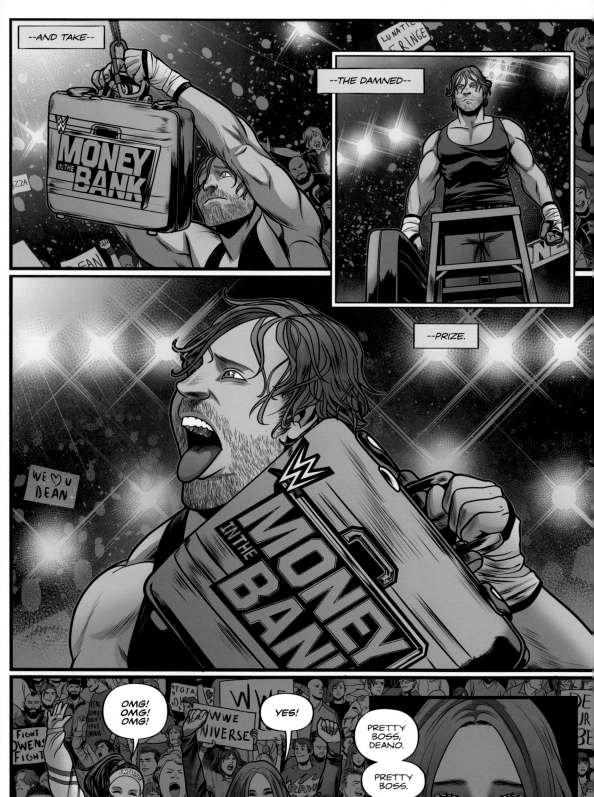

COVER GALLERY

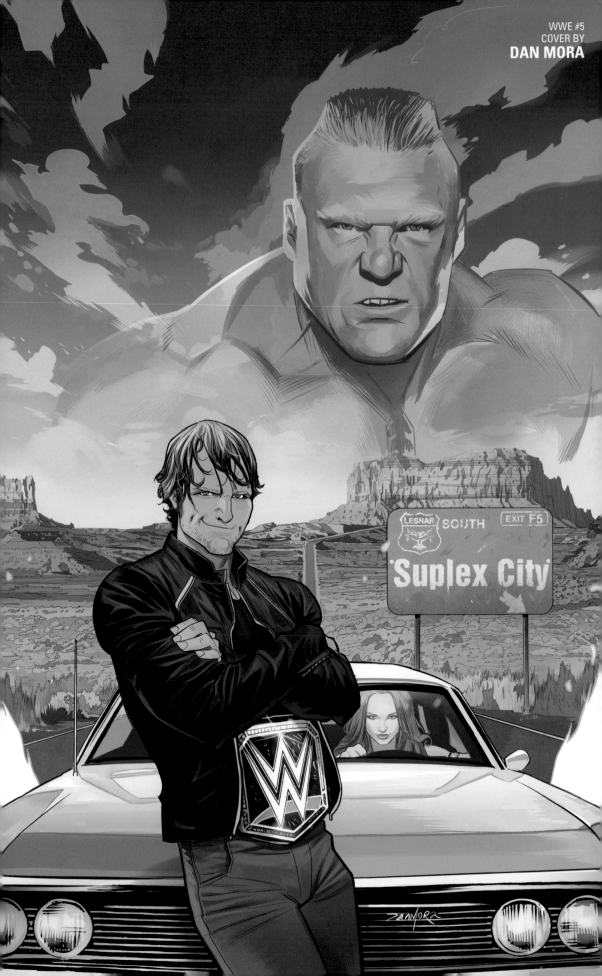

WWE #5
JOHN CENA COVER BY
JAMAL CAMPBELL

WWE #5
GOLDUST COVER BY
MARCO D'ALFONSO

WWE #7
COVER BY
DAN MORA

WWE #8
COVER BY
DAN MORA

WWE #8
MANKIND COVER BY
WILL ROBSON

ASUKA

RING ATTIRE: NXT TAKEOVER - DALLAS

"RAVISHING"
RICK RUDE

RING ATTIRE: WRESTLEMANIA V

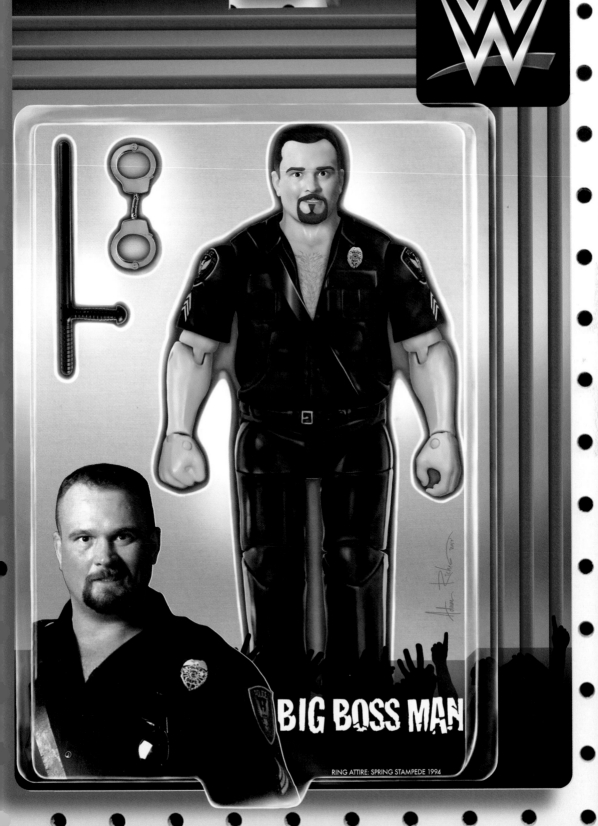

BIG BOSS MAN

RING ATTIRE: SPRING STAMPEDE 1994

WWE VOLUME THREE
THE ROMAN EMPIRE
COMING SOON

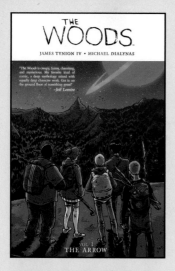

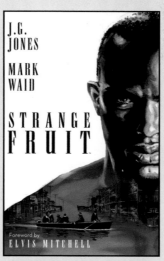